Water Utility Accounting

Third Edition

🔻 American Water Works Association

Water Utility Accounting — 3rd Edition

ISBN 0-89867-761-0

Project Managers: Kathleen A. Faller and Todd A. Shimoda
Cover design by Susan DeSantis
Text design by Carrie Henderson

Printed in the United States of America

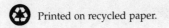 American Water Works Association

6666 West Quincy Avenue
Denver, CO 80235
(303) 794-7711

Printed on recycled paper.

CONTENTS

⊠ Part Three — Accounting-Cycle Implementation and Management

⊠ Part Four — Accounting Reports

⊠ Part Five — Financial Management Functions

FOREWORD

Increased complexities and difficulties surrounding the operation, replacement, and expansion of water systems and associated infrastructure have been well documented in recent years. Sound financial capabilities and effective financial information systems are key elements in managing these complexities and difficulties.

The purpose of *Water Utility Accounting* is to provide information concerning water utility management, accounting, and financial management functions. The text focuses on how the financial management function serves the overall operation of the utility and how the various activities associated with performing the financial management function are conducted. While the book is intended for both utility management personnel and utility financial personnel, certain portions of the text discussing technical financial management activities assume that the reader possesses a basic understanding of accounting principles and procedures. It should also be understood that accounting principles and practices change continuously and more recent pronouncements may not be reflected herein.

This third edition reflects the pronouncements of several regulatory bodies, including the Governmental Accounting Standards Board, the Financial Accounting Standards Board, the Securities and Exchange Commission, and the National Association of Regulatory Utility Commissioners. Since accounting practices for investor-owned utilities are usually prescribed by state regulatory agencies, emphasis has been placed on the practices of government-owned utilities.

Substantially reorganized from the previous edition, this third edition generally follows the accounting-cycle concept of budgeting, recording, and reporting. In addition, the text explores the finance, audit, and information systems functions that, together with the accounting function, comprise the major activities generally associated with financial management in water utilities.

It is hoped that this book, along with others planned for related topics, will add substantially to the resources available to water utility managers and staff.

ACKNOWLEDGMENTS

The Accounting/Financial Analysis Subcommittee of the Financial Management Committee, appointed by the Management Division of the American Water Works Association, prepared and reviewed the third edition of *Water Utility Accounting*. Subcommittee members included

Lawrence G. Shaw (Chair), KPMG Peat Marwick LLP, Dallas, Texas

Stanley M. Massarelli (Vice-chair), Ohio Water Service Company, Poland, Ohio

R.D. Ambrose, Buchart-Horn Inc., York, Pa.

A.L. Anders, J.P. Morgan, New York, N.Y.

F.L. Critelli, Elizabethtown Water Company, Westfield, N.J.

W.K. Ferry, Brown & Caldwell, Pasadena, Calif.

L.S. Graven, Bowling Green Municipal Utility, Bowling Green, Ky.

R.D. Hardten, Black & Veatch Engineers, Kansas City, Mo.

M.G. Hinkle, Blue and Company, Indianapolis, Ind.

R.E. Huber, City Water Board, San Antonio, Texas

D.O. Kalkwarf, Marion Water Department, Marion, Iowa

J.C. Kirner, Tacoma Department of Public Utilities, Tacoma, Wash.

H.G. Mülle, AUS Consultants, Moorestown, N.J.

P.M. Sachs, Arthur Andersen & Company, Kansas City, Mo.

R.M. Wilson, Denver Water, Denver, Colo.

Others who reviewed the manuscript and provided suggestions and illustrations include

D.L. Edgemon, American Water Works Service Company Inc., Charleston, W. Va.

W.G. Stannard, Black & Veatch, Kansas City, Mo.

Z.L. Snyder, Black & Veatch, Washington, D.C.

W.T. Pohl, American Water Works Company Inc., Voorhees, N.J.

R.H. Taylor, California Water Service Company, San Jose, Calif.

Miami–Dade (Fla.) Water and Sewer Authority Department

Seattle (Wash.) Water

San Antonio (Texas) Water Systems

Dallas (Texas) Water Utilities

PART ONE ━━━━━━━━

⊠ Water Utility Accounting Overview

CHAPTER ONE

Introduction

⊠ What Is Financial Management?

Financial management is (1) planning for and acquiring resources and (2) planning, monitoring, analyzing, and reporting the use of those resources. Its fundamental purpose is to ensure that resources are available when needed and that they are used effectively and efficiently in the accomplishment of the objectives of the organization.

⊠ Functional Responsibilities Included Under Financial Management

Financial management functions are required in every water utility, regardless of size or type of ownership. Typically, these functions include budgeting and forecasting, accounting and reporting, financing activities, auditing and analysis, and financial information systems. Custodial and resource management functions, such as facilities maintenance, personnel, and inventory control may also be included.

Budgeting involves developing monetary plans for specified time periods. Budgets are plans developed in response to forecasts of expected circumstances and events in the environment in which the utility functions. While forecasts are predictions about situations external to the organization, budgets are internal plans. By comparing budgeted activity to actual results of operations, management can pinpoint needed changes.

Accumulating, categorizing, and recording financial and other statistical data is the essence of the accounting and reporting function. Appropriate summaries of financial and management reporting are distributed to the organization's internal and external users.

The financing function manages the flow of funds into the organization and includes investing activities. Specifically, alternative potential funding sources are evaluated and recommended, and needed funds are acquired. Cash-flow requirements are determined and made available.

Analysis of the utility's operation is an important function in financial management. In addition to traditional annual financial audits performed by independent auditors, this function can include an internal audit function with wide-ranging inquiries into the organization and its operations. Management or performance-type audits are also used with increasing frequency and may be performed by internal staff or by outside consultants. Measuring performance lets management evaluate the effectiveness of the operation.

⊠ Generally Accepted Standards for the Functional Responsibilities

Even though the term "generally accepted accounting principles" has long been in use, no complete official list of such accounting principles exists. Professional organizations and governmental and quasi-governmental agencies have promulgated standards.

The Governmental Accounting Standards Board (GASB) establishes accounting and financial reporting standards for activities and transactions of state and local governmental entities. The Financial Accounting Standards Board (FASB) establishes standards for activities and transactions of all other entities. Thus, unless GASB pronouncements conflict with or contradict FASB Statements and Interpretations, Accounting Principles Board Opinions/Accounting Research Bulletins, then the GASB pronouncements rank above FASB pronouncements in the hierarchy of generally accepted accounting principles applicable to state and local governmental entities. GASB's Statement Number 20, issued in September 1993, provides interim guidance for proprietary fund account's entities on the hierarchy of accounting requirements. *Codification of Governmental Accounting and Financial Reporting Standards* and subsequent pronouncements contain relevant standards for governmental entities. FASB issues *Statements of Financial Accounting Standards* to guide in the preparation and auditing of financial statements. FASB pronouncements govern accounting standards for all investor-owned water utilities.

Investor-owned water utilities that issue securities falling within the provisions of the *Securities Act of 1933* and the *Securities Exchange Act of 1934* must comply with the reporting requirements of the Securities and Exchange Commission (SEC). Although SEC relies heavily on accounting principles developed by other organizations, it is nevertheless greatly concerned with the form and content of reports, including financial statements and supporting schedules. It has issued Regulation S-X, titled "Form and Content of Financial Statements" and published numerous Accounting Series Releases and Staff Accounting Bulletins. Compliance with SEC reporting requirements may require the assistance of expert outside accounting and legal consultants.

The Government Finance Officers Association (GFOA) has published documents related to municipal financial management. Its *Governmental Accounting, Auditing, and Financial Reporting*, while not authoritative, provides detailed guidance on the practical application of generally accepted accounting principles for governments. *Disclosure Guidelines for State and Local Government Securities*, also published by GFOA, provides useful information in the preparation of official statements for issuance of municipal securities. In addition, GFOA gives the GFOA Award for Distinguished Budget Presentation. This award is not a standard, but budgets of recipients are evaluated on general elements of good budgetary practices.

The American Institute of Certified Public Accountants (AICPA) has been vitally concerned with developing standards of professional practice for its members. Among its more important publications are *Statements on Auditing Standards*, which are authoritative pronouncements on auditing matters. It has also published *Audits of State and Local Governmental Units*, which provides guidance on audits of governmental units other than the federal government.

The United States General Accounting Office (GAO) has a history of providing standards for audits of recipients of federal financial assistance. It has published *Standards for Audit of Governmental Organizations, Programs,*

Activities & Functions, commonly called the "Yellow Book," which serves as the manual for compliance with federal requirements.

The National Association of Regulatory Utility Commissioners (NARUC) has published the *Uniform System of Accounts for Class A Water Utilities*, which provides guidance for accounting for regulated utility operations. NARUC has also published the *Manual On Management Audits* for guidance to member commissions on management analysis.

⊠ Utility Management Role

Financial management is an important element of utility management. It is concerned with the same objectives as management — the effective and efficient use of resources in the accomplishment of the organization's objectives. Financial management provides assistance in setting and achieving realistic financial and performance targets.

The importance of financial policy direction cannot be overstated. Where clear policy has not been established and communicated, financial managers may find they need to articulate and suggest policy alternatives to the policymakers.

⊠ Book Organization

This book is arranged in five parts: Part One provides a general description of the water utility industry and a discussion of the objectives of financial management for water utilities.

Part Two deals with the budgeting, recording, and reporting of financial information that comprises the accounting cycle for water utilities.

Part Three is devoted to a discussion of the implementation and management of the accounting cycle. Separate chapters are concerned with revenues, operation and maintenance expenses, depreciation and amortization, taxes, utility plant investment, current and other assets, liabilities and other credits, and equity/capital.

Part Four is concerned with accounting reports for water utilities. The discussion covers financial statements, management and other reports, and rate making and other regulatory reporting requirements.

Part Five discusses related financial management functions, including financing activities and auditing. Also included is a chapter devoted to a brief discussion of information systems for water utilities.

Examples are presented throughout the book. The examples illustrate accounting principles and procedures that are generally applicable to water utilities and emphasize sound accounting and reporting practices for water utilities.

CHAPTER TWO

Water Utility Industry Description

Almost every business enterprise is concerned with the public interest to some extent and, consequently, is subject to a measure of public regulation. Certain types of enterprises are so greatly concerned with the public interest that they have been subjected to far-reaching regulation by government. Among these enterprises are public utilities.

Within the extensive area of public utilities, one of the more important sectors is the water utility industry. The importance of this industry is great, particularly when the role it plays in everyday industrial and economic life is considered. With its many ramifications, the water utility industry touches almost every phase of national economic life.

In the case of business in general, the economic law of supply and demand will act, at least in theory, as an invisible hand to regulate the economy. The demand for a commodity should bring forth the capacity to produce the commodity in the quantities necessary to fulfill the demand. At the same time, the consumer is able to exercise his or her influence over the price of the commodity by choosing among alternative sources of supply. Thus, competition should act as a regulator.

With a public utility type of enterprise, duplication of productive facilities is usually considered to be unsound. In the water utility industry, large capital expenditures are required to build source-of-supply facilities, transmission lines, pumping stations, treatment plants, and water distribution systems. If duplicate facilities were constructed by competing water utilities, the consumer, in effect, would have to pay for such economic waste through higher prices for water.

Such conditions have resulted in the granting of monopolistic privileges by governmental units to water utilities as well as to other public utilities. When the economic law of supply and demand cannot perform its function and, as a result, monopolistic privilege is granted, then there arises the need for another form of regulation. Such regulation has been exercised by governmental bodies basically in one of the following two ways: (1) through direct operation of the water utility by an agency of government, such as a water department of the municipal government, a water district, or a water authority; or (2) through public utility commissions or other governmental agencies that regulate the operations of investor-owned water utilities. The fundamental purposes of utility regulation have been to establish and control reasonable rates of earnings of public utilities, to establish and maintain satisfactory levels of services rendered by the utilities, and to ensure the financial stability of utilities. Utility regulation has emphasized protection of consumers.

The legal organization of a water utility may take many different forms, all of which can be categorized either as investor-owned or government-owned. The most common form of organization of water utilities is as a department of a general purpose local government, either a city or a county. The term "municipally owned" is used in this book to refer to any governmental unit subordinate to a state.

The legal form of organization has little or no effect on most phases of water utility operation. Therefore, unless otherwise indicated, the discussion in this book applies to both investor-owned and municipally owned utilities. However, the legal form of organization does result in some significant differences in type and extent of regulation, financing, taxes, and organization as described briefly in Table 2-1. The effects of the differences are discussed in subsequent chapters.

Table 2-1 ⊠ Important differences in water utilities resulting from type of ownership

Subject	Municipally Owned Water Utility	Investor-Owned Utility
Chart of Accounts	Often no requirement to adopt the state public service commission's uniform systems of accounts.	Usually required to adopt a uniform system of accounts prescribed by the state public service commission.
Water rates	Rate schedules are usually not subject to control by state public service commissions. However, in some states, municipally owned utilities are subject to regulation by state public service commissions on the same basis as investor-owned utilities.	Rate schedules are usually subject to the approval of the state public services commission.
Financing	Acquisition, replacement, or expansion of facilities may be financed by existing cash balances, the issuance of bonds to be retired from the income of the utility, contributions from the municipality with the repayment of any resulting bond issue accomplished through taxation or other sources, long-term advances from the municipality, contributions and advances from customers for construction, and contributions from state and federal governments.	Acquisition, replacement, or expansion of facilities may be financed from existing cash balances, the issuance of various types of securities (including preferred stock, common stock, and bonds), contributions and advances from customers for construction, and contributions from state and federal governments.

Table continued next page

Table 2-1 ⊠ Important differences in water utilities resulting from type of ownership (continued)

Subject	Municipally Owned Water Utility	Investor-Owned Utility
Taxes	Do not pay income taxes and usually do not have to pay property taxes. In some instances, municipally owned water utilities are required to pay taxes on property (such as source-of-supply facilities) that is located outside their service-area boundaries and within the taxing jurisdiction of other municipalities. Municipally owned water utilities may also be required to render free services to other municipal departments or to make payments to the general fund in lieu of taxes.	Required to pay all forms of taxes. (In a few states, investor-owned water utilities are exempt from payment of certain taxes, such as those on property.)
Organization	May be a legal entity in itself, as in the case of a water district or authority; or the utility may be a subdivision of a municipality, as in the case of a water department.	Usually incorporated, although smaller utilities may be either partnerships or individual proprietorships.

Water utilities in North America vary from systems serving large urban areas to very small systems serving only a few connections. In the United States, approximately 22,000 publicly owned and 37,000 investor-owned water systems serve about 187 million people. Statistics relating to ownership of US water supply systems ranging from very small to very large are shown in Table 2-2. Publicly owned systems are operated by a great variety of governmental and quasi-governmental authorities including cities, towns, counties, and special-purpose districts.

Typically, a water utility consists of a source of supply, treatment, storage and distribution, measurement and customer billing operations, and administrative and support services.

Often a water utility is operated in combination with a wastewater utility. Like water utilities, wastewater utilities are most often organized as separate municipal utility districts or as units of local government. Wastewater utilities are investor owned much less frequently than water utilities.

Many similarities exist between water and wastewater utilities, particularly in financial structure. The policies on extensions, contributed assets, and significant capital expenditures are often similar. If operated as a unit of local government, utilities are almost always operated as enterprise funds. As enterprise funds, each utility may make a payment to the general fund for administrative and other services, or the utility may make a payment in lieu of taxes or a return on investment payment, which represents a repayment from

Table 2-2 ⊠ Characteristics of the water supply industry

	Very Small		Small		Medium			Large			Very Large	
					System Size							
					Population Size							
	25–100	101–500	501–1,000	1,001–3,300	3,301–10,000	10,001–25,000	25,001–50,000	50,001–75,000	75,001–100,000	100,001–500,000	500,001–1,000,000	Over 1,000,000
					Number of Systems							
Ownership Type												
Public	1,987	6,357	3,893	5,716	3,416	1,567	645	206	90	192	15	12
Private	17,394	11,653	2,343	2,175	787	207	114	34	14	41	14	1
Indian	297	320	74	49	7	1	0	0	0	0	0	0
Total	19,678	18,330	6,310	7,940	4,210	1,775	759	240	104	233	29	13

the utility to the municipality for its initial investment in utility construction. Both water and wastewater utilities may have wholesale and retail customers.

Water and wastewater utilities are both usually regulated by federal and/or state health or environmental authorities. Increasingly, water reclamation activities provide water supply for certain uses, such as park and golf course irrigation. Coordination of the two utilities then extends to the physical systems.

Where water and wastewater utilities are operated by a local government and separately financed and operated, it is common for revenues to be cross-pledged for revenue bonds. Such cross-pledging can strengthen the attractiveness of the securities to potential investors. In some cases, the utilities are actually operated jointly, and in other cases, some activities common to both utilities are operated jointly, such as equipment maintenance, laboratories, and administrative and financial management. Even where water and wastewater utilities are not operated by the same local government, they generally use the same database for billing.

CHAPTER THREE

Financial Management Objectives

⊠ Financial Management Cycle

Significant segments of utility financial management follow a definite pattern and timetable. The cycle of strategic planning, budgeting, recording, reporting, and analysis recurs on a predictable basis, usually annually. Since the strategic plan generally covers a longer period of time, its annual function is generally one of an updating process.

Monitoring and analyzing the environment in which the utility operates may be a low-level continuous activity, with noticeable peaks of activity in response to changes in the environment. Forecasts and assumptions regarding events and circumstances exterior to the utility are developed. The broad purposes of the utility are reviewed, explicit objectives set, and alternative strategies to reach those objectives analyzed. Strategic planning may concentrate on the strategies and goals of a selected department or division, or the process may be oriented toward developing overall utility strategies and goals.

Programs translate an externally oriented strategy into an internally focused set of functional plans designed to implement the strategy. A program consists of a set of activities executed in a coordinated and timely fashion in order to achieve a specified goal.

Budgeting uses the forecasts, strategies, and programs developed in the planning process to produce a plan for a specified time period and states the plan in financial terms.

Recording and reporting the financial transactions of a utility is the process of communicating historical information regarding the financial position, results of operations, and financial activities of the utility. The transactions of the utility are classified and summarized in terms of money and each is related to a period of time, usually a fiscal or calendar year. Reports may be classified according to the content and the purpose for which they are issued. Different types of financial reports may be targeted for specific user groups.

Completing the financial management cycle is the audit and analysis process. A formal independent financial audit may be performed annually. Some other types of analysis may be needed on a more frequent basis, and periodic major studies, such as operational audits, may be undertaken.

Figure 3-1 illustrates the responsibility accounting cycle.

Figure 3-1 ⊗ Responsibility accounting cycle

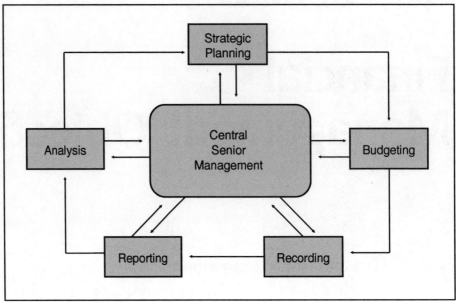

⊗ Budgeting and Forecasting

Budgets serve multiple purposes. They aid in making and coordinating short-range plans. Budgets are a mechanism for communicating these plans to the various responsibility-center (organization unit) managers and represent a way of motivating managers to achieve the goals set for their responsibility centers. Budgets can be used as benchmarks for controlling ongoing activities, as a basis for evaluating the performance of responsibility centers and their managers, and as a means of educating managers and others about the level of anticipated cash flows and noncash financial changes.

A budget is a set of estimated financial statements with appropriate supporting schedules. It has also been described as a plan stated in financial terms, a plan for spending money in a fiscal year, and as an estimate of what intends to be done in the future. All budgets deal specifically with money, thus distinguishing budgets from other plans. Budgets are future oriented. A typical budget period is a fiscal or calendar year.

Budgeting Process

Budgeting usually is accomplished annually in several distinct steps. First is the preparation step, sometimes initiated by a call for estimates from an executive officer. The estimates are prepared by the operating units, reviewed and revised as needed by financial and executive management, and consolidated into an overall organization budget. The next step is budget approval. In the case of governmental utilities, the budget is presented to the legislative authority and defended. Following legislative deliberation, the budget may be revised and subsequently approved. Governmental budgets as well as investor-owned utility budgets vary in their format, level of detail, and approval process. All types of ownership have one element in common — when the budget is approved, it is law. Budget approval is the legal authorization to expend funds to accomplish the intended purposes of the organization.

Types of Budgets

Budgets can be classified in a variety of ways. The classifications result from how one answers the question "Spend how much for what?" A budget-oriented purpose spells out in dollars and cents how much money is going to be spent for something in a specific time period.

A number of styles of budget formats can be found in municipal governments as well as in investor-owned utilities. Figures 3-2 through 3-5 show a typical budget format. Object-of-expenditure or line-item budgets are useful for control purposes. Program or activity budgets, such as maintenance or administration, are helpful in developing policy, but do not offer much control. Performance budgets based on a preferred level of service, such as improved customer service, need such output measures as time lapse to respond to customer complaints to be effective.

An operating budget is primarily concerned with annual revenues and expenditures. Capital budgets schedule expenditures for facilities needed as a result of anticipated growth, changing technology and/or regulation, and repair or upgrade of inadequate existing facilities. Capital budgets, or capital improvement plans, are usually planned several years in advance of actual project schedule commencement. This scheduling allows for preliminary planning, design, site acquisition, and construction. In municipal government, the approval of the capital improvements program may involve additional hearings and public-review meetings to ensure its consistency with adopted comprehensive plans. Funding sources for future capital improvements need to be identified well in advance of the needs for funds.

⊠ Financing

Acquiring adequate financing for day-to-day operations and needed improvements is essential for maintaining the long-term health of a utility. Revenues must be sufficient to provide for proper operation and maintenance, development and perpetuation of the system, and maintenance of the utility's financial integrity. The soundness of the utility's financial condition will be the primary criterion evaluated by rating agencies and will have a significant effect on the cost of debt.

Most government-owned utilities are operated as self-sustaining enterprise funds. According to GASB, enterprise funds are used "to account for operations (a) that are financed and operated in a manner similar to private business enterprises — where the intent of the governing body is that the costs (expenses, including depreciation) of providing goods or services to the general public on a continuing basis be financed or recovered primarily through user charges; or (b) where the governing body has decided that periodic determination of revenues earned, expenses incurred, and/or net income is appropriate for capital maintenance, public policy, management control, accountability, or other purposes."

User charges for services is a primary source of cash to meet the cash-flow requirements of the utility. AWWA believes the public can be served best by self-sustained enterprises adequately financed with rates based on sound engineering and economic principles (AWWA 1992). In addition to rates

Figure 3-2 ⊠ Typical budget format — operating budget summary

Miami–Dade Water and Sewer Authority Department Water System — Operating Budget Summary

For the period Oct. 1, 1990, through Sept. 30, 1994
($000)

	FY 90–91 Actual	FY 91–92 Actual	FY 92–93 Act/Est	FY 93–94 Budget
Operating Revenue	92,818	105,969	118,546	128,888
Operating & Maintenance Expense	36,479	39,104	41,861	47,183
Customer Accounting/ Service and General & Administrative Expense	13,576	14,876	17,331	22,487
Total Operating & Maintenance Expense	50,055	53,980	59,192	69,670
Operating Income Before Depreciation	42,763	51,989	59,354	59,218
Depreciation	11,427	11,775	12,206	12,967
Operating Income	31,336	40,214	47,148	46,251
Other Income (Expense)				
Interest income	7,437	6,035	5,154	5,480
Interest expense	(16,782)	(18,007)	(16,879)	(19,622)
Less: capitalized interest	2,927	4,036	4,842	4,939
Amortization of debt issue cost	(59)	(76)	(140)	(190)
Gain on sale of land	0	94	0	0
Loss of early extension of debt	0	(1,496)	0	0
Air-stripping grant	0	0	1,271	0
Total other income (expense)	(6,477)	(9,414)	(5,752)	(9,393)
Net Income (Loss)	$24,859	$30,800	$41,396	$36,858

and charges for water use and for fire protection service, specific charges for services can be developed. The unit of service to be priced should be narrowly defined. Services for which charges can be developed may include, but are not limited to, turn-on/turn-off; installation of remote meter-reading devices; meter resetting; appointment setting; meter testing; temporary hydrant permit; new account or account transfer; payment delinquency; NSF (insufficient funds) check; tapping; and application, engineering, and inspection fees. These charges should ordinarily be established at full cost and are based on the premise that services should be sold, not given away. The price should affect

Figure 3-3 ⊠ Typical budget format — operating revenues

Miami–Dade Water and Sewer Authority Department Water System — Operating Revenues					
For the period Oct. 1, 1989, through Sept. 30, 1994 ($000)					
	FY 89–90 Actual	FY 90–91 Actual	FY 91–92 Actual	FY 92–93 Act./Est.	FY 93–94 Budget
Retail Revenue	$63,703	$73,563	$85,784	$97,814	$105,449
Wholesale Revenue	14,198	16,217	17,236	18,042	20,297
Delinquency	1,120	1,294	1,295	1,370	1,380
Fire Protection	300	345	358	360	370
Service Charges	1,368	1,265	1,105	810	1,242
Miscellaneous	45	134	191	150	150
Total	$80,734	$92,818	$105,969	$118,546	$128,888

consumers' actions. Pricing on a prospective (future-oriented) basis is preferable to cost reimbursement.

AWWA Manual M1, *Water Rates*, fourth edition, provides guidance on developing rates for water service. The procedures outlined in the manual include (1) determination of the total annual revenue requirements for the period for which the rates are to be effective, (2) allocation of the total annual revenue requirements to basic functional cost components, (3) distribution of the component costs to the various customer classes in accordance with their requirements for service, and (4) design of water rates that will recover from each class of customer, within practical limits, the cost to serve that class of customer.

A number of alternative financing sources are available to the management of both municipally owned and investor-owned water utilities. The major sources of money available to both municipally owned and investor-owned water utilities include long-term debt, short-term debt, retained earnings, cash flows covered by depreciation charges, and contributions and advances in aid of construction. In addition, lease financing has become a more important and increasingly used source of funds in recent years. Municipally owned utilities may also be subsidized from available general funds. Although their use is no longer prevalent, some grant funds from state or federal sources include stock ownership, either common or preferred.

Ensuring the availability of funds on a day-to-day basis requires management and planning of cash flow. Cash-flow planning assures that sufficient cash is available when it is required and minimizes the necessity for short-term borrowing. Excess cash not required for balances can be temporarily invested. Cash management involves synchronizing cash inflows and outflows. Some methods to optimize cash flow include accelerating collections

Figure 3-4 ⊠ Typical budget format — direct operating expense by object

Miami–Dade Water and Sewer Authority Department Water System — Direct Operating Expense By Object

For the period Oct. 1, 1990, through Sept. 30, 1994
($000)

	FY 90–91 Actual	FY 91–92 Actual	FY 92–93 Act./Est.	FY 93–94 Budget
Personnel				
Source of supply (SOS)	261	261	381	435
Pumping	987	1,062	1,173	1,551
Treatment & purification (T&P)	8,617	9,575	9,729	11,035
Transmission & distribution (T&D)	6,832	7,159	7,970	9,227
Total	16,697	18,057	19,253	22,248
Electrical Service				
Source of supply	2,082	1,670	1,876	1,846
Pumping	837	877	902	951
Treatment & purification	3,191	4,098	4,718	5,051
Transmission & distribution	26	26	28	54
Total	6,136	6,671	7,524	7,902
Supplies				
Source of supply	175	130	228	293
Pumping	267	304	270	317
Treatment & purification	2,014	2,364	2,623	2,505
Transmission & distribution	1,898	1,916	1,935	2,269
Total	4,354	4,714	5,056	5,384
Vehicle Expense				
Pumping	11	15	47	102
Treatment & purification	363	287	349	307
Transmission & distribution	565	544	667	694
Total	939	846	1,063	1,103
Maintenance Expense				
Source of supply	31	16	50	52
Pumping	159	165	226	444
Treatment & purification	407	496	621	834
Transmission & distribution	310	389	350	291
Total	907	1,066	1,247	1,621
Purchased Water (SOS)	1,508	1,455	1,691	1,908
Geological Survey (SOS)	207	167	167	184
Fuel (T&P)	2,305	1,376	499	606
Natural Gas (T&P)	1,196	1,742	2,940	3,168
Chemicals (T&P)	1,159	1,241	1,064	1,525
Lime (T&P)	89	849	558	714
Security Service (T&P)	210	147	139	144
CaCO$_3$ Removal (T&P)	274	314	199	199
Security Service (T&D)	92	95	114	118
Paving (T&D)	406	364	347	359
Total	7,446	7,750	7,718	8,925
Total Direct Oper. Expenses:	$36,479	$39,104	$41,861	$47,183

Figure 3-5 ⊠ Typical budget format — direct operating expenses by function

Miami–Dade Water and Sewer Authority Department Water System — Direct Operating Expenses By Function

For the period Oct. 1, 1990, through Sept. 30, 1994
($000)

	FY 90–91 Actual	FY 91–92 Actual	FY 92–93 Act./Est.	FY 93–94 Budget
Source of Supply				
Personnel	261	261	381	435
Electric service	2,082	1,670	1,876	1,846
Geological survey	207	167	167	184
Purchased water	1,508	1,455	1,691	1,908
Maintenance expense	31	16	50	52
Supplies	176	130	228	293
Total	4,265	3,699	4,393	4,718
Pumping				
Personnel	987	1,062	1,173	1,551
Electric service	837	877	902	951
Supplies	267	304	270	317
Vehicle expense	11	15	47	102
Maintenance expense	159	165	226	444
Total	2,261	2,423	2,618	3,365
Treatment & Purification				
Personnel	8,617	9,575	9,729	11,035
Electric service	3,191	4,098	4,718	5,051
Supplies	2,014	2,364	2,623	2,505
Vehicle expense	363	287	349	307
Fuel	2,305	1,376	499	606
Security service	210	147	139	144
Chemical	1,159	1,241	1,064	1,525
Natural gas	1,196	1,742	2,940	3,168
Lime	89	849	558	714
$CaCO_3$ removal	274	314	199	199
Maintenance expense	407	496	621	834
Total	19,825	22,489	23,439	26,088
Transmission & Distribution				
Personnel	6,832	7,159	7,970	9,227
Electric service	25	26	28	54
Supplies	1,898	1,916	1,935	2,269
Vehicle expense	565	544	667	694
Paving	406	364	347	359
Security service	92	95	114	118
Maintenance expense	310	389	350	291
Total	10,128	10,493	11,411	13,012
Total Direct Oper. Expenses:	$36,479	$39,104	$41,861	$47,183

of checks received and slowing collections of checks written. Many utilities use a lockbox plan for payments of accounts receivable, allowing funds to be credited as soon as they are received. Arrangements with banks can include compensating balances and overdraft systems.

⊠ Accounting and Reporting

Accounting information is used to answer the following three kinds of questions:

- score-card questions, for example, "How am I doing?"
- attention-directing questions, for example, "What problems should I look into?"
- problem-solving questions, for example, "Of the several ways of doing the job, which is the best?"

Although budgeting, forecasting, and financing are all concerned with future activities of the utility, accounting and reporting are concerned with its history. The objective of the accounting function is to classify and summarize the transactions of the utility and to report the summaries in meaningful ways to various interested groups. Information is used to make decisions, and the information needs of various groups are determined by the types of decisions each is required to make.

The following major groups are among the users of water utility information:

- regulatory authorities
- taxing authorities
- owners
  1. Stockholders, in the case of investor-owned water utilities.
  2. Citizens and legislative-approval officials, in the case of municipally owned water utilities.
- creditors
- customers (rate payers)
- employees
- management

The information needs of any one of the above groups are not mutually exclusive of the needs of others. However, within each group there may be advantages to stratified reporting. For example, not all employee levels have the same "needs to know." Differences in information needs primarily have to do with the level of summarization. The information requirements of internal and external decision makers differ. Internal requirements for information are much more demanding in terms of deadlines, range of requirements, scope, and measurement characteristics. A typical set of external requirements for accounting information regarding a business organization's activities is normally completely contained within the set of internal requirements for information. In general, internal information systems for coping with the information requirements of decision makers can simultaneously satisfy all the information requirements of external decision makers.

Concepts of Management Accounting

Two broad categories of accounting reports are financial and management. Financial reporting conforms with generally accepted accounting principles. Specific statements are usually mandatory and have an historic focus. The most commonly reported accounting period is a fiscal or calendar year. Financial reports are precise and deal with the entire organization.

Management accounting, on the other hand, has no single unified structure. Reports do not necessarily conform with generally accepted accounting principles. The reporting periods are likely to be shorter than one year and are reported frequently. The focus of management reports is usually on the future and such reports tend to be less precise than financial accounting reports. Where financial accounting reports may be ends in themselves, management accounting reports are usually a means to an end.

Auditing and Analysis

A financial audit is an examination of the water utility's financial statements by a firm of independent public accountants. The audit consists of verifying the accuracy of accounting records and other evidence supporting those financial statements. Through the study and evaluation of the utility's system of internal control, inspection of documents, observation of assets, making appropriate inquiries, and other auditing procedures, the auditors will gather the evidence necessary to determine whether or not the financial statements provide a fair and reasonably complete picture of the utility's financial position and its activities during the period being audited. The responsibility for engaging the auditors usually rests with a committee of the utility's board of directors or another governing body of the utility.

A management or operating audit may consist of a systematic and objective review of the entire organization, including its management and operations. A specific segment may be audited independently or internally in relation to specified objectives and relevant standards. The purpose of a management audit is to evaluate performance, identify opportunities for improvement, and develop recommendations for improvement or further action.

Financial audits are performed by outside independent accountants; management audits may be performed by internal staff or outside experts. The techniques of analysis and the objectives of the audit are different. Financial audits are usually performed annually. Management audits are done less frequently. A management audit is more thorough and more time-consuming than routine monitoring of operations.

Performance Measurement

Often evaluating the performance of a water utility can be enhanced by using performance measures. Three general types of performance measures exist. Work-load measures express the amount of work performed for an activity in a given amount of time. Efficiency measures express output produced compared to the amount of input required to produce it (or inversely, it relates the amount of input to unit of output). Effectiveness measures indicate the extent to which an activity or program meets and fulfills an objective or need, or brings about desired results. Examples of each type of performance measure are given in Table 3-1.

Table 3-1 ⊠ Performance measure examples

Work Load	Efficiency	Effectiveness
Peak day demand	Treatment cost per million gallons or litres treated	Percent of time met peak demand
Number of meters read	Average number of meters read per meter reader per day	Percent accuracy of meter readings
Number of paychecks processed	Cost per paycheck	Percent of time paychecks issued on time

Some general rules of thumb regarding performance measures include the observation that some measure of output is usually better than none. The focus should be on important measures and where feasible, related to measures available from outside sources. Different performance measures should be developed for different purposes. Measures that can be reported in a timely manner should be used. A list of other commonly used performance measures follows:

1. Water treatment cost per millions of gallons (litres) produced.
2. Cost of chemicals per thousand gallons (litres) of production.
3. Transmission and distribution cost per mile (kilometre) of main.
4. Customer service cost per customer.
5. Administrative and general cost per customer.
6. Total operation and maintenance cost per customer.
7. Annual revenue per residential customer.
8. Jurisdictional taxes per customer.
9. Number of customers per employee.
10. Metered ratio, that is, total gallons (litres) of water sold divided by total water delivered to the system.
11. Number of bill adjustments per 1,000 bills prepared.
12. Composite depreciation rate.

Resource Management

Financial management staff may be assigned responsibility for management of all resources of the enterprise in addition to its financial resources. The most important of these are the utility's human resources and its buildings, machinery, and equipment. Personnel management is vital to any organization.

Developing and implementing purchasing and procurement policies, inventory control, and insurance are areas of responsibility that may be assigned to financial management staff. Facilities maintenance or property management, particularly in a smaller utility, may also be included. The condition and adequacy of the plant and equipment are matters of considerable concern to managers. Studies of plant and operating procedures may be required. Water utilities of all sizes often retain engineering consultants for periodic intensive study of the entire plant and system.

Internal Control

One of the most important considerations in the design of a water utility accounting system is the provision for internal control. Internal control is a management responsibility and therefore its discussion could logically be included in the section of this chapter concerned with the information needs of management. However, since internal control should be important to all interested groups, the subject deserves separate emphasis.

The American Institute of Certified Public Accountants defines internal control as comprising "the plan of organization and all of the coordinate methods and measures adopted within a business to safeguard its assets, check the accuracy and reliability of its accounting data, promote operational efficiency, and encourage adherence to prescribed managerial policies" (Committee on Auditing Procedure 1949).

This definition implies using all appropriate management control techniques to attain adherence to plans. In this section, however, emphasis is placed on those aspects of internal control designed to minimize errors and fraud and to discourage waste. The principal purpose of an internal control system is to promote efficient operation of the utility. It extends beyond the accounting and financial functions and includes methods for delegating authority and assigning responsibility. An internal control system consists of measures employed to safeguard assets from waste, fraud, and inefficient use; to promote accuracy and reliability in the accounting records; to encourage and measure compliance with utility policies; and to evaluate the efficiency of operations. Certain principles involved in the establishment and maintenance of an adequate system of internal control are discussed in the following paragraphs.

High-quality personnel. The water utility accounting system will be ineffective unless reliable, trained personnel are employed. The utility must follow sound employment practices, use employee training programs, and adopt procedures for measuring employee performance in order to attract and retain highly qualified personnel. Over the long run, the use of inferior personnel is likely to prove costly from the standpoint of productivity and possibly fraud.

Separation of duties. Personnel having record-keeping responsibilities should not have access to the physical handling of assets. Ideally, there should be a complete separation of the accounting, operating, and custodial functions. For example, the person receiving payments from customers should not have access to the accounts receivable subsidiary ledger. Such procedures will help to eliminate errors in accounting records and prevent fraud by requiring the collusion of at least two persons in any dishonest activity.

Adequate supervision. The organizational structure of a water utility should be such that every employee has a superior who supervises and evaluates his or her performance to ensure that the job is being effectively and efficiently performed.

Assignment of responsibility. The organizational structure of the utility should provide for proper allocation of responsibilities. The effect of assigning responsibilities is that individuals are more diligent in carrying out their assigned tasks and tend to perform their jobs more efficiently. Another important consideration is that the qualifications of personnel should be commensurate with responsibilities.

Establishing routine procedures. Written instructions should be issued to specify procedures to be followed in carrying out routine functions. Such instructions should include procedures for general operations, authorizations, reviews, and record keeping as a means of providing control over assets, liabilities, revenues, and expenses. The requirement that checks be signed by authorized personnel only after presentation of a voucher prepared from supporting source documents is an example of a routine established to control disbursements. Procedure development will also facilitate temporary and permanent personnel transfers.

Job rotation. Rotating routes among meter readers and rotating accounts among receivables clerks is a useful method of preventing dishonesty. The requirements that all employees take vacations to rotate responsibilities among more employees and that key personnel be bonded are additional measures for providing against fraud.

Investigations. Water utility activities should be reviewed periodically to ensure that established procedures are being followed. This may be accomplished through investigations conducted by internal auditors or outsiders, such as certified public accountants.

Physical control over property. Protective facilities and other safeguards should be installed to prevent the removal of property by unauthorized persons.

The extent to which these principles of internal control can be applied will vary with the size of the water utility. For example, a small utility having a limited number of employees may not be able to attain complete separation of duties. However, sufficient separation must always be maintained to ensure adequate control over such key assets as cash, securities, and receivables.

This section has dealt only with the general nature and principles of internal control. The subject of internal control, as applied to specific areas of a water utility's operation, is discussed within each of the appropriate chapters of this book.

⊠ References

American Institute of Certified Public Accountants. 1949. *Internal Control.* New York: AICPA, Committee on Auditing Procedure.

American Water Works Association. 1991. *AWWA Manual M1, Water Rates.* Denver, Colo.: AWWA.

———. 1992. Organization and Management of Publicly Owned Water Utilities. Statements of Policy on Public Water Supply Matters. Denver, Colo.: AWWA.

PART TWO

⊠ Accounting-Cycle Overview

CHAPTER FOUR

Financial Planning and Control

The effective management of any entity, government or private, requires accurate planning and the ability to govern, or control the execution of those plans. Financial planning is a process by which the organization establishes both long- and short-term goals and objectives. This planning process is a necessary step that must be followed regardless of the level of autonomy experienced by the entity. Even entities that are under larger departments or are controlled by other bodies have the need to establish accurate goals and objectives for their own operations.

The financial planning process is composed of the following three major elements: (1) the strategic plan, (2) the annual operating plan, and (3) the annual capital or construction plan. All of the elements are interrelated and each relies on or flows from the other. Once strategic plans have been developed, annual operating plans as well as annual capital and/or construction plans can be derived using the general guidelines established by the strategic plans. Since the business environment is a dynamic one, the planning phase is a continuous effort. The entity stops only long enough to take a "picture" of the requirements necessary to meet short-term goals and objectives during the following year. This "picture" is the annual operating, capital, and/or construction budget.

The second aspect of business planning is the ability to govern, or control, the execution of the annual plans. This is called the financial control process. The typical measure by which performance is judged is the difference between actual and planned results. This measure can best be achieved through timely, accurate, and consistent reporting of activities. The level of concern and accountability for variances from planned activities is a matter for top management to determine.

The final aspect of financial planning and control is the physical presentation of the strategic and annual financial plans. The final form of the printed documents can either enhance the effectiveness of the financial plans or detract from them by causing confusion. Properly organized and prepared budget documents are essential to the success of any financial plan.

⊠ Financial Planning Process

Strategic Plan

The strategic plan for an entity defines goals and objectives that are long-range in nature. Strategic plans often start with and evolve around the basic mission statement of the entity. A typical mission statement for a water utility might be to provide the highest-quality water in a cost-effective manner. Given this basic mission statement, the task becomes one of identifying secondary goals and objectives that make the attainment of the mission statement possible. Factors that influence these secondary goals and objectives need to be considered. An analysis of the environment in which the entity operates is essential. No entity exists in and of itself. Any long-range plan would necessarily have an impact on or be impacted by long-range plans of other related entities or governing bodies. It is essential that business environments and long-range goals of other entities be considered in the formulation of long-range, financial plans. Often the long-range plans of a utility are coordinated by central planning departments.

An additional factor to be considered in the definition of long-range goals and objectives is the ability to react to changes. While long-range plans are intended to be general in nature they must also be able to provide functional parameters for the formulation of shorter-term plans. Because the business environment is dynamic and because management objectives change over time, it is necessary to continually update and restate long-range plans. The planning process is an iterative one and as such should not be thought of as "static."

Strategic plans are the framework for the successful completion of both short- and long-term goals and objectives. They provide the guidance necessary for the formulation of more immediate operational plans. It should be the responsibility of top management to produce mission statements, identify long-range goals and objectives, and implement and monitor the strategic plan.

Annual Operating Plan

A refinement and expansion of the strategic plan in the short term results in the annual operating plan. The annual operating plan is most often described as the "annual budget." The annual budget is considered a refinement and expansion of the strategic plan because it provides management with the tools necessary to implement, guide, and monitor efforts towards the attainment of the goals and objectives as set forth in the strategic plan. When considered as an operating guide, the annual budget covers operating requirements for a specific period of time. When thought of as a "process," however, the budget cycle becomes more difficult to define. The cycle could refer to the fiscal or calendar year defined by the annual budget, the preparatory phase plus the fiscal or calendar year, or the period commencing with the preparation phase and concluding with the final postaudit. As a "process," the annual budget could easily span a two-year period (i.e., six months to plan and prepare the budget, one year for the actual annual results to evolve, and six months to evaluate the variances).

Annual operating plans consist of two primary sections, an estimation of expected revenues and an estimation of expected expenses. By and large these two primary categories represent two opposing sets of parameters. Revenue projections are to a large extent influenced by factors that are external to the organization. The political environment has a considerable impact on rates needed to derive revenues. The physical environment in the form of weather has an even greater impact on revenues by influencing the demand for water. Other external factors include the level of employment, business cycles, economic conditions, and any number of uncontrollable events that cloud the issue of revenue production.

On the other hand, estimates of expenses are mostly internal to the organization. Management can, to a certain extent, control the levels of expenditures by controlling the amount and type of activities that are undertaken. Although the organization has little influence on the prices paid for goods and services, it does have the ability to control the timing, amount of activity, and type of activity that is performed.

The estimation of revenues during the proposed budget period is normally the first step in the budgeting process. This part of the budgeting process is made easier by following a standard guideline. One such guideline might be the preparation of an estimated statement of revenues and the disposition of revenues for the budgeted period (Figure 4-1). The statement should be divided into two separate sections. In the estimated revenue section, a functional breakout of revenue classifications should be followed. Revenues derived from operations should be listed by classification. It becomes an easier task to project individual revenue classifications rather than attempting to judge the effect on total revenues of each external factor. Other revenues that are nonoperating in nature are listed separately by classification and are projected in the same manner.

The second section of the statement should be the requirements of revenue necessary to sustain operations during the budgeted period. By aligning the expense categories in their order of priority, management can assure themselves of ordinance compliance during the budgeted period. Details of annual operating expenses can be determined either by a "top-down" or a "bottom-up" information gathering process.

The "bottom-up" approach involves individual profit centers in the budgeting process. Each center is required to provide estimated expenditures for the coming period. It becomes the task of the budget department to collate and organize the information provided by the individual centers. A simple test for reasonability is the only control exercised by the budget department in the early phases of the "bottom-up" budget compilation. It is the job of each successive level of managerial control to keep estimated expenditures within the scope of the parameters established by the strategic plan.

"Top-down" budgeting takes the opposite approach. Top management decides the level of expenditures allowable. These expenditure levels are then divided among the lower levels of control as management perceives the need to do so. The task of the budget department in "top-down" budgeting is to follow the directives of top management and prepare the actual planning guide for each subordinate department.

Regardless of the method of budget planning, it is important that the adopted budget be flexible. The business environment is dynamic and changes often occur that result in a change in plans. In order to meet long-term strategic goals and objectives, it is expected that changes in short-term plans will occur. The budget, or planning process, should be a continuous one. Quarterly amendments to annual operating plans are often standard. Needed budgetary amendments are usually discovered through the monitoring

Figure 4-1 ⊠ Statement of revenues and their disposition

	Amended Budget 1992	Proposed Budget 1993
Revenues		
Operating Revenues		
Metered water sales	$57,696,549	$59,432,333
Revenue from federal grants	3,109,752	3,720,457
Customers' penalties	1,153,931	1,468,647
Fire protection and miscellaneous	2,875,471	2,981,750
	64,835,703	67,603,187
Nonoperating Revenues		
Interest earned and miscellaneous	8,103,729	6,979,000
Total Revenues	$72,939,432	$74,582,187
Disposition of Revenues		
Maintenance and Operation		
Water works system	$34,549,905	$35,495,745
	34,549,905	35,495,745
Operating Reserve Requirement	320,000	380,000
Revenue Bond Debt Requirement		
Interest costs	17,239,090	16,682,456
Retirement of bonds	6,007,500	6,614,167
Reserve funds provision	1,671,214	1,663,966
	24,917,804	24,960,589
Capital Requirements		
Capital outlay	1,080,630	1,274,805
Equipment additions	242,400	216,150
	1,323,030	1,490,955
Other Requirements		
Debt service on annexed water systems	598,043	702,792
Debt service on purchased water systems	680,478	478,555
Debt service on equipment purchases	44,470	38,650
	1,322,991	1,219,997
Revenues Available for Construction and Contingencies	10,505,702	11,034,901
Total Disposition of Revenues	$72,939,432	$ 74,582,187

process. A series of reports detailing actual expense variance from the budget provides the key to monitoring the budgetary health of the organization (see Figure 4-2).

Annual Capital or Construction Plan

As was the case with the annual operating plan, the annual capital or construction plan is a refinement and expansion of the strategic plan. Through the implementation of specific projects, management can continue to move toward the final goals and objectives of the organization. Programs that are designed to meet those goals should be identified and prioritized. As was pointed out earlier, it is important that the construction budget be flexible as the priority of specific projects tends to be dynamic as well. Having established, identified, and prioritized specific projects, it becomes necessary in the planning process to identify possible financing alternatives for specific projects. Examples of possible funding sources include sales-generated revenues; receipts derived from the issuance of debt; monies made available from local, state, or federal programs; contributions from developer customers or other nontypical sources, such as funds from successful litigations. Since the prioritizing of specific programs plays such an important part in the construction budget, it becomes imperative that top management be involved at each step of the budget-preparation process.

⊠ Financial Control Process

In order to effectively manage and control expenditures it is necessary to monitor the performance of the entity as it relates to the annual budget. Overexpenditures (actual expenditures exceeding budgeted expenditures) need to be identified as quickly as possible in order to apply corrective measures before major variances occur. Underexpenditures (budgeted expenditures exceeding actual expenditures) can either indicate that some portions of the short-term plan are not being performed or that expenditure estimates were overstated. The former requires management attention to determine how shortages will be funded or if program revisions are necessary; the latter may indicate a possible source of additional revenue that could be applied to other projects experiencing underexpenditures. Similar precautions must be taken when variances in revenues are identified.

The degree of control depends on the degree of detail provided in the budget variance analysis. Alerts can be identified either by a dollar variance or by a percentage variance. Often a combination of the two is used. Percentage variances become less and less significant as the dollar value of the actual expense increases. Conversely, a poorly performing budgeted item that has a lower dollar value could go unnoticed if a system of dollar variances were used as alerts.

In addition to the degree of control exercised by management, it is important that the information be timely. Budget variance reports should be compiled at regular intervals, such as monthly or quarterly, and presented at the first opportunity following the completion of the chosen interval (Figure 4-3). In some instances, the availability of an on-line mainframe computer system could provide budget variance alerts on a daily basis. Management should define the level of detail and the timing required to produce the optimal amount of financial control.

Figure 4-2 ⊠ Proposed amendments to the 1993 annual operating budget

	Adopted Budget 1993	Amendment Number 1*	Amendment Number 2†	Proposed Budget 1993
Revenues				
Operating Revenues				
Metered water sales	$59,432,333	2,650,000	300,000	$62,382,333
Revenues from federal grants				3,720,457
Customers' penalties	1,468,647	53,000	6,000	1,527,647
Fire protection and miscellaneous				2,981,750
	60,900,980	2,703,000	306,000	70,612,187
Nonoperating Revenues				
Interest earned and miscellaneous	101,363	11,475		7,091,838
Total Revenues	$74,582,187	2,804,363	317,475	$77,704,025
Disposition of Revenues				
Maintenance and Operation				
Water works system	$35,495,745		180,000	$35,675,745
	35,495,745		180,000	35,675,745
Operating Reserve Requirement	380,000		1,800	381,800
Revenue Bond Debt Requirements				
Interest costs	16,682,456			16,682,456
Retirement of bonds	6,614,167			6,614,167
Reserve funds provision	1,663,966			1,663,966
	24,960,589			24,960,589
Capital Requirements				
Capital outlay	1,274,805		345,000	1,619,805
Equipment additions	216,150		85,000	301,150
	1,490,955		430,000	1,920,955
Other Requirements				
Debt service on annexed water systems			582,075	1,284,867
Debt service on purchased water systems				478,555
Debt service on equipment purchases				38,650
	1,219,997		582,075	1,802,072
Revenues Available for Construction and Contingencies	2,804,363	(876,400)		12,962,864
Total Disposition of Revenues	$74,582,187	2,804,363	317,475	$77,704,025

*Amendment Number 1 — rate increase as approved by City Council.
†Amendment Number 2 — Annexation of Rural City and Rural City Water Company.

Figure 4-3 ⊠ Sample budget variance sheet

Current Period Allotment	Current Period Activity	Variance Over/(Under)	Classification	Annual Allotment	Year-to-Date Budget	Year-to-Date Expense	Variance Over/(Under)	Percent Variance
$14,090	13,973	($116)	Administrative Sal/Wages	$183,180	88,065	85,958	($2,106)	(2.39)
14,090	13,973	(116)	**Personnel Services**	183,180	88,065	85,958	(2,106)	(2.39)
0	0	0	Operating Expense	50	20	18	(1)	(7.50)
0	0	0	Maintenance Expense	3,910	3,910	3,257	(653)	(16.70)
0	0	0	Membership/Subscription	240	200	40	(159)	(79.60)
0	0	0	Data Processing Services	0	0	0	0	0.00
0	0	0	Teleprocessing Charges	0	0	0	0	0.00
0	0	0	**Contractual Services**	4,200	4,130	3,316	(813)	(19.70)
330	111	(268)	Operating Materials	4,600	2,280	1,845	(434)	(19.07)
330	111	(268)	**Materials and Supplies**	4,600	2,280	1,845	(434)	(19.07)
0	1,748	1,748	Bank Charges	7,160	4,050	3,992	(57)	(1.42)
670	645	(24)	Insurance	8,040	4,020	3,874	(145)	(3.62)
1,490	1,476	(13)	Retirement	19,390	9,690	9,492	(197)	(2.03)
2,160	3,870	1,710	**Other Charges**	34,590	17,760	17,359	(400)	(2.25)
16,630	17,955	1,325	**Gross Operating Requirements**	226,570	112,235	108,479	(3,755)	(3.35)
(420)	(471)	(51)	Transfers to Other Funds	(5,660)	(2,820)	(2,830)	(10)	0.36
(420)	(471)	(51)	**Interfund Transfers**	(5,660)	(2,820)	(2,830)	(10)	0.36
$16,210	17,483	$1,273	**Total Operating Requirements**	$220,910	109,415	105,649	($3,765)	(3.44)

LAST PAGE OF REPORT

⊠ Presentation of Annual Financing Plans

The presentation of the actual budget document is important. When properly presented, the budget document conveys the data in a clear, concise, and readable format. A solution to the problem of providing only the required information to a specific category of reader lies in using a comprehensive approach to the presentation of the data. Detailed line items for each profit center should be addressed in the body of the report. Each level of supervision should have its own summary. As the budget is compiled, each successive summary is rolled into the next higher supervisory level. In this manner it is possible to address every item of control and responsibility.

A comprehensive budget will provide much more detail than is ordinarily required by management. Because of this, it is necessary to provide a narrative overview of the budget. This overview should explain the organizational aspects of the budget and provide a listing of total dollars expected in revenue as well as the expected distribution of those revenues. A summary of financial information should accompany the narrative. The financial information summary should provide details at the organizational level with total dollars presented for each expense category. A further breakdown of financial information at the summary level can be done for each major group within the organization. Detailed financial information should flow from the comprehensive body of the budget report to the summaries. It is often helpful to provide the reader a description of the structure of the organization. This can be accomplished by including an organizational chart and a listing of account codes and their descriptions in the appendix of the report.

⊠ Summary

Financial planning is a process by which the top management of a utility can first define its long-range goals and objectives and then implement those plans through a short-term annual plan. The financial planning process is composed of three major elements — (1) the strategic plan, (2) the annual operating plan, and (3) the annual capital or construction plan. The financial control process provides the ability to govern, or control, the execution of the annual plans. Properly organized and prepared budget documents provide the means to monitor the efforts of the individual profit centers of the organization in meeting short-term goals. Flexible budgets are essential in attaining organizational goals because of the dynamic business environment in which entities operate.

CHAPTER FIVE

Record Keeping

The recording of information and reporting on the information gathered in a meaningful context is one of the objectives of the accounting function. This information has many uses and purposes, including external financial and regulatory reporting and internal management reporting. This chapter explains the process of the accounting function in providing its support and management role.

⊠ Accounting Function — Nature and Objectives

Support Service

The accounting function provides support to all other areas of the organization. This support comes through the accumulation and processing of information on the organization's activities. Information by definition can be quantitative or nonquantitative. Accounting information falls within the quantitative category as it is usually expressed in monetary terms in the currency of the country. The accounting function processes operating information, financial reporting information, and management information.

In providing support to other areas of the organization, the accounting function uses other statistical information to more completely fulfill its role. Data such as miles of vehicle use, hours of equipment operation, or kilowatt hours are nonmonetary information required to complete the process within the accounting function.

Accountability for the Utility's Physical Resources

The safeguarding of the utility's physical resources is one of the objectives of the accounting function. The procedures for the gathering of data must be designed to capture *all* data relative to the transaction and *all* data that define the area of operation affected and time period covered.

All transactions must be recorded. Activities such as movement of materials and supplies, which are daily occurrences, are usually controlled through procedures that capture and summarize the transaction. Transactions such as the sale or abandonment of fixed assets, which occur less frequently, must be incorporated within procedures designed to capture all the information required to report thereon.

All data necessary to record the transaction should be captured. The integrity of the transaction usually includes more data than quantity and costs. The recording of the acquisition of an asset may include additional financial data (such as the incurrence of debt or a lease), the computation of an estimated useful life, or additional statistical data, such as age.

Provide Information to Users

The accounting function also provides information to users. In addition to financial reporting, which is further discussed in chapter 15, information for management and operating use is an important goal of the accounting function. The accounting function primarily processes operating information. Operating information is data generated during the course of operations and usually provided in great detail to accounting. It is then reported to users and management after summary, analysis, and comparison.

As an example of operating information, metered water sales is discussed. In a monthly operating report, water sales is reported perhaps as a one-line item. However, when the data was captured it began with the sales to each customer, then was grouped by sales to different customer classes, meter sizes, and route or location code. Another form of operating information is budget variance reports. These reports are provided to each functional area or department in a utility.

Figure 5-1 presents the flow of accounting information.

Maintain the System of Internal Control

Maintaining a system of internal controls is not only the responsibility of the accounting function, it is the responsibility of everyone in an organization. However, certain controls are strictly accounting responsibilities in that the process of control resides in the accounting function. Procedures such as reconciliations of customer deposits, accounts receivable, and bank statements provide important internal controls for utilities.

Figure 5-1 ⊠ Flow of accounting information

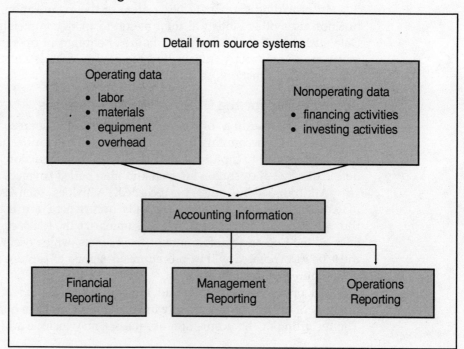

Policies and procedures are the basic guidelines and instructions to the utility and staff for the processing of transactions. Standard operating procedures allow a consistent method of handling transactions occurring under different circumstances or processed by different individuals. Consistency in reporting also allows for comparison between reporting periods and expedites management analysis and decision.

Certain principles involved in the establishment and maintenance of an adequate system of internal control were discussed in chapter 3.

⊠ The Accounting Process

Accumulate and Record Financial and Other Statistical Data

The record-keeping phase of the accounting process begins with the accumulation of information. Financial and statistical data flow into the accounting function both from within and from other areas. The integrity of the data flowing into accounting is reliant on the systems and controls discussed earlier.

Categorization and summarization of data sometimes begins at the source level, especially in automated systems and in areas of high volume, such as water sales. Before the accounting staff of a water utility can meaningfully record the transactions of the utility, its assets, liabilities, equities, revenues, and expenses must be classified using a comprehensive system of accounts that provides a logical and pertinent summary for reporting.

Recommended System of Accounts

A system of accounts should be designed to facilitate record keeping and report preparation and to provide for control and accountability. The system of accounts must provide for the accumulation of data in sufficient detail, and in such a manner as to facilitate the preparation of reports to meet the needs of all interested groups. In designing the system of accounts, it is important to balance the desirability of increased information with the cost of obtaining it.

Minimum requirements concerning the system of accounts to be kept by an investor-owned water utility are usually prescribed by the appropriate utility regulatory agency of the state in which the utility operates. Some states also require municipally owned water utilities to follow a prescribed uniform system of accounts. In fact, the need for accounting information by state utility commissions to aid in fulfilling their regulatory obligations is so important that the general design of accounting systems used by regulated water utilities is usually based on commission requirements. This basic design must be adjusted, as appropriate, so that the information requirements of other interested groups are also met.

The basic system of accounts set forth in this chapter, and the detailed listing of accounts given in the appendix of this book, is predicated on the recommendations of the National Association of Regulatory Utility Commissioners (NARUC) and is representative of systems required by most state utility regulatory agencies. Since the NARUC system is designed for investor-owned water utilities, it must be modified slightly to meet the needs of municipally owned operations, which are discussed later in the chapter and in the appendix, based on recommendations of the National Council on Governmental Accounting (NCGA).

The NARUC-published system of accounts for each class of water utilities consists of the following: (1) general instructions and definitions, (2) instructions concerning utility plant and operating expense, (3) a prescribed list of accounts, (4) a definition of each account and instructions concerning the types of transactions to be recorded in each account, and (5) the general sequence for balance sheet and income statement items. NARUC also issues, periodically, interpretations of the *Uniform System of Accounts for Class A Water Utilities*. It is recommended that interested readers obtain copies of the *Uniform System of Accounts for Class A Water Utilities* and related interpretations in order to gain a full appreciation of NARUC accounting requirements.

Basic framework of the recommended system. In this section, the logic of the NARUC system is explained. Figure 5-2 is a graphic presentation of the interrelationships of the groups of accounts provided in the recommended system. This figure, as well as the detailed listing of accounts given in the appendix, reflects the coding scheme employed by NARUC, adjusted to accommodate municipally owned water utilities. Accounts are assigned code numbers to facilitate identification and to allow for proper consolidation or combination of accounts when preparing and presenting reports to regulatory agencies or other interested groups. The account numbers are shown in parentheses in Figure 5-2.

The accounts in Figure 5-2 are divided into two major sections; the first consists of summary balance-sheet accounts, and the second consists of summary income accounts. A third section, comprised of the retained earnings accounts, forms the connecting link between income accounts and balance-sheet accounts.

Balance-sheet accounts. Summary balance-sheet accounts are grouped within the following two categories: (1) "asset and other debits" (accounts numbered 100–199), and (2) "liabilities and other credits" (200–299). These two broad categories are further divided into eleven groups of summary accounts, as shown in Figure 5-2. Many of the individual, summary balance-sheet accounts are supported by subsidiary accounts or records that provide additional details as to specific components of the summary or controlling accounts. One particular group of summary balance-sheet accounts, "utility plant" (101–116), is supported by six functional groups of detailed subsidiary utility plant accounts (300–399) under the NARUC system. This detailed structure is necessary because of the importance of plant facilities information to regulatory bodies for determining the appropriate rate base and to appropriately record depreciation. Detailed utility plant information also facilitates effective management control of plan assets.

Income accounts. The summary income accounts shown in Figure 5-2 are grouped into the following four categories: (1) utility operating income, (2) other income and deductions, (3) interest charges, and (4) extraordinary items. Operating income is the income derived from the normal operations of the water utility during a stated period of time. Operating income is computed by subtracting operating expenses (401–412.2), which include all expenses applicable to the furnishing of water utility services, from operating revenues (400), which summarize the revenues derived from normal operations of the water utility. In situations where the utility has income derived from the leasing of the utility plant to others (413) or gains or losses from the disposition

Figure 5-2 ⊠ A system of accounts for water utilities

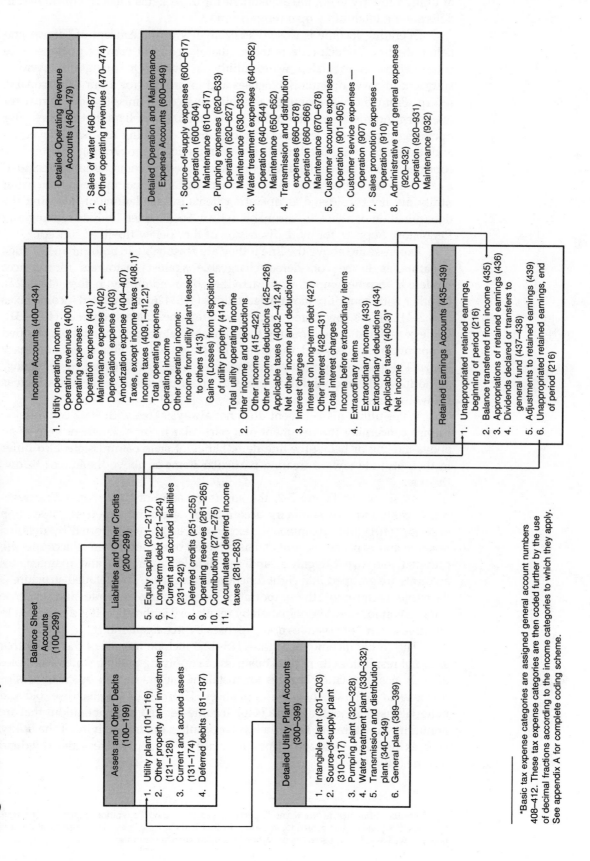

*Basic tax expense categories are assigned general account numbers 408–412. These tax expense categories are then coded further by the use of decimal fractions according to the income categories to which they apply. See appendix A for complete coding scheme.

of utility property (414), the adjustment for these items must be considered in determining total utility operating income.

Operating income is closely associated with the concept of "above and below the line," which reflects the regulatory point of view of public service commissions. A regulated water utility is entitled to operating revenues sufficient to cover operating expenses and to provide for a fair or reasonable return. From the viewpoint of a public service commission, the return (or operating income) to a water utility is the amount in dollars that remains after operating expenses have been subtracted from operating revenues. Revenues and expenses recognized in the determination of operating income are considered to be above-the-line items. Below-the-line items, although included as adjustments of operating income in arriving at the net income of the water utility, are not considered as operating items in calculations of rates and the determination of a fair or reasonable return. See chapter 16, Rate-making and Regulatory Reports, for more discussion of the "below-the-line" concept.

Expenses are above-the-line if they are reasonable in amount and of such a nature as to be considered chargeable against customers for services rendered. Income gained from activities of a nonutility nature (415–422), together with nonutility income deductions (425–426) and related income taxes (408.2–412.4), are considered to be below-the-line. Interest charges (427–431), while considered in determining the allowable rate of return, are not classified as operating expenses and, therefore, are below-the-line. Finally, extraordinary items (433–434), net of related income taxes (409.3), considered by regulatory authorities to be of doubtful propriety as operating items, are also classified as below-the-line.

Water utility management does not always agree with state commission rulings concerning the treatment of a particular income statement item as an above-the-line or below-the-line item. Different state commissions also differ in their attitude toward treating particular items as above-the-line or below-the-line.

As shown in Figure 5-2, the summary account titled "operating revenues" (400) and two summary accounts for operating expenses, "operation expense" (401) and "maintenance expense" (402), are supported by detailed revenue and expense accounts.* The detailed operating revenue accounts are grouped into two categories, and the detailed operation and maintenance accounts are grouped into eight functional categories. The detailed structure is desirable because of the importance of operating revenue and expense information for rate determination by regulatory authorities. It is also an aid to effective control of revenues and expenses by management.

The "other income" accounts (415–422) include income of the utility that does not result from its normal business of supplying potable water. Examples of such income include charges for installing meters owned by customers or revenues from the sale of water appliances (415); cost of merchandise sold and materials used for jobbing work (416); income derived from operations that are nonutility in nature but nevertheless constitute a distinct activity of the utility, such as providing sewage disposal service (417); and interest and dividend income (419).

---

*Note the difference in the terms "operating expenses" and "operation expense." The term "operating expenses" has a broader meaning in that it includes depreciation, amortization, and taxes, as well as the charges to the operation and maintenance accounts.

The "other income deductions" accounts (425–426) include miscellaneous amortization charges not included in the expenses used to compute utility operating income (425) and miscellaneous income deductions (426). Examples of the latter account include charitable donations, expenditures for the purpose of influencing public opinion with regard to the election or appointment of public officials, and losses on write-downs or sales of securities.

Interest charges (427–431) include interest on both long-term and short-term debt; the amortization of debt discount, debt premium, and debt-issue expenses; interest on debt to associated companies; and all other interest expense. Extraordinary items (433–434) include atypical, infrequently recurring gains and losses that would significantly distort the income of the current year if such items were reported as operating revenues or expenses.

Retained earnings accounts. The net income of the water utility, determined from the accounts previously described, is transferred to an account titled "balance transferred from income" (435) in the retained earnings category. The retained earnings category is composed of a group of accounts used to determine net income of the water utility and the balance-sheet accounts. The purpose of the retained earnings category is to explain changes in a water utility's retained earnings balance over a particular time period. Such changes may be caused by net income, appropriations of retained earnings during the period, transfers to the municipal general fund (or in the case of investor-owned water utilities, dividend declarations), and other accounting adjustments related to prior periods.

Limitations of the recommended system of accounts. Any system of accounts, including that suggested in this chapter, is based on a set of assumptions as to the organizational structure and operating activities of a water utility. If a given utility varies in organizational plan or in operating activities from the assumptions underlying the suggested system, then the details of the system should be adapted to fit the actual conditions. The essential features of the suggested system should be retained by all water utilities because the system is based on accounting principles advocated by NARUC and NCGA. Use of the essential features of the suggested system of accounts will promote uniform reporting by water utilities, which is a prerequisite to effective regulatory control. In addition, uniform reporting allows financial reports to be more easily understood and permits comparisons both between individual utilities and the industry in general.

Interfund transactions. In most municipalities, a municipally owned water utility, as a separate accounting entity, has important and continuing relationships with other funds for such centralized services as purchasing and transportation. Centralized services are usually accounted for through a working-capital fund. Conversely, various activities of the municipality use the services provided by the water utility. There may be other important transactions between the water utility and other funds of the municipality. Such transactions may include the transfer of a portion of the utility's retained earnings to the general fund, the transfer of resources from the general fund to the utility for financing purposes, and payments by the water utility to the general fund or special revenue funds in lieu of property taxes or a return on investment. With regard to all of these interfund relationships, it is most important to recognize a strict adherence to individual fund entities; therefore, the system of accounts must be designed to record the interfund transactions resulting from the relationships between municipal funds.

Restricted assets. A water utility may have cash and investments, the use of which is restricted by statute, contractual agreement, a special trust relationship, or utility management policy. Although the restrictions can pertain to both investor-owned and municipally owned water utilities, the latter group is more frequently subject to such restriction.

To meet the requirements imposed by the restrictions, the appropriate liquid assets are segregated within the utility enterprise fund. The segregated assets may include assets restricted for debt service (for both general obligation bonds and revenue bonds), assets restricted for replacement of utility plant, and assets derived from customer deposits. Although the restricted assets bear some resemblance to funds, they are offset by corresponding liabilities or restrictions of retained earnings. Since restricted assets are not completely independent self-balancing entities, they are not funds, as that term is defined in government accounting. Although these segregated assets are commonly referred to as "funds" (for example "sinking funds" and "construction funds"), NCGA has recommended that, in order to avoid confusion, the portions of a water utility's assets restricted for a particular purpose be referred to as "restricted asset accounts."

The restricted assets of a municipally owned water utility are offset by corresponding liabilities or restrictions of retained earnings. The recommended system of accounts differentiates between operating reserves and the restriction of retained earnings (called "appropriated retained earnings"). Accretions to operating reserve accounts are made by charges to operating expenses; the reserve accounts represent provisions for estimated liabilities or contingent losses. Appropriations of retained earnings arise directly from charges to the unappropriated retained earnings (216) account (refer to Figure 5-2).

The operating reserves category includes accounts called "property insurance reserve" (261), "injuries and damages reserve" (262), "pensions and benefits reserve" (263), and "miscellaneous operating reserves" (265). The appropriated retained earnings (215) account includes restrictions of retained earnings for bond debt service, constructions, replacement, and similar purposes. Restricted assets are discussed in detail in chapter 12. Operating reserves and appropriations of retained earnings are discussed in chapter 14.

Management Accounting and the Recommended System of Accounts

The central idea of management accounting is that managers should be provided with sufficient, timely, relevant information so that the entity may be managed efficiently and effectively. Management accounting for water utilities is concerned with providing accounting and statistical information to facilitate the performance of utility management functions, particularly those of planning and controlling.

The NARUC *Uniform System of Accounts for Class A Water Utilities* emphasizes the grouping of cost data on a functional basis, such as source of supply, pumping, water treatment, and transmission and distribution. For planning and control purposes, management is interested in cost information based on a natural classification, such as labor, fuel, and rent. Therefore, within each functional group, costs are identified according to their natural classification.

Effective cost control requires that definite responsibility for costs be established. A manager should be held responsible only for those costs that he or she can control. Therefore, the system of accounts must allow for identification and presentation of costs incurred by each responsibility segment (organization unit) of the water utility organization. Cost data and related operating statistics enable utility management to set standards of performance and to prepare realistic operating plans (budgets). Comparison of actual costs and operating statistics with planned costs and performance standards, by responsibility segment, enables management to control cost and performance and to improve future planning.

In addition to providing information to facilitate planning and controlling current activities of the water utility, a good system of accounts should be designed to facilitate the evaluation of proposed alternatives to current technology and current activities. Proposed alternatives often involve capital expenditures. Information needed for capital expenditure decisions is discussed in chapter 11.

Use of the Double-Entry System

The assets of a water utility equal its liabilities and equities. Liabilities and equities represent the rights or interests of various groups in the property held by the utility. The equating of assets with liabilities and equities is the foundation on which the double-entry system is constructed. Transactions carried out by the utility bring about changes in the assets and equities; accounts based on the double-entry system record these changes.

The double-entry system provides a continuous and complete record of the utility's transactions. Further, double-entry accounting assists one in understanding the significance of the relationship between balance-sheet and income accounts, as well as between asset, liability, and equity accounts.

The discussion in this book is based on the assumption that the double-entry system is employed.

Use of Accrual Accounting

There are two bases that can be followed in accounting — cash and accrual. Under the cash basis, revenues are recognized as earned when cash is received, and expenses are charged when cash is disbursed. Under the accrual basis, revenues are recorded in the period in which service is given, although payments may be received in a prior or subsequent period. Expenses are recorded in the period in which the benefits are received, although payments may be made in a prior or subsequent period. Systems may also be partly accrual and partly cash. Such systems are described as modified accrual or modified cash systems.

To obtain a statement of revenues and expenses for an accounting period, it is essential that all revenues and expenses for the period be recorded. The use of the accrual basis allows a water utility to match costs against the revenues generated by these costs, thereby producing a statement of revenues and expenses that is more accurate than one based on cash accounting.

In general, the accrual basis of accounting is recommended for use by both municipally owned and investor-owned water utilities. The illustrations and discussion in this book are based on the assumption that the accrual basis of accounting is employed.

⊠ Key Elements of the Accounting Function

The resources of an organization are the elements that make it possible for the organization to perform. The performance of the accounting function is dependant on its three major resources:

- personnel
- systems
- procedures

The personnel of an accounting division or department usually include the following types of staff and associated training:

- Professional staff has a university degree in accounting and adequate experience for the position.

- Paraprofessional staff usually has a combination of some formal studies and experience enabling them to perform certain tasks with minimum supervision.

- Clerical staff usually has little formal studies but has been trained in the procedures of the function. This group usually requires more supervision.

The systems available to an accounting division or department are very important as these are the tools accountants work with to process the information received. Accounting and finance systems were among the first to be transferred to computerized environments at the beginning of the age of computers. The first programs were quite simple, compiling only the basic data for generation of ledgers and transaction reports. Today, however, the most sophisticated packages are fully integrated systems, including everything from fleet management to project tracking.

The basics of an accounting system should integrate the data flow from one function to the next with minimum duplication of data files or data entry. Whether computerized or not, the system tracks the same basic data.

⊠ Distinctive Features of Government-Owned Utilities

Government-owned utilities share accounting features with private business enterprises, such as accounting for the utility as a separate enterprise fund. The municipal utility, however, may profit, break even, or lose money depending on legal agreements between the utility and municipality. Municipal utilities differ from private utilities on regulations governing financing and cost-recovery options for the physical plant, opportunities for centralized support services, and simplified accounting costs for services provided by other utilities within the same municipality.

Concept of Self-Sustaining Operations

Utilities may be operated financially to result in a break-even, profit, or loss, depending on the legal and contractual conditions of the relationship between the utility and the municipality.

Privately owned and operated businesses rely on profitability as the incentive for investment. Utilities operated for profit require the generation of revenues sufficient to cover all financial requirements, including operations and maintenance costs, debt service, and profit as defined in the private sector.

The financial requirements covered by the revenues of a utility can also vary depending on the legal and contractual conditions of the relationship between the utility and the municipality. A utility operated as a self-sustaining operation generates revenues to cover all expenses, which may include taxes or payments in lieu of taxes and depreciation. It must additionally generate revenues for expansions of the system if it is required to finance expansions.

Sometimes a utility is operated under conditions where earnings do not generate sufficient funds to cover all the utility's financial requirements. In certain circumstances, governments have as a matter of public policy decided that a subsidy will exist.

In contrast to this situation, under certain circumstances the utility must generate earnings and or make payments to the municipal government as a return on the investment of the utility.

Fund Versus Enterprise Accounting

Governmental accounting systems typically are organized and operated on a fund accounting basis. GASB defines a fund as a fiscal and accounting entity with a self-balancing set of accounts recording cash and other financial resources, together with all related liabilities and residual equities or balances, and changes therein, which are segregated for the purpose of carrying on specific activities or attaining certain objectives in accordance with special regulations, restrictions, or limitations. A fund represents a particular aspect of the activities of a governmental unit, and the classification of accounts must be designed to record all the financial transactions and yield reports pertaining to the fund as a separate and complete accounting entity. Funds are established in order to demonstrate compliance with laws or for reasons of policy and administration.

A municipally owned water utility should be accounted for as a separate enterprise fund. GASB states that the purpose of an enterprise fund is

> to account for operations that are financed and operated in a manner similar to private business enterprises — (a) where the intent of the governing body is that the costs (expenses, including depreciation of providing goods or services) to the general public on a continuing basis be financed or recovered primarily through user charges; or (b) where the governing body has determined that periodic determination of revenues earned, expenses incurred, and or net income is appropriate for capital maintenance, public policy, management control, accountability or other purposes.

Focus on Plant Investment and Financing

Plant in service is the largest asset on the balance sheet of utilities. Because of the large investment, state and municipal regulations have established certain financing and cost-recovery mechanisms in some states. These mechanisms, identified by such terms as capital-recovery fees, impact fees, and land development fees, may require special accounting consideration. By definition these may have strict restrictions and requirements on the use of proceeds and reporting requirements. Additionally, special uses may impact rate calculations under different cost-of-service, rate-making methods.

Allocation of Support Services

Centralizing support services is a common practice in municipalities. It provides efficient provision of services to other areas of an organization by eliminating duplicated functions in each area. Services such as a centralized inventory store, central fleet management, and centralized purchasing, are all effective in controlling the costs of the function and in providing better services through a more efficient organizational structure.

Through a system of cost allocations, the costs for these services are distributed to other areas, including the utilities. Interfund transfers are required to place costs onto the function that caused their incurrence. Proper cost allocations are necessary to set rates for the services rendered by a utility.

Allocations Between Water, Wastewater, and Other Service Functions

Cost allocations include the provision of services from one utility to another. Whether or not the service functions are in separate departments, boards, or commissions, expenses of another service function continue to be a cost and should be allocated between the respective entities. If the service functions exist within the municipality, cost allocations through accounting entry can be done. If they exist in separate legal entities, then cost allocations can be accomplished through billing of services.

⊠ References

National Association of Regulatory Utility Commissioners. 1977. *Uniform System of Accounts for Class A Water Utilities 1976.* Washington, D.C.: National Association of Regulatory Utility Commissioners.

National Association of Regulatory Utility Commissioners, Committee on Accounts. 1974. *Interpretations of Uniform System of Accounts for Electric, Gas and Water Utilities, January 1974.* Washington, D.C.: National Association of Regulatory Utility Commissioners.

National Committee on Governmental Accounting. 1968. *Governmental Accounting, Auditing, and Financial Reporting.* Chicago, Ill.: Municipal Finance Officers Association.

National Council of Governmental Accounting. 1979. *Statement 1: Governmental Accounting and Financial Reporting Principles.* Chicago, Ill.: Municipal Finance Officers Association.

CHAPTER SIX

Reporting of Financial Information

⊠ Financial Reports

Financial reports are the end product of the accounting cycle. The purpose of financial reports is to convey information about the financial condition and results of operations of the water utility. The financial condition and results of operations are of importance and interest to a variety of users. These users are generally classified as management, creditors, regulatory agencies, customers, stockholders, and other properly interested parties. The financial information contained in financial reports serves as a key ingredient in the decision-making process of these users.

Regardless of the user of the financial report, four principles of reporting should be adhered to. First, the financial information presented in the report should be accurate. Accuracy involves the concept of materiality and such limits of accuracy should be a consideration in the development of any system of accounting and reporting controls.

Second, the financial information presented in the report should be consistent. The principle of consistency requires like treatment of like transactions from one accounting period to the next. Financial information presented on a consistent basis fosters meaningful financial analyses. Changes in accounting principles or estimates may result in the need to restate or reclassify prior-year data in order to promote the consistency principle.

Third, financial reports must be timely. For any information to be useful in the decision-making process it must be provided in a relevant time frame. In order to report information by the time it is needed or required, the information demands of the intended users must be anticipated and a system designed to provide the needed information routinely. The design of the information system should also facilitate the presentation of data needed occasionally but not routinely.

Fourth and finally, the format and content of financial reports must consider the requirements of the readers and users of the report. Data should be arranged in a logical and readily understandable manner. The wording of the report should be concise and convey the precise meaning intended.

Language used in the report should be familiar to the reader and technical terminology should be avoided if possible. As much or as little detail should be shown as the intended reader is expected to need.

Chapter 15 contains more detailed information on the reporting of financial information.

⊠ Management Accounting and Reporting

Purpose and Use of Management Accounting

The responsibility of management in conducting the affairs of a water utility is to meet the enterprise goals set by the utility's policy-making group. In meeting these goals, management must determine the needs of customers for quality water service, provide and organize water production and distribution facilities to satisfy customer desires, and plan and control the activities of the water utility.

Planning and controlling are the responsibilities of every manager at every level within the water utility organization. The character and scope of planning and controlling vary with the responsibility and authority of a manager. Thus it is necessary that the organizational structure of the utility be clearly defined.

Effective planning and controlling by water utility management requires the use of relevant information for making decisions. Accounting is one of the main management aids for making its planning and controlling efforts productive.

Management Accounting — General

Traditional water utility accounting is concerned with measuring the net income of the utility for each time period of its life and determining the asset, liability, and equity balances at the end of a given time period. The measurement of what has happened to the stream of revenue and related expense, and to the asset, liability, and equity balances, is complex. The traditional accountant believes that the job is done when the data is obtained, arranged according to best practice, and reported.

Unlike traditional accounting, management accounting for water utilities is concerned with providing accounting and statistical information to facilitate the performance of utility management functions, particularly those of planning and controlling.

The central idea of management accounting is that managers should be provided with sufficient timely information so that the water utility can be managed efficiently and effectively. If this central idea is accepted, then the following corollary ideas follow:

- The focus of management accounting is on the future. The past is of importance only as a guide to the future.

- All important information relevant to a decision should be provided at the time it is needed. Implicit in this statement are the ideas that

    1. Information as to legal, political, and social conditions, as well as economic and business conditions (and expected changes in these conditions), is often more important than internal information. Much of the external information must be derived from judgment and instinct. Therefore, although the expected

effects of external forces often must be expressed numerically, the reliability of the numbers should be questioned.

2. Internal information relating to employee attitudes and behavior must be considered, as well as accounting and statistical information related to the production of water, distribution of water, and other activities' outcomes of the water utility.

3. No more time or money should be spent in obtaining an item of information than the item is expected to be worth. Thus, it is true that

    a. Accuracy is often less important than timeliness; estimates may be adequate for many purposes.

    b. Integration of all information systems must be accomplished. It is inconsistent with the objective of efficient and effective operation of the water utility to allow accountants, statisticians, economists, and operating executives to maintain overlapping systems for deriving information. In order to determine if data should be collected routinely or only on occasion, the system requires anticipating what data will be needed, by whom, in what form, and when.

Basic Concepts of Management Accounting

For accounting to fulfill the role that it can and should play in assisting management planning and controlling, a number of basic concepts of management accounting should be employed in the design of a water utility accounting system. Table 6-1 presents a concise statement of the basic concepts of management accounting. These concepts are described in the following paragraphs.

Collection of cost and revenue data by responsibility center. The first basic concept of management accounting is that costs and revenues must be measured routinely for each responsibility segment of the water utility.

The responsibility of the owners of a water utility is to state the major objectives of the utility and to communicate these objectives to the managers so that they will know what goals they are expected to attain. The owners must also set the major policies under which water utility management will operate the enterprise. If the ownership is far removed from the operation of the water utility, then setting major objectives and policies becomes the duty of the representatives of the owners (the citizens) or the members of the city council (or water commission, city water board, or water authority board). In the case of an investor-owned water utility, the representatives of the owners (the stockholders) are the members of the board of directors.

Setting objectives and policies for a water utility does not in itself require any management accounting or information system. Rather, the system must be designed so that the owners or their representatives are informed of the degree to which water utility management is attaining the goals set for the utility, and the extent of the water utility management's adherence to major policies.

Within the framework of the major objectives and policies established by the owners or their representatives, and considering forecasts of social, economic, and political conditions, the general manager of a water utility must

Table 6-1 ⊠ The basic concepts of management accounting for water utilities

Basic Concepts	Example of Techniques Used to Apply the Basic Concepts
1. Historical costs and revenues should be collected routinely for each responsibility center.	Responsibility accounting.
2. Historical cost and revenue data for each responsibility center must be related to the factors that caused the behavior of past data, so that the manager of each center may prepare realistic future plans.	Budgets or profit plans that consider all important items of cost and revenue.
3. Standards of performance are established for each activity and communicated to the managers so that the managers know how they are being judged. Formal cost standards are established when the expected benefit exceeds the cost of establishing the formal standards.	Standard or estimated costs, return on investment, or other measure of performance.
4. Alternatives to present operations are evaluated before management makes a decision or takes action.	Return on investment.
5. Actual performance is compared with budgeted or standard performance, and variances are investigated to determine necessary management control action.	Periodic reports flowing from responsibility accounting and work measurement programs, and special reports.
6. Adequate internal control is established over resources, including physical control, insurance coverage, accounting and statistical controls.	Control accounts and subsidiary ledgers, perpetual inventory systems, locked storerooms, night watchman, etc. (See chapter 3 for other examples.)
7. Internal and external audits are used to make sure management plans and policies are being followed, and that the internal control system and information system are functioning as they are supposed to.	Generally accepted auditing standards and procedures.

establish objectives and policies for each major segment of the utility. This is because overall objectives must be achieved through the operation of each segment.

Responsibility accounting. Responsibility for the operation of each segment of the water utility, and commensurate authority to perform the operations, must be assigned to specific individuals. Through these individuals, the general manager is able to control the segmental operations.

Each manager responsible for the operations of a major segment of a water utility is implicitly responsible for the preparation of realistic plans and budgets to attain the objectives that the general manager has set for the segment. Ordinarily, each major segment must be further divided. Responsibility for these subdivisions must be delegated to specific individuals who are assigned goals and who prepare realistic plans to meet the goals.

In order to aid water utility managers in preparing the realistic plans described above, the management accounting or management information system must provide information that relates past cost and revenue data to all conditions that caused the past data to behave as it did. Such conditions are both external to the water utility and each responsibility segment, as well as internal to each responsibility segment.

Effective planning by water utility management, however, does not simply involve the forecasting of causative conditions and the subsequent computation of cost and revenue figures on the same basis as in past periods. Effective planning by water utility management involves a determination of whether the relationships that existed in the past should continue to exist in the period for which plans are being prepared. Thus, the first question to be asked by each water utility manager in charge of a responsibility segment is: "Should a particular activity be performed at all?" — not "How much will it cost to perform a particular activity next year?"

Standards of performance. If it is determined that a particular activity needs to be performed in order to help the water utility meet the goals that have been set by the owners or their representatives, then the standards by which the results of the activity are to be judged — standards that are consistent with the objectives and policies of the water utility — must be determined. Thus, a third concept of management accounting for water utilities is that standards should be established for the performance of each activity. It is fundamental that standards be established for the quality of output of each activity and communicated to the person responsible for the activity, so that he or she knows how his or her output will be judged. Standards related to procedures, quantity of output related to input, and costs, are desirable refinements in all instances in which the expense of establishing such refinements can be justified by the expected benefits.

Evaluation of alternatives. After standards have been established and translated into requirements for staffing, material, equipment, and money, then the decision must be made by water utility management as to whether a particular activity (extension of water mains, for example) should be performed by the utility itself or by an outside contractor. If it is to be performed by the utility, then the decision must be made as to the most logical and efficient manner in which to fit the activity into the organizational structure of the utility.

The process of planning the future operations of each activity or responsibility segment of a water utility may disclose a number of alternatives to present operations. A system needs to be established so that the alternatives are objectively and impartially evaluated before management commits the resources of the utility. Logically, the information for this evaluation comes from the management accounting system; therefore, the evaluation of alternatives may be considered as the fourth basic concept of management accounting.

From the previous discussion, it is clear that the role of the management accountant in the planning function is to foresee what information will be needed at all levels of water utility management in the planning process and to provide that information. Usually, it is also considered the duty of the management accountant to coordinate the preparation of the plans by submanagers so that they all employ the same assumptions and adhere to the same time schedule.

Control of operations. "Controlling" describes the function of water utility management that has to do with guiding all parts of the water utility organization along planned paths. Therefore, a fifth concept is that the management accounting system should provide for the routine comparison of actual data with planned data and for the prompt reporting of significant variances to individuals responsible for both investigation of variances and corrective action. Comparison of actual costs and operating statistics with planned costs and performance standards, by responsibility segment, enables water utility management to control costs and performance effectively and to improve future planning.

Control of resources. If the operations and changes in the operations have been planned and controlled as outlined previously, then it would appear that management has done its best to preserve and enhance the capability of the water utility to make a profit, to be self-sustaining, to furnish quality water service, and to attain any other goals set for it. Clearly, preservation of the capability of a water utility to achieve the goals set for it by its owners or their representatives requires more than merely safeguarding the resources used by the water utility. However, the resources must be safeguarded or there is considerable possibility that they will not remain available to the utility.

The sixth concept of management accounting for water utilities is that, in order to safeguard the resources of the water utility, the management control system must provide for internal control in the broadest sense: accounting control, physical control, adequate and appropriate insurance coverage, and statistical control. A further discussion of the main concepts involved in the establishment and maintenance of an adequate system of internal control is provided in chapter 3.

Internal and external audit. Provision for internal and external audit is the seventh basic concept of management accounting. Any management information system for a water utility is incomplete if it does not provide for continuing internal checks to make sure that the proper data is being correctly processed and reported to the proper managers of the utility.*

Internal audits must also be made to ensure that plans and policies of the owners and managers of the water utility are being followed and that

---

*Within the context of internal control, the reader should be aware of the major provisions of the *Foreign Corrupt Practices Act of 1977*, which became effective on Dec. 19, 1977. Under this act, imposed by the US Congress, publicly held companies and their officers and employees are subject to civil liability and criminal prosecution under federal securities laws for failing to have a sufficient system of internal control.

The law requires that publicly held companies (1) devise and maintain a system of internal control that is sufficient, among other things, to provide reasonable assurance that transactions are properly authorized and recorded, and (2) keep records that "accurately and fairly" reflect financial activities in reasonable detail. Because of the law, it is recommended that publicly held companies review their present system of internal control to ensure reasonable compliance with the standards established.

For further information as to specific provisions of the law, refer to the text of the *Foreign Corrupt Practices Act of 1977*, Pub.L.95-148, tit. I,91 Stat. 1232 (Oct. 31, 1977). See also "Notification of Enactment of Foreign Corrupt Practices Act of 1977." Accounting Series Release No. 242. Securities and Exchange Commission, Washington, D.C. (1978).

necessary changes and exceptions are brought to the attention of appropriate managers. A management accounting system for a water utility should also have periodic independent or external audits to ensure that the system is functioning as it is supposed to.

Summary of Management Accounting

A management accounting system for a water utility should provide utility management with sufficient timely information to facilitate planning and control. Plans (budgets) should be prepared for each responsibility segment of a water utility by those persons responsible for the operation of the segment, within the framework of the policies that have been set for that segment. The plans for each segment must be an expression of the action to be taken by the segment to reach concrete objectives. Each segmental plan must relate inputs of all resources (personnel, material, equipment, and money) to outputs of services, so that proposed plans for each segment of the water utility can be evaluated and coordinated by the general manager to ensure the optimum allocation of resources available to the utility.

Effective control requires that actual performance be compared with budgeted or standard performance by responsibility segment, and that deviations from plans be investigated to determine necessary management control action. In addition, effective control over the activities of the water utility requires an adequate system of internal control over resources and a provision for internal and external audits.

Chapter 17 contains more detailed information on the reporting of information to management.

Financial Trends and Ratios

Financial trends and ratios are key indicators of a utility's financial strength, stability, credit worthiness, and growth capabilities. Financial-trend and ratio analysis provides valuable information for management in planning for the future growth and development of the enterprise. It is also very beneficial to obtain industry medians for the various trends and ratios being investigated for comparison purposes. Deviations from the industry median do not always signal a negative factor, but may simply identify a unique feature or element of the individual utility's operations or a temporary condition brought on by unforeseen occurrences.

Following are a selected number of trends and ratios commonly used in assessing the financial condition or balance-sheet components of a water utility:

- *Working capital* is computed by subtracting current liabilities from current assets. This is a key indicator of a utility's ability to meet its short-term obligations from available business-cycle resources.

- *Current ratio* is computed by dividing current assets by current liabilities. The current ratio is an often-used measure of short-term solvency because it indicates the extent to which the claims of short-term creditors are covered by assets that are expected to be converted to cash in a period roughly corresponding to the maturity of the claims.

- *Net funded debt* is computed by dividing total assets less balances in debt-service funds and reserve funds by net funded debt.

Following are a selected number of trends and ratios commonly used in assessing the operating or income statement components of a water utility:

- *Net revenues* are gross revenues minus operation and maintenance expenses. This amount represents the amount of funds generated by the utility that are available to support debt service and also fund capital and construction requirements.

- *Operating ratio* is computed by dividing maintenance and operation expense by operating revenues.

- *Net take down* is computed by dividing net revenues by interest requirements for the year.

- *Debt-service coverage* is computed by dividing net revenues by principal and interest requirements for the year. This ratio may also be based on average annual or maximum annual debt-service requirements stipulated by debt-maturity schedules. The selection of average annual or maximum annual debt-service requirements is normally specified in the governing bond order.

- *Debt-service safety margin* is computed by dividing net revenues less principal and interest requirements for the year by gross revenues.

⊠ Financial Accounting Standards

Guidelines for reporting financial information have been developed in order to promote consistency and comparability of data disclosed. This is particularly true for financial reports prepared and intended for use by those outside the water utility, such as rate and regulatory reports. All utilities should have ready access to these guidelines in order to assure that complete, consistent, and comparable financial reports are produced.

Selection of the appropriate set of standards applicable for each individual utility is important. Standards for financial accounting and reporting are promulgated by the Governmental Accounting Standards Board (GASB) and the Financial Accounting Standards Board (FASB).

GASB is empowered to review and promulgate accounting and reporting standards for state and local government entities. FASB is empowered to promulgate accounting standards for entities other than state and local government organizations. Obvious conflicts may arise when a general industry, such as a water utility, finds itself under the jurisdiction of both bodies, as some utilities are municipally owned while others are privately owned.

Guidance on resolving this jurisdictional conflict is addressed in "Report of the Committee to Review Structure for Governmental Accounting Standards," issued by the Financial Accounting Foundation and Governmental Accounting Standards Advisory Council, and dated Jan. 26, 1989. The report states

> The division of jurisdiction between the GASB and FASB with respect to the separately issued general purpose financial statements of "Special entities" (groups of entities, such as utilities and hospitals, that may be owned by either governmental or nongovernmental entities) was stated in

the 1984 Structure Agreement to be based solely on whether the entity's owner is governmental or nongovernmental. We believe jurisdiction should be determined based on this principle: The separately issued general purpose financial statements of groups of entities properly considered to be an industry for accounting purposes should be subject to standards of a single board, and practices that have worked well in the past should be continued. The principle incorporates a concept of industry based on accounting practices and the behavior of users of separately issued general purpose financial statements. Under this principle, the separately issued general purpose financial statements of groups of special entities that are not considered industries for accounting purposes and that show no signs of practice problems under jurisdiction assigned by ownership would have their jurisdiction assigned by ownership. Three groups fit the concept of an industry for accounting purposes: hospitals; gas, water, and electric utilities; and colleges and universities (other than two-year colleges with the power to tax).

We conclude that hospitals; gas, water, and electric utilities; and colleges and universities (other than two-year colleges with the power to tax) constitute industries for accounting purposes and that prior standard-setting, which has been within the purview of the FASB and its predecessors, has worked reasonably well in practice for many years. However, we recognize that government-owned entities have unique public account-ability obligations. The public interest would therefore be best served by having the FASB responsible for the standards applicable to the separately issued general purpose financial statements of these three groups of special entities, and the GASB responsible to promulgate, only for those entities that are government-owned, requirements to present such additional information as the GASB determines is necessary in the interest of public accountability.

Standards developed by GASB and FASB are issued as "Statements" of the respective bodies and are numbered consecutively as issued. The format of the statements typically consists of

1. Introduction and background information.
2. Standard of accounting and reporting, as it relates specifically to the situation being addressed.
3. Effective date.
4. Appendices, often including examples of disclosure and basis of conclusions (majority and minority opinions) reached regarding the standard promulgated.

Both GASB and FASB offer subscription services, or statements can be ordered separately. Statements are also published in monthly editions of the *Journal of Accountancy*. Of particular interest is the September 1993 Statement Number 20, "Accounting and Financial Reporting for Proprietary Funds and Other Governmental Entities that Use Proprietary Fund Accounting." Also, chapter 16 in this book presents detailed information on rate and regulatory reporting.

PART THREE

⊠ Accounting-Cycle Implementation and Management

CHAPTER SEVEN

Revenue

Maintaining an adequate level of revenue, which is collected equitably from all classes of customers using water service, is a major responsibility of water utility management. Other secondary considerations gaining increased public attention are attempts to use the revenue rate-making process to promote water conservation and to provide a subsidy to low-income or elderly customers or for other social purposes.

Whether municipally owned or investor-owned, total revenues must be sufficient to enable the utility (1) to provide adequate customer service to maintain and perpetuate the water system, (2) to pay taxes or make payments in lieu thereof when required, (3) to earn an appropriate return, and (4) to have the secure financial status necessary to obtain money at reasonable cost for system expansion or improvement. Adequate revenues result from establishing and charging appropriate rates for the water sold and fees for services furnished by the utility.

Customer payments for water service provide the main continuing flow of cash to most water utilities. Maintaining an adequate and continuing flow of cash to the utility requires effective planning, management, and control of revenues and funds on hand by water utility management.

Sources of revenue are usually constrained by the enabling legislation, charters, governing ordinances, or board or commission policy. State public utility commissions often must approve revenue proposals of investor-owned utilities before the proposals can be implemented. Governmental utilities are usually subject to an elected or appointed board or commission.

The revenues of a water utility are divided into the following two broad categories, depending on their source: "operating revenues" and "nonoperating revenues." (A suggested system of accounts for classes A and B water utilities is included in appendix A.) Operating revenues include revenues derived from the sale of water and from other activities closely allied to the sale of water. Nonoperating revenues are not derived from the utility's normal business of supplying water. Sources of nonoperating revenues may include rents derived from nonutility property, interest and dividends earned, recreational fees, and revenue for rendering supervision, management, engineering, and similar services to other organizations. Ordinarily, revenues from merchandising, jobbing, and contract work are also classified as nonoperating. Nonoperating revenues, together with the nonoperating expenses incurred in obtaining the revenues, are usually classified in the "other income" section of the income statement.

⊠ Operating Revenue Sources

Water Sales

Revenues derived from the sale of water represent the major source of operating revenue to the water utility. Water sales should be categorized to match the significant revenue flows arising from services provided by the utility, such as general customer water sales, fire protection service, wholesale, irrigation, or other special classes of service.

Sales to general customers are usually subclassified as residential sales, commercial sales, industrial sales, and sales to public authorities. Subclassification is based on the type of customer and the use made of the water supplied to the customer. Residential sales include all sales of water service to individuals for home or domestic uses. Commercial sales include uses by multiple-family, master-metered accounts; retail and wholesale businesses; and occupants of office buildings. Industrial sales include sales of water to manufacturing firms for use in manufacturing. Sales to public authorities include sales of water to municipal, state, and federal government units for services billed under general service classifications, as opposed to special contracts or agreements.

Metered and unmetered sales. Sales of water to general customers may be metered or unmetered. Under the category "metered sales to general customers," the charge to the customer is based on a rate schedule applied to the amount of water delivered through each meter or combinations of meters. Under the category of "unmetered sales to general customers," the charge to the customer is based on a flat rate per period of time per housing unit, footage of frontage on the water main, or some other unit. Although the flat-rate basis still is used, meter-based rates are more widely employed and are generally considered to result in more equitable charges to consumers. In addition, when compared with unmetered service, metered service promotes conservation and results in more economical use of a water plant by reducing unaccounted-for water and waste by customers due to leaks or overwatering.

Fire service. Fire service protection can be broken into two categories, private fire protection service and public fire protection service. The category of private fire protection service includes revenues obtained for maintaining fire protection service. This category includes revenues for water delivered to customers through specific facilities, such as hydrants, that can be either privately or publicly owned, provided the service is billed under separate fire protection rate schedules. The public fire protection service category includes revenues obtained from municipalities or other public authorities for fire protection service rendered to the general public. In the case of investor-owned water utilities, charges for public fire protection typically are levied against the municipality on the basis of the number of hydrants, miles of mains, or "inch–foot" calculations (where "inch" refers to the diameter of mains and "foot" refers to the length of mains). In the case of municipally owned water utilities, a charge for public fire protection may be levied against the municipality or directly against property owners on the basis of assessed valuation. The latter procedure is an equitable way of distributing the cost of public fire protection among those benefiting from such service, as opposed to a charge based on water consumption.

Public authorities. The "sales to the public authorities" category includes revenues from municipalities or other governmental authorities for such purposes as supplying water to public buildings, parks, swimming pools, fountains, and median strips. Sales to public authorities can be made under special contracts or agreements that call for the application of either metered or flat-rate schedules.

Irrigation. In some utilities, sales to irrigation customers may comprise a significant portion of total water sales. The "sales to irrigation customers" category includes revenues for water supplied for commercial irrigation purposes. These revenues are generally billed under rate schedules applicable solely to irrigation customers and can be either metered or unmetered.

Resale. The "sales for resale" category includes revenues from water supplied to investor-owned water utilities or to public authorities for resale, including water supplied for standby or for mutual assistance agreements. Water supplied for resales is usually billed under special rate schedules or contracted agreements.

Interdepartmental. The "interdepartmental sales" category includes amounts charged for water supplied to other departments of the controlled entity under specified rate schedules. An example would be a case in which the water department sold water to the electric utility or wastewater treatment department of the same city.

There may be other special sales of water which, if significant in amount and billed under special rate schedules, should be classified separately. These special sales include revenues from water supplied for air conditioning, refrigeration, large industrial users, or institutions that consume a significant portion of the total water delivered by the utility and that are billed under special rate schedules or agreements. In addition, revenues from water furnished to builders or contractors during construction, and other customers who use water for a limited time without permanent connections should be classified separately if their consumption is significant.

Other Operating Revenues

Although revenues derived from the sale of water represent the major source of operating revenues, other operating revenues may also be significant. For example, ad valorem taxes for a governmental water utility and power sales can provide a significant source of revenues for some utilities. The sources of other operating revenues should be reported separately when their impact is meaningful to the operations of the utility.

Some of the classifications suggested clearly have limited impact on many utilities. For example, forfeited discounts include the amount of billed water-revenue discounts forfeited and the amount of additional charges to customers who do not pay their water bills within a specified time. This may or may not be significant to a utility. However, "miscellaneous service revenues" includes items such as fees for changing or reconnecting service and charges for maintenance of appliances, piping, or other installations on customers' premises. Such fees could provide a significant revenue base to cover the cost of these services. Rents from "water property and interdepartmental rents" includes rents received from other organizations or departments for use of property devoted to water operations. "Other water revenues" includes revenues incidental to water operations and not included in any of the previous accounts, such as income from the sale of material and supplies not ordinarily purchased for resale and commissions on the sale or distribution of water of other utilities.

Operating Revenue Accounts

State public service commissions generally require that separate accounts and subsidiary records be kept for each specified type of operating revenue. At a minimum, separate accounts and subsidiary records are generally required for each type of operating revenue discussed in the preceding sections (shown in the system of accounts presented in appendix A). In addition, operating revenue derived from other sources, if significant in amount, should also be classified in separate operating revenue accounts.

The careful maintenance of detailed operating revenue accounts (including the subdivision of sales to general customers in terms of residential customers, commercial customers, industrial customers, and public authorities) is essential to water utility management and to regulatory authorities for determining and establishing rate schedules. Water utility management can use the information contained in the detailed operating revenue accounts to analyze trends in revenue and to aid in forecasting future water requirements. Trends and forecasts of water revenue requirements can, in turn, affect management decisions regarding the amount and type of capital expenditures to be undertaken by the utility, the securing of additional water rights and franchises, and other preparations for expansion.

⊠ Projecting Operating Revenues

Sound planning on the part of water utility management is a prerequisite to obtaining an adequate level of revenue. Total operating revenues must be sufficient to enable the water utility to provide adequate water service.

The operating budget is an important planning aid to water utility management. It allows management to develop plans to meet the water utility's revenue requirements, or costs of rendering service. The nature of revenue requirements differs among water utilities. In the case of investor-owned water utilities and municipally owned water utilities subject to rate regulation by state commissions, revenue requirements customarily include operating expenses and an allowance, as measured by operating income, intended to provide a fair and reasonable return on a defined rate base. In the case of municipally owned water utilities not subject to commission jurisdiction, the revenue requirements of the utility are frequently a function of "cash needs." The composition of cash needs varies. Cash needs typically include, but are not limited to, operation and maintenance expenses, debt service requirements, and outlays for normal plant replacements, extensions, and improvements.

Developing the Operating Budget

An early step in the development of the operating budget is to estimate the revenue component of the budget. The statement of estimated operating revenues will show the projected revenues by major components, generally forecasted for a budget period of one year or more. Operating revenues are a function of the demand for water service. In turn, the demand for water service in a given locality is a function of factors such as the population level, industrial concentration, weather conditions, and economic conditions.

Operating revenues should be estimated for each category of service to which a separate rate schedule applies (sales to general customers, public and private fire protection service, wholesale, and any other significant revenue category). Forecasting revenues by residential, commercial, industrial, and public authority components is recommended if the accuracy of the forecast can be materially improved by separately forecasting the revenue to be derived from each component. Forecasting by residential, commercial, industrial, and public authority components could improve the accuracy of the forecast if the historical water-consumption pattern for each of these classes of general customers reflects a different trend in water usage or when future trends may be expected to diverge.

In addition, if a water utility serves more than one community or district, each of which is subject to different rate schedules or reflects different water usage characteristics, then operating revenues should be estimated for each community or district served. To increase the accuracy of the forecast, large-use customers or customers having extraordinary demands for service may be requested to supply estimates of their probable demands for water during the budget period.

Because sales to residential customers typically produce the greatest portion of total operating revenues, it may be desirable to forecast residential sales by components, such as single-family houses, multifamily houses, and apartment houses. The extent to which the revenue forecast is made by separate customer classes and by components of classes depends on (1) the extent to which different customer classes and components of classes are subject to differing rate schedules, (2) the extent to which different classes and components of classes reflect differing consumption characteristics, and (3) the degree of accuracy desired in the operating revenue forecast.

The preparation of a statement of estimated operating revenues may be considered as a two-step process. In the first step, an estimate must be made of either the quantity of water required by each customer class and the projected number of accounts in each customer class, or other quantity measures used as a basis for applying rate schedules. In the second step, the rate schedules must be applied to the estimated quantity components to determine the estimated revenue obtainable from each customer class.

Interrelation of Operating Budget and Capital Expenditures Budget

The forecast of demand for water service is the starting point of the entire budgetary process; that is, estimated customer demand for water service is the basis for quantification of the entire water utility operations plan. The estimate of the quantity of water required by customers will in turn affect the level of budgeted operating revenues (assuming that at least a portion of customers' water usage is metered).

The estimated amount of water required by customers will also affect the level of budgeted operating expenses. Many of the operating expense items of a water utility do not vary in amount in response to changes in operating activity by the utility. Accountants call such cost behavior "fixed." There are other operating expenses that do vary in amount in response to changes in operating activity. The accounting term for this behavior is "variable." Fuel expenses (for pumping) and chemical expenses (for treatment) are examples of expenses that vary in relation to the quantity of water demanded by customers. Meter reading, billing, and collection expenses do not vary directly with consumption, but can vary to some degree with the number of customers served by the utility.

In addition to serving as a basis of budgeting operating revenues and some operating expenses, a forecast of future water consumption is used by water utility management in planning a capital expenditures program that will provide facilities sufficient to meet future demands for water. Total system capacity must be provided to meet the peak hourly demand placed on the system during the year by general customers, and additional capacity must be available to provide adequate public fire protection service even during times of peak demand by general customers. The impact of planned additional facilities on operating expenses (including the level of preventive maintenance and improvements) and on revenue requirements must be considered. In order to be an effective capital budgeting tool, the forecast of annual customer water requirements should be made for at least a five-year period, and should include anticipated peak demands for service. Inasmuch as the forecasts for the period beyond the first year are not used as a basis for the current operating budget, the forecasts need not be as detailed in terms of customer or service components.

Forecasting Sales of Water to Metered Customers

Historical water consumption information accumulated from individual customer records may be used as a basis for estimating the amount of water to be sold to each class of metered customer, or component thereof, during the budget period. For example, the amount of water sold within each block of a block-rate schedule for each year in a series of years for each customer class or class component may be charted. A trend line can then be fitted to the historical data. The trend line can be extrapolated in order to estimate the amount of water to be sold to the class of customer or class component for the budget period.

If, in addition to the block rate schedule, a service charge or minimum charge is levied on customers, an estimate must also be made of the revenue to be obtained from service charges or minimum charges. The estimate of the revenue from service charges or minimum charges involves forecasting the number of customers who will be subject to the charges. This forecast can be made on the basis of historical information in the same manner as the forecast of water consumption. If the service charge or minimum charge is based on the size of meter or other measure, then the historical data must be assembled on that basis.

Forecasting Unmetered Sales

Unmetered sales charges to a particular class of customer are based on quantity components or measures other than the amount of water consumed. Thus, budgeted revenue for a particular unmetered customer class depends on (1) the estimated number of customers in the class and (2) the estimated number of units on which water charges are based. Such units might include dwelling units, front footage on the main of the customers' premises, or hydrants. Customer records should provide historical data for these factors, which can then be extrapolated.

Modification of Historical Trends

Historical data, such as per capita consumption records, must be examined to ensure that underlying conditions have not changed. Economic and social conditions in the service area of the utility can change, causing corresponding changes in the number of customers in a particular class, the quantity of water sold within each block of a block rate schedule, the number of meters of various size, or other demand and revenue factors. Therefore, projections of historical consumption trends must be adjusted to account for changing conditions in the service area. Specifically, the estimated number of customers should be modified to reflect increases resulting from building permits projected to be issued, the number of new houses built, and other similar factors. Likewise, historical projections of the quantity of water sold within each block of a block rate schedule should be adjusted for the estimated effects of changes in pricing policies, advertising and other promotional activities, and general and local socioeconomic conditions.

Applying the Rate Schedules

After the quantity components are estimated, they must be related to the appropriate rate schedule in order to determine total projected revenues. In the case of metered sales to a particular customer class or class component, for example, the appropriate block rate schedule is applied to the estimated water volume to be sold under the rate schedule in order to obtain a revenue estimate for that class or class component. If a service charge or minimum charge is levied on metered customers, then the appropriate charge must be multiplied by the estimated number of customers (or number of meters, if the charge is based on meter size) to determine the total estimated revenue obtainable under the service charge or minimum charge.

To determine the budgeted amount of revenue from unmetered sales, the appropriate flat-rate schedules are applied on the basis of some common denominator, such as housing units, bedrooms, front footage, or hydrants used by each customer class.

Ultimately, the adequacy of forecasted operating revenues must be judged in terms of covering the cost of rendering water service. In an inflationary and capital-expansion environment, the existing rate schedule may be judged inadequate for meeting the various costs of rendering water service (revenue requirements). In such instances, either the existing rate schedule must be increased to reflect the inflationary environment or a rate study undertaken to develop an alternative rate schedule that will generate the necessary revenues.

⊠ Planning the Rate Schedule

The particular rate-making procedure to be followed in establishing a rate schedule for a water utility depends on many factors, including differences in the form of ownership (investor-owned or municipally owned), differences in regulatory control over water rates (control by a state public service commission or by a local authority), and differences in individual viewpoints or preferences concerning the appropriate procedure to be followed to meet local conditions and requirements. Nevertheless, there are basic considerations involved in planning a rate schedule for almost any water utility. (Refer to AWWA Manual M1, *Water Rates*, for specific information and principles of water rate structure design.)

The development of an adequate rate schedule represents a joint effort between various experts, particularly accountants and engineers. The accounting records (property and expense records) supply the basic data for the cost-of-service study. From these records, the accountant must develop pro forma statements of expense. The engineer generally is responsible for converting original cost records to rate-base values (when applicable) that fall somewhere between original cost less depreciation and replacement cost less depreciation. Subsequently, the accountant and engineer must work together to allocate utility plant and operating costs to each class of customer in order to develop an equitable water rate schedule.

Water rates must be established at levels that will produce sufficient total revenue to allow the water utility to (1) operate and maintain the water system in a manner that will provide adequate service, (2) meet financial obligations, (3) attract capital to maintain and improve facilities, and (4) provide additional facilities required by customer demand.

Depending on the circumstances under which the water utility operates, total revenue requirements are determined in accordance with the traditional public utility approach, the "cash needs" approach, or a combination of both. In order to attain reasonable equity, differences in rates and charges for water service applicable to different classes of customers and users should be based, insofar as possible, on the cost of serving the different customer classes and uses.

Revenue Requirements Under the Traditional Public Utility Approach

In the case of investor-owned water utilities subject to rate regulation by state public service commissions, revenue requirements are generally established by applying the traditional public utility approach, that is, by determining the total revenues sufficient to permit a given return on a defined rate base.

In instances where state regulatory bodies have jurisdiction over rates of municipally owned water utilities, the approach to the determination of revenue requirements can vary. In some cases, the public utility approach is employed, whereas in other cases, the "cash needs" approach is required. The usual exemption of municipally owned water utilities from a state commission regulation does not necessarily hold when the utility renders service to customers located outside the municipality or service areas. When commissions do regulate outside-service-area water charges, the related revenue requirements are generally determined using the traditional public utility approach.

In the case of municipally owned water utilities not subject to rate regulation by state public service commissions, the determination of revenue requirements according to the traditional public utility approach also provides an alternative to the use of the "cash needs" approach. The public utility approach recognizes that the water utility is the property of the citizens of the municipality and that outside users should be charged amounts to cover operation and maintenance expenses, depreciation expense, local taxes, and a reasonable return on the value of all property devoted to providing service to the suburban user who is not at risk of otherwise contributing to the funding of the utility (i.e., general fund transfers of citizen's taxes paid).

If the public utility approach is used inside the service area, as is required of investor-owned water utilities and of some municipally owned water utilities subject to commission regulation, then differences between inside-the-service-area and outside-the-service-area rates may be justified on the basis of variations in the cost of serving the two groups of customers. Rates developed under the "cash needs" approach will often result in rates that are significantly different from rates developed under the public utility approach.

Using the public utility approach, operating revenues must be sufficient to cover operation and maintenance expenses, depreciation and amortization charges, and taxes, and must allow a return on the rate base.

There is almost always some time lapse between the date an application for new rates is prepared and submitted to the state public service commission for approval and the date the new rates become effective. If rates are predicated on past or present costs, and if operating expenses increase markedly, then the revenues derived from the new rate schedule may become inadequate shortly after it goes into effect. Therefore, a realistic forecast of expenses should be based on past operation and maintenance expenses, depreciation and amortization charges, and taxes, all adjusted for known or anticipated changes for the applicable future period.

Recent trends favor regular rate increases to cover the impact of inflation and the often sharply increasing marginal costs of service as available water supplies become more difficult and costly to develop.

Although periodic changes in rates are necessitated by changing requirements, too frequent changes in rates could be undesirable because of the cost incurred in conjunction with rate cases and the adverse effect on customer relations. On the other hand, regular annual rate increases that reflect inflationary costs in current dollars are most equitable to both current and future customers.

Properly matching costs with revenues will assure that current customers pay only their fair share of costs of services incurred by the utility. However, in the case of water utilities subject to public service commission regulation, the rate base and operating expense figures are usually historical in nature and generally are developed for a "test year." The rate base and operating expense figures for the test year are typically those that existed during the 12 months prior to the rate study, adjusted for conditions that are expected to prevail in the future.

The amount of the rate base and rate of return to be allowed on the defined rate base are established by the public service commission for those water utilities subject to its jurisdiction. The determination of rate base differs between states. Methods employed by public service commissions may be original cost less depreciation, replacement cost less depreciation, or some combination of the two approaches. In any event, a rate base and a rate of return must be established to ensure a regulated water utility an income sufficient to attract the capital necessary to maintain and improve the facilities as required by customer demand.

Revenue Requirements Under the "Cash Needs" Approach

Most municipally owned water utilities elect, or may be required by law, to use the "cash needs" approach to rate determination.

Depending on local policy and conditions, there is a wide variation among municipally owned water utilities as to the types of cash outlays that are to be covered by revenues. The rate study, in accordance with the "cash needs" approach, generally would determine the amount of operating revenue needed to cover operation and maintenance expenses; debt-service requirements, including revenue bond coverage requirements if any; plant replacements; and normal plant extensions and improvements not otherwise funded. In some instances, operating revenues may also be required to cover other cash outlays, such as appropriations for major improvements, contributions to other municipal funds, payments in lieu of taxes, and return on investment.

The emphasis on cash needs in determining the revenue requirements for a municipally owned water utility not subject to commission regulation is primarily a result of two factors. First, most municipally owned water utilities are financed by serial revenue bonds that must be annually serviced with cash generated by the utility. Second, municipally owned water utilities are ordinarily expected to recover the cost of service (measured in terms of normal annual cash outlays) through operations, but are not expected to earn a profit. Municipally owned utilities may, however, be required to maintain debt-service and other management reserves. Further, the "cash needs" approach is similar to the budget basis used by other municipal departments or agencies and, therefore, may be more easily explained and justified to municipal administrators.

It should be noted that, in accordance with the "cash needs" approach, no explicit provision is made for depreciation expense. Depreciation charges are noncash expenditures and, as such, are properly excluded. However, the use of the "cash needs" approach does not imply that depreciation expense should be ignored in determining utility operating income. The application of sound accounting principles requires that provisions be made for depreciation and other noncash or multiperiod expenses in the statements of account. Multiperiod expenses include items that can benefit more than one accounting period, such as prepaid insurance or bond issue discounts.

Revenue requirements under "cash needs" should be based on the average requirements for the period to which the new rate schedule will apply. Operation and maintenance expenses should be forecast as described in chapter 8. Forecasted debt-service requirements should include payments on principal and interest to be made on outstanding debt and on any borrowing expected to take place during the budget period. Coverage requirements on revenue bond debt service also may necessitate attention in establishing revenue requirements.

The amounts estimated for replacements should be sufficient to provide for current renewals and replacements of water utility property that is no longer serviceable. This ensures that current customers do not receive service at costs below the long-run average of providing service. The requirement for normal extensions and improvements should provide for small main extensions, services, meters, hydrants, and other minor items. The amount of funds needed for major extensions and improvements often is not included in the estimate, since it is assumed that major improvements will be financed by applicants for service or by borrowing.

Required contributions to other municipal funds, particularly if made in lieu of payment of taxes or return on investment, should also be included in the computation of revenue requirements. If the policy of a utility is to minimize or avoid debt, operating revenues may be required to cover the cost of major extensions as well as improvements not otherwise financed from contributions.

Determining the Rate Schedule

The definition of rate base varies from one public service commission to another, as does the allowable rate of return. Consequently, the level of rates in rate schedules developed by two similar water utilities subject to regulation by two different public service commissions may vary. In the case of municipally owned water utilities not subject to the jurisdiction of state public service commissions, the level of rates in rate schedules also may vary markedly depending on the capital structure of the utility, the requirements for payments of taxes (or payments in lieu of taxes or return on investment), and capital financing policies.

Historically, many water utilities employed a rate schedule of three to seven blocks applicable to all general customers (residential, commercial, industrial, and public authorities). Under the block rate schedule, charges per unit of water consumed by customers vary depending on the amount of water consumed within successive consumption blocks. Separate rate schedules are often provided for private fire protection, public fire protection, sales for resale, and other classes of use.

Block rate schedules often provide for decreasing incremental charges to customers as consumption is increased. This has been a common characteristic of block rate schedules for water utilities. Two justifications for charging decreasing unit water rates as consumption increases are that (1) savings are realized by transporting water in large quantities for delivery to a single customer and (2) the ratio of peak demand to average demand typically is smaller for the large water user than the small user. Therefore, the extra capacity costs necessary to meet peak demand are relatively less for large users.

Recent trends have reduced the number of consumption blocks contained in rate schedules. Many utilities have settled for a single-unit volume rate for water. Agencies anticipating inadequate sources of water, which could result from drought conditions or rapid growth without ready access to new supplies, sometimes turn to inclining or seasonal rate structures as an attempt to limit water consumption. The success of these inclining rate structures depends on a number of variables, such as the significance of the water bill to the customer, local weather conditions, and public education. The demand for water generally appears to be inelastic at present rates, and attempts to decrease water usage (for example, through advertising campaigns emphasizing the need for conservation) are not always effective.

Developing an equitable schedule of rates and charges applicable to various classes of customers and uses requires periodic cost-of-service studies. The process often involves three major steps (1) allocation of the costs of service to cost functions, (2) allocation of the functional costs to customer classes, and (3) development of the rate schedules. For more detailed information about cost-of-service studies, refer to AWWA Manual M1 and chapter 16 of this book.

⊠ Monitoring Revenues

A general rule in accounting is that revenue is recognized at the time possession, title, or use of a product or service is transferred to the customer. The accrual basis of accounting is generally used in following this rule. Under accrual accounting, the major item of revenue for a water utility — sales of water — is recognized on the basis of customer billings. (If a utility is required to follow cash-basis accounting, then revenue is recognized when cash is received from customers.) Revenue from other sources should also be recognized, to the extent practicable, as it is earned during the accounting period.

The use of meters for measuring the quantity of water delivered to customers results in a lag between the time that water is consumed and the time that meters are read. There is an additional interval between the time a meter is read and the time the bill is rendered to a customer. These lags result in some inaccuracies in assigning revenues to accounting periods. As remote reading systems become practicable, such lags will be reduced.

In an effort to decrease inaccuracies, some utilities currently estimate the amount of water delivered to customers, but not represented by meter readings, and determine the prospective billing based on monthly pumping figures and customers' past consumption records. This method may be particularly useful if a water utility reads customers' meters every two months but prepares a monthly statement of revenue.

Even if all meters are read and all customers billed during the accounting period, revenues from the sales of water service based on meter readings and billings during the period will be understated by the amount due to the utility for water service rendered between the time meters are read and the end of the accounting period. For example, if meters are read regularly throughout the month, the deficiency is approximately equivalent to 15 days' revenue. The deficiency may be largely offset by water service that was delivered to customers during the preceding accounting period, but which is represented by meter readings and billings during the current accounting period. Variations in customer consumption from one accounting period to another, therefore, make reported revenue somewhat inaccurate, but the inaccuracy is seldom considered to be material or large enough to mislead users of water utility financial statements.

⊗ Comparing Budgeted and Actual Revenue

Actual revenues usually differ to some extent from budgeted revenues. Budgeted revenue estimates serve as useful standards only to the extent that they are valid and reasonable. Variations from budgeted revenue figures are to be expected. Significant variations in actual revenues from budgeted revenues should be investigated to determine the reason and if management action is necessary. In some cases, variations arise from faulty budgeting procedures. In other cases, managers or employees have erroneously failed to follow the operating plan. Random events that cause variation, such as weather, can be self-correcting over time.

Revenue totals should be reported to management on a periodic basis, typically at monthly intervals. Revenue statements should be designed to display results both in total and in detail by geographical area and customer classes. During each year, monthly statements should present both actual and budgeted data.

Variations in revenue from the budget standard due to unanticipated changes in the volume of water used by customers may be largely beyond the control of management.

Variations in water delivered into the distribution system from anticipated levels are not necessarily an indication that the water used by customers has varied from anticipated levels. Variations may be caused by such factors as leaks in the water delivery system, underregistration or overregistration of meters, and unauthorized use of unmetered water. For revenue control purposes, water utility management is primarily interested in assuring that

(1) user demands for water are met, (2) the water produced is actually used by customers, and (3) metered customers are billed correctly for the amount of water that they use. User demands for water are met primarily by ensuring that plant capacity is adequate to meet the water requirements of all customers and by remedying customer complaints concerning water service. Control over water use and billing for this use is discussed in the following section.

⊠ Accounting for Water Output

The control of water produced and delivered to the distribution system is closely allied with the control of revenues. This control assists a water utility in increasing the effectiveness and efficiency of its operation.

Total delivery to the distribution system (measured, for example, by a master meter installed in the mains that supply the distribution system with treated water) less water used by customers (metered use and estimated flat-rate use) is considered "unaccounted-for water." Determining customer use of water is improved when all users are metered. Even in a completely metered system, some estimate of use is necessary because all meters cannot be read simultaneously. In addition, water used through unmetered hydrants, to fight fires, or lost when mains break also results in "unaccounted-for water."

Residential, commercial, and industrial use is metered by the majority of water utilities. Public use, with the exception of fire protection, also may be metered. In order to account for all treated water, unmetered water use should be estimated. Estimates of water use for fire fighting could be based on the number and size of hose streams, pressure, and the length of time water is used. Estimates of water used by street department water trucks, if not metered, may be based on the capacity of each truck and the number of tank loads used. Unmetered, treated water used by the utility itself, for example, to clean filter beds, can also be estimated. The ratio of total water used by customers to total water delivered to the distribution system provides one index to the efficiency of utility operation. In addition to the immediate concerns related to revenue, it should be kept in mind that leakage may allow the backflow of groundwater into the mains, resulting in contamination of the treated water before it reaches the customer. Factors influencing the ratio of unaccounted-for water include the age and condition of the distribution system (including meters), ground conditions, pressure, and source of supply.

A program of systematic meter reading, testing, and repair; leak control; maintenance of operating statistics; and controlling unauthorized use will help a utility attain or maintain an acceptable percentage of accounted-for water in relation to total treated water delivered to the distribution system.

In summary, the increasing cost of expanding water utility plant capacity and the limited supply of water, makes it imperative that existing plant capacity be used efficiently and effectively. The total accounted-for water (or revenue-producing water) in relation to the total water delivered to the distribution system is an effective measure of the efficiency and effectiveness of operations. By increasing the ratio of accounted-for water to water delivered, the need for expensive programs to increase plant capacity may be minimized. Increased net income should also result from increasing the percentage of treated water that can be charged to users.

CHAPTER EIGHT

Operation and Maintenance Expenses

Operating income is computed by subtracting operating expenses (expenses applicable to the furnishing of water utility services) from operating revenues (revenues derived from the normal operations of a water utility). Planning and controlling revenue items are discussed in chapter 7. Planning and controlling operating expense items are the subject of this chapter.

A water utility's expenses are classified by regulatory bodies as "operating expenses" and "nonoperating expenses." Operating expenses include all expenses applicable to the furnishing of water utility services. Nonoperating expenses include expenses not associated with a utility's normal business of supplying water. Such expenses typically are small in relation to operating expenses.

Operating expenses are usually subdivided into operating expenses, maintenance expenses, depreciation expenses, amortization expense, taxes other than income taxes, and income taxes. Planning and controlling operation and maintenance expenses are discussed in this chapter; planning and accounting for depreciation and amortization expenses are discussed in chapter 9; and planning for taxes is discussed in chapter 10.

⊠ Nature and Classification

Operation expenses for a water utility include the expenses incurred in operating the source-of-supply and pumping facilities, water treatment facilities, and transmission and distribution facilities. In addition, operation expenses include customer accounts expenses. Examples of customer accounts expenses include meter reading, maintaining customer records and collections, uncollectible accounts, and miscellaneous expenses incurred in maintaining customer accounts. Customer accounts expenses also include customer service costs related to supervision, labor, and providing customer service and informational activities to encourage the safe and efficient use of a utility's service, to promote conservation of water, and to assist customers in answering specific questions regarding the proper and economical use of a utility's service and of customer's equipment that uses the service. Operation expenses also include the administrative and general expenses of a utility that have not been charged directly to a particular operating function and sales expenses in promoting the use of water service.

Maintenance expenses for a water utility include maintenance of the source of supply and pumping, water treatment facilities, transmission and distribution facilities, and general plant facilities. In general, expenses for repairing a water utility plant, or for replacing parts of structures and equipment of a size less than that of a "retirement unit" for the purpose of maintaining a utility plant, are called maintenance expenses. The state PUC or the utility generally will define retirement units. The cost of replacing significant parts of a water utility plant that prolong the useful life of the asset should not be charged to maintenance expense accounts but should be capitalized. See chapter 11 on plant investment.

The "operation expense" account and the "maintenance expense" account, which are summary accounts, are supported by subsidiary operation and maintenance expense accounts. Subsidiary operation and maintenance expense accounts are designed to show in detail a portion of the cost of rendering water service to customers.

Functional Classifications

The National Association of Regulatory Utility Commissioners (NARUC) classification of detailed operation and maintenance accounts reflects the fact that water utilities are enterprises subject to rate regulation. As illustrated by the chart of accounts presented in appendix A, detailed operation and maintenance expense accounts are provided for each functional division of the utility. The functional expense categories are as follows:

- source of supply and pumping expenses:

    operation
    maintenance

- water treatment expenses:

    operation
    maintenance

- transmission and distribution expenses:

    operation
    maintenance

- customer accounts expenses

- administrative and general expenses

The development of the uniform system of accounts by NARUC serves two purposes — uniformity and consistency. Since regulatory commissions perform reviews of the operations of utilities, it is necessary for the accounting information to be consistent from period to period as well as uniform in treatment. The NARUC Committee on Accounts, through its "Interpretations," has also defined accounting procedures in detail for the uniform system of accounts. This accounting guidance allows regulators to distinguish capital expenditures from operating and maintenance expenses and to separate utility activities from nonutility operations. In addition, utility management, share-holders, and creditors find the uniformity and consistency important in their use of the accounting information. Periodically, the uniform system of accounts is formally updated to reflect needed changes.

In applying a uniform system, an individual utility is not prohibited from developing subaccounts, departmental accounts, and other accounting records that are supplemental to those required by the uniform system.

Expense Classification for Planning and Control

Each management team member of the water utility must be responsible for planning all expense items under her or his control. Each manager's plans should be expressed in terms of wages and salaries expense, materials and supplies expense, and other natural classifications of expenses. For example, Figure 8-1 shows the comparison of budgeted operating expenses with actual expenses for a water utility's meter maintenance shop. Expense items are shown in Figure 8-1 at a level of detail beyond that provided by the NARUC classification of accounts. Similarly, managers of other segments of a water utility need information in greater detail than that provided by the accounting system designed by regulatory authorities.

The following sections describe how to obtain supplementary information to that found in the accounts.

⊠ Planning

Within the framework of the major objectives and policies established for the water utility, management must plan and control the utility's operation and maintenance activities. As noted in chapter 6, a forecast of demand for water service is the starting point for the entire budgetary process. Demand for water service (in terms of both volume of water and number of customers) is an important factor in determining the level of operation and maintenance activities.

Evaluation of Alternatives

The first step in planning any activity is to determine if relationships that existed in the past should continue to exist in the future. Therefore, the first question to be asked by each water utility manager is: "Should a particular activity or procedure be performed at all?" The decision to perform or not to perform an activity involves analysis of the estimated value of expected benefits. If it is determined that an activity needs to be performed in order to help a water utility reach its goals, a choice must be made among alternative procedures for performing the activity.

Consistent with forecasted demand for water service, each alternative (including the alternative presently employed) for performing an operation or maintenance activity must be translated into, and evaluated in terms of, estimated requirements for personnel, material, and plant facilities. Frequently, each alternative procedure for performing an activity requires the use of a different combination, or mix, of varying types of personnel and labor skills, material resources, and plant facilities. For example, using computers to perform the customer accounting functions requires a different mix and type of personnel, material, and equipment than does the use of manual procedures. After selecting alternatives to be followed during the budget period, estimates of required personnel, material, and other operating and maintenance expenses become the basis of operating budgets. If alternatives selected

Figure 8-1 ⊠ Meter maintenance operating expenses

Operating Expense Control Report — Meter Maintenance Shop

	Month of June			Year to Date		
	Actual	Budget	Over (Under)	Actual	Budget	Over (Under)
Salaries and Wages:						
Foreman	$ 430	$ 410	$ 20	$ 2,695	$ 2,575	$120
Meter repairmen	1,155	1,090	65	7,185	6,720	465
Laborers	740	740	0	5,090	5,055	35
Total salaries and wages	$2,325	$2,240	$85	$14,970	$14,350	$620
Materials and Supplies:						
Small tools	$ 10	$ 20	($10)	$ 105	$ 100	$ 5
Maintenance materials and supplies	910	890	20	5,325	5,450	(125)
Other	480	510	(30)	175	355	(180)
Total materials and supplies	$1,400	$1,420	($20)	$5,605	$5,905	($300)
Other Expenses:						
Maintenance of meter testing equipment	$ 5	$ 20	($15)	$ 115	$ 105	$ 10
Utility services	25	30	(5)	180	180	0
Incidental expenses	15	10	5	40	60	(20)
Total other expenses	$ 45	$ 60	($15)	$ 335	$ 345	($ 10)
Total Operating Expenses	$3,770	$3,720	$50	$20,910	$20,600	$310

require facilities not currently available, then acquisition or construction of facilities must be included in the proposed capital expenditures budget.

The Use of Historical Data

Historical data serve as a useful guide for estimating personnel and material requirements for activities that have been performed by the utility in the past. For example, in cases where it is reasonable to establish a physical standard of performance (such as the number of labor hours required to paint a given number of fire hydrants), past performance is a helpful guide for setting the standard. The standard can then be used to estimate labor or material requirements for the level of the operation or maintenance activity expected to be attained during a budget period.

In addition to physical components, historical data are useful for developing price components, such as labor wage rates and unit costs for materials and supplies. The price components are then applied against personnel and material requirements to obtain budgeted operation or maintenance expense. For minor items of expense (such as telephone bills and magazine subscriptions), physical and price components do not require separate estimation. To the extent that past circumstances are not expected to exist in the future, historical data must be modified in order to develop budgeted operating and maintenance expenses.

Cost Behavior

A knowledge of cost behavior (why costs rise and fall) by water utility management is necessary for the effective planning and control of operation and maintenance expenses. Many operation and maintenance expense items do not vary in amount in response to changes in volume of water sold. For example, the level of materials and supplies expense for maintenance purposes depends to a large degree on the size of a water utility plant rather than the quantity of water sold. Of course, the level of maintenance materials and supplies expense in relation to the physical size or cost of plant assets varies among particular types of utility plant assets. For example, for such plant items as source-of-supply tunnels and reservoirs, the level of materials and supplies expense normally is small in comparison to plant items such as distribution mains. The level of expense for wages and salaries depends primarily on the number of permanent employees required to operate and maintain water utility facilities. The level of customer accounts expenses depends more on the number of customers than on the volume of water sold. There are some major expense items, such as chemicals and fuel or other sources of power for pumping, that do vary with the volume of water produced for customer use.

Many of the factors that influence cost behavior are interdependent. The number of employees depends on the size of the water utility plant and the number of customers served. The size of the water utility plant depends on the number of customers served and the volume of water produced for customer use. Therefore, for the purpose of understanding and determining cost behavior, expense items should be related to those factors that both directly and indirectly affect the level of the expense items.

Considerations in planning major categories of water utility operation and maintenance expenses are discussed in the following sections.

Planning Source-of-Supply and Pumping Expenses

Major items of expense incurred in operating and maintaining source-of-supply facilities include labor, materials, and supplies. Operation expenses also may include purchased water and rent of leased source-of-supply facilities. Major items of expense incurred in operating pumping facilities include labor, materials and supplies (other than fuel), fuel or power used for pumping, and rent. Major items of expense incurred in the maintenance of pumping facilities include labor, materials, and supplies.

Labor. Source-of-supply and pumping labor expense is a product of personnel requirements and wage and salary levels, both of which must be forecast in the budget process. The number of employees required to operate and maintain source-of-supply and pumping facilities effectively depends on the physical conditions, design, and extent of the facilities. The personnel requirements for operation activities is largely unresponsive to changes in the amount of water demanded by customers; within wide ranges of water production, personnel requirements for pumping facilities are fixed. The introduction of new pumping facilities incorporating the latest technological developments, or increases in the size of pumping facilities, will probably cause changes in personnel requirements. Historical data concerning operating personnel requirements for the operation of facilities during a budget period will provide a basis for forecasting labor expense.

The number of employees required to maintain source-of-supply and pumping facilities is a function of utility maintenance policy. In the language of operations researchers, a proper maintenance policy is one that minimizes the total of the cost of maintaining a facility plus the cost of not maintaining the facility. The cost of maintenance is a familiar concept; the cost of not maintaining includes those costs incident on an interruption of service supplied by the facility. Within the framework of this overall maintenance policy, a maintenance program based on the physical condition, design, and extent of facilities and on replacement policy, must be established for each budget period. Maintenance personnel required to fulfill the budgeted maintenance program is thus determined. Practical experience shows that personnel must be provided for emergency maintenance as well as routine maintenance.

Existing wage and salary schedules, modified by expected changes in the schedules and expected changes in the number of employees at each level in the schedules, serve as a basis for translating personnel requirements into labor budgets.

Materials and supplies. The usage of materials and supplies for operation and maintenance purposes depends on the physical condition, design, and extent of source-of-supply and pumping facilities and the estimated or scheduled work load. Historical data concerning materials and supplies usage, adjusted for anticipated changes in the nature and extent of the work load, are useful for budgeting requirements. The estimated usage then must be multiplied by anticipated unit prices of materials and supplies in order to arrive at a budget figure for materials and supplies expense.

Purchased water. The cost of purchased water, if any, also must be budgeted. The estimated amount of water to be purchased depends on the difference between the estimated volume of water demanded by customers (as forecast by procedures discussed in chapter 6) and the estimated amount of water to be supplied by a utility's source-of-supply facilities. The amount to be supplied by utility facilities is based on historical data adjusted for anticipated changes in the capabilities of source-of-supply facilities to meet the demand for water. An estimate of the cost of purchased water during a budget period is then obtained by applying the appropriate rate schedule to the estimated volume of water to be purchased for resale.

Fuel and power. A water utility may (1) purchase fuel for use in producing its own power to operate pumps, (2) purchase fuel or power to operate pumps, (3) purchase fuel or power for use directly in operating pumps, or (4) employ a combination of methods. The amount of fuel (such as coal) used in the production of power to operate pumps and the amount of fuel or power (such as diesel fuel or electric power) used directly in the operation of pumps depends largely on the amount of water produced for customers.

Historical data concerning the amount of fuel and power required to pump a million gallons (or litres) of water serve as a basis for forecasting fuel and power requirements for a budget period. Forecasted fuel and power usage during a budget period is determined by multiplying historical fuel and power usage per million gallons (litres) pumped by estimated pumpage (in terms of millions of gallons [litres]) for the budget period. Estimated fuel and power usage must then be multiplied by anticipated unit prices to arrive at a budget figure for fuel and power expense.

Consistent with the capabilities of the pumping facilities, forecasted fuel and power expense should reflect the least-cost combination of fuel and power sources available for use during a budget period.

Rent. Rent expense depends on the extent to which property of others is used in connection with the source-of-supply system. A budgeted figure for rent expense, applicable to source-of-supply facilities, can be determined from existing or anticipated lease agreements. Rent expense applicable to other facilities can be estimated in a similar manner.

Before a water utility commits itself to leasing property, the advantages and disadvantages of leasing as opposed to purchasing should be considered. Purchasing has the advantage of allowing the cost of the property to be included in the rate base and, for investor-owned utilities, the advantage of tax savings from the additional depreciation expense. Disadvantages of purchasing include those normally accompanying ownership, such as the expenses of property taxes, insurance, maintenance, and the cost of having to finance the purchase. The advantages of leasing include eliminating the problems of financing the purchase and, for investor-owned water utilities, the tax savings from the treatment of rental payments as deductible expenses. Disadvantages include the lack of flexibility to changing conditions resulting from the commitment to a long-term fixed obligation and the lack of any interest in the residual value of property on termination of the lease. The choice of leasing as opposed to purchasing depends on the circumstances surrounding a particular item of property.

Water Treatment

The major items of expense incurred in operating and maintaining water treatment facilities include labor, materials and supplies (other than chemicals), chemicals, and rent.

Labor, materials, and supplies. Water treatment labor expense is a product of personnel requirements and wage and salary levels. Materials and supplies expense incurred in the operation and maintenance of water treatment facilities is a product of usage and unit prices of materials and supplies.

As with source-of-supply and pumping facilities, the number of persons employed and the usage of materials and supplies (other than chemicals) for operation and maintenance activities depends largely on the physical condition, design, and extent of the water treatment facilities. Requirements for personnel, materials, and supplies (except chemicals) for operation and maintenance activities are largely unresponsive to changes in the amount of water demanded by customers, at least within wide ranges. Technological changes incorporated into new water treatment facilities, or the enlargement of existing facilities, will affect personnel, materials, and supplies requirements.

The earlier discussion about forecasting personnel requirements, wage and salary levels, and materials and supplies expense (see "Planning Source-of-Supply and Pumping Expenses"), is equally applicable to planning and forecasting water treatment labor, materials, and supplies expense for a budget period.

Chemicals. The level of chemical usage is dependent, to a large extent, on the volume of water produced for customer use. The amount of chemicals used also is affected by the quality (in terms of purity) of raw water received for treatment from the source-of-supply facilities.

Historical data concerning chemicals used per million gallons (or litres) of water produced serve as a useful guide for determining chemical usage during the budget period. The historical data should be adjusted for anticipated changes in the level of chemical usage due to changing raw-water quality. For each type of chemical used, the estimated usage per million gallons (or litres) of water is multiplied by the estimated volume of water to be supplied to customers in order to get total chemical usage. Total usage for each chemical is multiplied by the anticipated per-unit cost for that chemical to obtain budgeted chemical expenses.

Transmission and Distribution

Labor, materials, supplies, and rent are among the major items of expense incurred in operating and maintaining transmission and distribution facilities.

Labor. Transmission and distribution labor expense is a product of personnel requirements and wage and salary levels, both of which must be forecast in the budget process. The number of persons employed for operation and maintenance activities depends largely on the physical condition, design, and extent of transmission and distribution facilities. The growth of a transmission and distribution system will, of course, affect personnel requirements. Personnel requirements for operating storage facilities, transmission and distribution mains, and fire mains generally are not subject to wide fluctuation. Historical data concerning personnel requirements for operating the facilities, adjusted for contemplated changes, serve as the basis for forecasting personnel requirements during a budget period.

Personnel requirements for maintaining customer meters depend on the numbers of customer services and meters installed, removed, relocated, turned on, and shut off. Historical data concerning personnel requirements for the handling of customer meters, adjusted for anticipated changes in the number of customer meters and services to be installed, removed, relocated, turned on, and shut off, serve as a basis for forecasting personnel requirements during a budget period.

The number of employees required to maintain transmission and distribution facilities is a function of the utility maintenance policy. Within the framework of the overall maintenance policy, a maintenance program must be established for a budget period. The extent of the maintenance program will depend on (1) the physical condition, design, and extent of distribution reservoirs and standpipes; (2) the physical condition, size, and length of transmission and distribution mains and fire mains; (3) the physical condition, size, and number of customers' services, meters, and hydrants; and (4) the replacement policy. Maintenance personnel requirements for a budget period are forecast based on the scheduled maintenance program and on estimated emergency repairs.

Existing wage and salary schedules, modified by expected changes in the schedules and expected changes in the number of employees at each level in the schedules, serve as the basis for translating personnel requirements for transmission and distribution activities into labor budgets. Based on past experience, utility management may desire to budget at overtime rates the probable number of labor hours expected to result from emergency repair work on transmission and distribution facilities.

Materials and supplies. The usage of materials and supplies for operation and maintenance purposes depends on the physical condition, design, and extent of the transmission and distribution facilities, and on the estimated or scheduled work load. Historical data concerning materials and supplies usage, adjusted for anticipated changes in the nature and extent of the work load, are useful for budgeting materials and supplies requirements. The estimated usage must then be multiplied by anticipated unit prices of materials and supplies in order to arrive at a forecast of expense for a budget period.

Customer billings for work performed. Amounts billed to customers for operation and maintenance work performed on customer service connections and meters also should be estimated for a budget period. The estimated billings then should be credited against the costs incurred in performing the work to determine estimated net expense incurred by the water utility during the budget period. In accordance with NARUC recommendations, any estimated excess of billings over costs incurred should be transferred to miscellaneous service revenues, thus becoming a component of estimated operating revenues. Historical data, adjusted for anticipated changes in work billed to customers, serve as a basis for forecasting customer billings for work performed during a budget period.

Customer Accounts

Customer accounts activities include opening and closing customer accounts, meter reading, billing, collecting, maintaining customer records, and handling customer complaints and requests for information. Major items of expense incurred in performing customer accounts activities include supervision, labor, materials and supplies, losses from uncollectible utility revenues, and expenses associated with the use of data processing equipment. As noted previously in this chapter, the purpose of these expenditures is to encourage the safe and efficient use of water, to promote water conservation, and to assist present customers by answering specific inquiries as to the best use of the utility's service and the best use of customer's equipment that uses the service.

The careful use and preservation of all scarce natural resources has become increasingly important in recent years. Many municipalities have found it necessary to ration water during periods when sources of supply have been drawn to very low levels or depleted. The increasing use of newspapers and television to promote conservation in water consumption and to educate the general public about the limitations of water supply sources has resulted in a relatively new cost classification for many water utilities. Therefore, attempts to forecast customer service expense should include particular attention to water utility plans regarding future public education programs designed to promote water conservation and more efficient water usage.

The level of customer accounts expenses largely depends on the number of customers served. Customer accounts activities should be organized to minimize expenses for a given number and type of customer served. The attempt to minimize customer accounts expenses involves evaluating alternative procedures for conducting customer accounts activities. As an example, by extending the period covered by meter readings and billings, personnel requirements and labor expenses can be reduced. However, the savings in labor expense from extending the billing period would be offset at least partially by the cost of additional working capital required to tally unbilled water sales, the increased loss from uncollectible accounts, the overall reduction in available cash flow, and the increased loss of sales of water resulting from the lack of timely correction of underregistration of meters. The practice of billing large customers (such as industrial customers) more frequently than small customers (including residential customers) may minimize the unfavorable effects of extended billing periods. Also, if meters are read every two months, then estimated bills may be rendered in alternate months to reduce the unfavorable effects cited above.

Within the context of a given meter-reading and billing schedule, there are a number of alternatives available for conducting customer accounts activities. In the case of meter reading, the method of recording metered water usage (for example, by using meter sheets instead of meter sensing cards) and the location of meters (for example, locating meters in outside pits instead of basements) will affect equipment and personnel requirements. In the case of billing and customer record keeping, a manual system, a system employing bookkeeping or accounting machines, a computer system, or a combination thereof may be employed. Each of these alternatives affects personnel and equipment requirements.

Labor. Historical data concerning personnel requirements for performing customer accounts activities serve as a useful guide in forecasting needs during a budget period. Historical personnel requirements must be adjusted for anticipated changes in the nature and extent of the work load resulting from changes in procedures for conducting accounts activities and from estimated changes in the type and number of customers served during a budget period. Existing wage and salary schedules, modified by anticipated changes in the schedules and expected changes in the number of employees at each level in the schedules, serve as a basis for translating forecast personnel requirements into a labor expense budget for customer accounts activities.

Materials and supplies. Materials and supplies expense also can be estimated from past experience. Historical data concerning materials and supplies expense should be adjusted for anticipated changes in usage due to changes in the nature and extent of the work load for a budget period. The estimated materials and supplies usage must then be multiplied by anticipated unit prices in order to determine a budget figure for materials and supplies expense.

Rent. The level of rent expense depends on the extent to which property such as computers and other equipment is used in connection with customer accounts activities. A budget figure for rent expense should be based on existing or anticipated lease agreements.

Uncollectible utility revenues. Uncollectible utility revenue is a function of the water utility's credit and collection policies. Unless credit and collection policies are to be changed during a budget period, past experience, in terms of bad debts as a percentage of accounts receivable or of operating revenues, serves as a basis for estimating uncollectible water utility revenues for the budget period. Anticipated changes in local economic conditions or demographic composition during a budget period should also be considered in estimating uncollectible revenues.

Administrative and General

Administrative and general expenses typically comprise a significant portion of operation and maintenance expenses. Major administrative and general expense items include the following:

- salaries and bonuses of officers, executives, and office staff employed in connection with the general administration of a water utility's operations
- the cost of outside services (for example, legal, accounting and auditing, engineering, labor negotiating, and similar services) generally applicable to all operating functions
- property insurance expense incurred to protect against losses and damages to property employed in a utility's operations
- insurance expense incurred to protect a water utility against injury and damage claims of employees or outside parties, and expenses incurred in settlement of injury and damage claims
- payments under employee pension plans and payments with respect to other employee benefits (for example, employee accident, sickness, hospital, and death benefits)
- rent charges with respect to property employed in performing administrative and general functions
- assessments against a water utility to cover expenses incurred by state public service commissions
- labor, materials, and supplies expense incurred for the maintenance of general plant facilities

Administrative and general expenses may vary significantly from one accounting period to another due to the performance of nonroutine functions, such as the preparation and presentation of rate cases before a public service commission. Note that many commissions require that costs of preparing and presenting rate cases be deferred and amortized over a stipulated time period. Expenses also vary because of the use of outside services on other than a routine basis. Expenses incurred in performing these nonroutine activities, to the extent that they can be foreseen, should be reflected in the operating expense budget. Administrative and general expenses also vary in settlement of injury and damage claims. Other expense items are incurred on a routine basis and can be budgeted on the basis of past experience. Such items include salaries, bonuses, office supplies, the cost of legal or other services used on a continuing basis, property insurance, insurance against injury and damage claims, costs of pension plans and other employee-benefit programs, rent, labor, and material expense for general plant maintenance. Some of these routine expense items are detailed below.

Labor. Personnel requirements for performing administrative and general functions are relatively fixed over reasonably long periods of time. Therefore, personnel requirements for a budget period can be based on past experience. The introduction of new office equipment during a budget period may, of course, require adjustment of past experience regarding personnel needs. Existing wage and salary schedules for administrative personnel, modified by changes in the schedules and expected number of employees at each level in the schedules, serve as a basis for translating personnel requirements into a labor expense budget for administrative personnel.

Office supplies. Estimates for office supplies expense can be reasonably based on past experience and historical trends; adjustments may be required for changes in the nature and extent of work load and for anticipated changes in unit prices applicable to each office supply item. The expense associated with outside services also may be estimated from past experience, adjusting for anticipated changes in use of services and for changes in fees and expenses paid under contract for services.

Property insurance. The level of property insurance expense depends on the size and value of water utility plant facilities and the degree of insurance coverage desired. Property insurance expense can be estimated by referring to existing or proposed insurance contracts. To the extent that property insurance coverage is not purchased from an insurance firm, but provided on a self-insured basis, a reasonable allowance for expected property loss may be budgeted on the basis of past experience. Budgeted property loss serves as the basis for making a charge to the property insurance expense account with a corresponding credit being made to the property insurance reserve account (when the loss actually occurs, the reserve account is decreased).

Injuries and damages. Insurance expense incurred to protect a water utility against injury and damage claims of employees and outside parties also can be estimated by referring to existing or proposed insurance contracts. To the extent that insurance coverage is not purchased from an insurance company but provided on a self-insured basis, a reasonable allowance for expected losses due to injuries and damages to employees or outside parties may be budgeted. The budget is based on past experience and, in the case of litigation in progress, on the advice of attorneys. The budgeted loss due to injuries and damages serves as the basis for making a charge to the injuries and damages expense account, with a corresponding credit being made to the injuries and damages reserve account.

Employee pensions. Payments under a pension plan depend on the terms of the pension contract or agreement and on the number of water utility employees covered by the plan. If accruals are made to a reserve account to provide for future pensions, then employee pensions expense, based on actuarial studies, is equal to the amount of the accrual made during the accounting period. A pension fund from which pension payments are made also may be established and maintained through contributions to the fund equal in amount to the periodic reserve accruals. If pension payments are made to retired water utility employees by an insurance company, employee pension expense is determined by the payments to be made by the water utility to the insurance company during the accounting period. In cases where accruals are not recorded in a pension reserve or where annuities are not purchased, employee pensions expense is determined by direct payments made by the water utility during the accounting period to, or on behalf of, retired employees.

Employee pensions expense for the budget period can be estimated by referring to the terms of the pension contract or agreement that indicate the basis for determining the expense. Where accruals are made to pension reserves (and contributions equal to the reserve accruals are made to a pension fund), the amount of the reserve accrual (and associated pension fund contribution) typically is determined by the number of water utility employees and the employees' salaries and wages. If an annuity is purchased from an insurance company, the periodic payments for the purchase also are based on the number of employees and level of employees' salaries and wages. If no reserve accruals are recorded and no annuities are purchased, pension payments depend on the number of retired employees and the level of the retired employees' salaries and wages earned during the time of their employment by the utility. While past experience may be useful in estimating employee pensions expense during a budget period, adjustment in historical data will be required for changes in contract terms based on new actuarial studies, for changes in the number of employees covered, and for changes in other factors influencing pensions expense. When pension contract terms are complex, it may be advisable to hire an actuary.

Retirement systems of municipally owned water utilities usually fall into three main categories (1) employees may be covered by a plan for all municipal employees; (2) a water utility by itself, or as one of many departments of the municipality, may belong to a statewide plan; or (3) a utility may have its own retirement system. The amount of employee pension expense under any one of these plans depends on the regulations and laws establishing the plan. Reference must be made to the particular regulations and laws in order to forecast pension expense.

Other employee benefits. Expenses associated with other employee-benefit programs (for example, accident, sickness, hospital, and death benefits) also can be estimated by referring to the appropriate contracts or agreements giving rise to the benefit plans and by using past experience regarding the cost of these plans. Historical data will require adjustment for changes in the terms of the contracts, changes in the number of employees covered, and changes in other factors affecting the cost of the employee-benefit plans.

Other administrative and general expenses. Rent expense associated with property used for administrative and general activities can be estimated by referring to existing and proposed lease agreements. Assessments to cover the expenses incurred by state public service commissions, and labor, materials, and supplies expense incurred for the maintenance of general plant facilities, may be estimated by projecting historical trends. Adjustments of historical data will be required for extraordinary changes in factors influencing the level of these expenses.

Centralized Activity

A water utility organization typically incudes certain centralized entities that provide services to other segments of the organization. Examples of such entities are a central garage that provides transportation services and a central stores department that receives and issues materials and supplies. Since each centralized unit represents a responsibility center, costs associated with rendering centralized services should be budgeted for each centralized activity. Actual costs associated with rendering centralized services are accumulated in clearing accounts and allocated to particular operation and maintenance activities and to particular capital expenditure projects. Allocation of centralized activity expenses is discussed later in this chapter. Depending on the size and the complexity of the utility organization, separate clearing accounts may be established for the expenses of transportation, power-operated equipment, stores, fuel stock, shops, and similar activities.

In connection with stores and fuel stock expenses, the undistributed balances in the clearing accounts at the date of the balance sheet (that is, the amount of stores and fuel stock expenses reasonably attributable to being on hand at the balance sheet date) are classified by NARUC as current assets (see account 161, "stores expense," and account 151 "plant material and supplies," in appendix A. In the case of expenses for transportation, the clearing accounts as of the balance-sheet date are classified by NARUC as deferred debits (see account 184, "clearing accounts," in appendix A). To illustrate the budgeting process associated with centralized activity expenses, the remaining discussion in this section is devoted to forecasting two of the more common types of centralized activity expenses: transportation expenses and central stores expenses.

Transportation. Transportation services are primarily used by operation and maintenance personnel in the transmission and distribution division, meter reading and bill collecting personnel, and supervisory personnel. The size of the central garage depends on the requirements of the entire water utility organization for transportation services.

Based on the anticipated needs of a water utility for transportation, the personnel, equipment, and materials and supplies requirements must be determined for a budget period. Wages and salaries of the garage supervisor, equipment operators, and equipment maintenance personnel may be budgeted in a manner analogous to the budgeting of other wages and salaries expense previously described in this chapter. Other expenses incurred in operating and maintaining equipment (for example, gas, oil, maintenance materials and supplies, depreciation of equipment and garage, and taxes on equipment) may be estimated by using historical data regarding each individual piece of equipment modified in accordance with anticipated changes in equipment.

Central stores. In the case of central stores, the major items of expense include wages and salaries, and materials and supplies. Requirements for personnel to operate central stores and the level of materials and supplies needed to perform central-stores activities depend on the requirements of a water utility organization for the services rendered by central stores. Adjustments in historical data may be required due to anticipated changes in factors affecting the expense items.

Summary of Planning Operation and Maintenance Expenses

Effective planning requires that alternative procedures for conducting operation and maintenance activities be evaluated. The combination of procedures that is expected to result in the most efficient use of resources should be the one selected. After determining the procedures to be employed, operation and maintenance expenses should be budgeted for each organization responsibility segment, including those performing centralized service

activities (such as central garages and central stores) and those directly
involved with the operation and maintenance of water utility plant facilities,
customer account activities, sales promotion and advertising activities, and
administrative and general activities.

The end result of planning operation and maintenance activities, as
described in the preceding sections of this chapter, is an annual budget of
operation and maintenance expenses such as that shown in Figure 8-2.

⊠ Controlling Operation and Maintenance Expenses

Effective control over operation and maintenance expenses is mandatory
from the standpoint of avoiding frequent requests for changes in water utility
rate schedules in response to increasing expenses. Unless operation and
maintenance expenses are kept in strict control, frequent and costly rate
studies may become necessary, and there is no assurance that rate increases
will always be approved.

Comparing Budgeted and Actual Expenses

Effective management control of operation and maintenance expense
requires that actual results be compared with planned (budgeted) expenses on
a routine basis. The comparisons should be made by developing a system of
monthly comparative reports of actual and budgeted operation and maintenance expenses for each responsibility segment of a water utility organization.
Figure 8-1 presents an example of a monthly control report for a meter
maintenance shop. Similar reports should be prepared for each segment of the
utility.

Significant variations between budgeted and actual amounts should be
investigated to determine needed corrective action. For example, an unfavorable variation between actual and budgeted chemical expenses might be
explained by unanticipated price increases of various kinds of chemicals, an
unanticipated increase in the volume of water supplied to customers, or
lower-than-expected-quality raw water being received for treatment.

In the case of significant unfavorable variations between actual and
budgeted figures, the manager or supervisor in charge of the organizational
unit experiencing the variation should be required to indicate on the monthly
report what corrective action, if any, is being taken to alleviate the problem. In
no case should a manager or supervisor in charge of a responsibility segment
of the water utility be held responsible for expenses over which he or she has
no control. For example, expense variations due to inefficiency in a centralized
activity (such as a central garage or central stores) should be attributed to the
management of the centralized activity and not to the serviced segments as a
controllable variance.

Use of Unit Cost Standards Based on Historical Data

For certain types of work performed by various segments of a water
utility, unit cost standards can be developed to judge the efficiency of work
performed. Unit cost standards also allow for distributing certain expenses
(such as those incurred by central garages and central stores) among operation
and maintenance activities and among construction projects.

The efficiency of operations is best measured by the relationships
between costs incurred and amount of work accomplished. Work is usually

Figure 8-2 ⊠ Structure of an annual operating budget

Statement of Estimated Revenue and Expense

	Budget, 19BY
Operating Revenues	$6,930,000
Operating Expenses:	
Operation Expense	$1,663,200
Maintenance Expense	346,500
Depreciation and Amortization Expense	485,100
Taxes	2,564,100
Total Operating Expenses	$5,058,900
Utility Operating Income	$1,871,100

Budgeted Utility Operation and Maintenance Expenses

Cost Center	Budgeted Amount, 19BY
Office of the General Manager	$ 36,400
Production Division	748,370
Transmission and Distribution Division	324,850
Commercial Division	268,960
General and Administrative Division	631,120
Total Budgeted Operation and Maintenance Expenses	$2,009,700

Transmission and Distribution Division Budgeted Operating Expenses

Cost Center	Budgeted Amount, 19BY
Office of the Division Manager	$ 23,200
Operations Section	116,485
Maintenance Section	185,165
Total	$324,850

Maintenance Section Budgeted Operating Expenses

Cost Center	Budgeted Amount, 19BY
Maintenance Supervision	$ 12,480
Maintenance of Mains and Storage Facilities	61,120
Maintenance of Customer Services	70,365
Maintenance of Meters	41,200
Total	$185,165

Meter Maintenance Shop

Budgeted Operating Expenses	Budgeted Amount, 19BY
Salaries and Wages:	
Foreman	$ 5,150
Meter Repairers	13,435
Laborers	10,105
Total Salaries and Wages	$28,690
Materials and Supplies:	
Small Tools	$ 200
Maintenance Materials and Supplies	10,900
Other	710
Total Materials and Supplies	$11,810
Other Expenses:	
Maintenance of Meter Testing Equipment	$ 210
Utility Services	360
Incidental Expenses	130
Total Other Expenses	700
Total Budgeted Operating Expenses	$41,200

measured in terms of physical units, the cost per unit being determined by dividing total costs applicable to a number of units of work performed by the number of units. The procedure for developing unit cost standards is (1) to establish units of work for the activity, (2) to compile all the elements of cost entering into the performance of the work, and (3) to divide the total cost by the number of units in order to arrive at the cost per unit. Unit cost standards are usually developed from historical cost data for a particular period of time. Periods reflecting abnormal operating conditions should be eliminated from consideration.

One maintenance activity lending itself to the development of a unit cost standard is painting fire hydrants. The standard cost per hydrant can be used to evaluate the efficiency of current performance of this activity. Unit standards should also be developed for all other maintenance activities that involve a significant annual expense.

Unit cost standards also may be used to judge the performance of pumping and water treatment activities. For example, the current cost of chemicals used per million gallons (or litres) of water pumped could be compared with standard unit costs. In addition, customer accounting costs over a period of time could be compared on a per-customer basis. The cost of operating and maintenance transportation and other power-operated equipment could be compared on a per-mile (or kilometre) or per-hour-operated basis.

It should be noted that unit cost standards require periodic updating. For example, changes in wage and salary levels and changes in the cost of materials and supplies affect the applicability of existing cost standards for that activity and will necessitate changes in the cost standards. Further, increases in productivity resulting from improved technology or improved management techniques also may affect the applicability of existing cost standards associated with particular activities and, therefore, require the determination of new cost standards.

⊠ Reconciling Expense Classification for Planning and Control With Functional Expense Classifications

There are some expense classifications used for management planning and control purposes that are directly comparable with the functional classification of expenses shown in the suggested system of accounts in appendix A. Included among these expense classifications are chemicals expense (for water treatment), and fuel or power-operated equipment, which could be compared on a per-mile-driven or per-hour-operated basis.

Wages and Salaries Expense

It is apparent that records must be maintained for the amount of wages and salaries expense incurred for specific activities and jobs performed by each responsibility segment. Generally, wages and salaries expense is allocated among various jobs and activities on the basis of time expended by employees performing particular activities or jobs. The time expended is recorded and maintained on individual or group time sheets. Normally, not all wages and salaries paid to employees of a water utility will be classified as expense. If construction work is performed by the utility, the wages and salaries paid to employees engaged in construction activity should be capitalized.

Materials and Supplies Expense

As in the case of wages and salaries expense, records must be maintained for each responsibility segment regarding the amount of materials and supplies expense incurred for specific activities and jobs performed. Generally, the cost of materials and supplies used is allocated among activities and jobs on the basis of information contained in stores requisition forms. As in the case of labor costs, a portion of the cost of materials and supplies used may require capitalization in the "construction work in progress" accounts, whereas the remaining portion is allocated to the various operation and maintenance expense accounts shown in the suggested system of accounts (appendix A).

Centralized Activity Expenses

The expenses incurred in performing centralized service functions must also be allocated to particular activities and jobs, including those related to stores, fuel stocks, transportation, power-operated equipment, and shop expenses.

Stores expense represents the cost of handling materials and supplies. As materials and supplies are charged to activities and jobs, a proper proportion of the stores expense should be allocated to each activity and job. The amount to be charged is arrived at by applying a predetermined percentage to the cost of materials used. Estimated or actual total stores expenses are divided by the total estimated or actual cost of materials and supplies handled in order to determine the applicable percentage. As noted previously in this chapter, the balance in the "stores expense" account at the end of the accounting period should not exceed the amount of stores expenses reasonably attributable to the inventory of materials and supplies. This balance is classified as an asset on the balance sheet, as are balances in other centralized activity accounts. Fuel-stock expenses are allocated to activities and jobs in a similar manner.

Transportation expenses and power-operated equipment expenses must also be allocated to specific activities and jobs. The wages and salaries of equipment operators are allocated to activities and jobs on the basis of information contained on time sheets. The costs of operating and maintaining equipment (for example, costs of gas, oil, maintenance materials and supplies, maintenance labor, depreciation of equipment and garage, taxes on equipment, and general overhead) typically are allocated to activities and jobs on the basis of a rate established for each piece of equipment. That is, an individual equipment record sheet is maintained for each piece of equipment to record the costs of operating and maintaining the piece of equipment. Each activity or job is then charged the cost of operating and maintaining the equipment on the basis of a rate per hour or per mile operated.

Shop expenses include all the costs connected with operating a central shop. Labor costs and shop overhead may be charged to activities and jobs on the basis of an hourly rate. The cost of materials and supplies may be charged on the basis of an hourly rate or on the basis of actual costs incurred for each activity or job.

Administrative and general expenses ordinarily are not allocated to other functional expense accounts. However, administrative and general expenses directly traceable to construction activity should be transferred to construction costs and capitalized in construction work-in-progress accounts.

⊠ Capitalization of Costs

Water utility companies are required by regulators to capitalize certain allowable costs. Allowable costs are used to determine rates that produce revenues to match those costs. Costs are to be estimated during the period in which rates are in effect and specific prior costs cannot be recovered. According to the Financial Accounting Standards Board's (FASB's) Statement of Financial Accounting Standards Number 71 (SFAS 71), *Accounting for the Effects of Certain Types of Regulation*, an enterprise shall capitalize all or part of an incurred cost that would otherwise be charged to expense if both of the following criteria are met:

a. It is probable that future revenue is an amount at least equal to the capitalized cost that results from inclusion of that cost in allowable costs for rate-making purposes.

b. Based on available evidence, the future revenue will be provided to permit recovery of the previously incurred cost rather than to provide for expected levels of similar future costs. If the revenue will be provided through an automatic rate-adjustment clause, this criterion requires that the regulator's intent clearly be to permit recovery of the previously incurred cost.

Regulators can require utilities to capitalize the cost of financing construction into plant and equipment. On completion of construction, the total amount capitalized will be the basis for depreciation and unrecovered investment for rate-making purposes. These amounts shall be capitalized only if it is probable that they will be included as allowable costs. When the allowance for earnings on shareholder's investment is capitalized for rate-making purposes, it cannot be capitalized for book purposes other than during construction or as part of a phase-in plan (described in a following section).

⊠ Plant Abandonments and Disallowances of Costs

To specify accounting for planned abandonments and disallowances of costs, FASB amended SFAS 71 with the issuance of SFAS 90. This statement requires that a loss shall be recognized when disallowed costs on an abandoned plant are both probable and reasonably estimable, whether full, partial, or no return on investment is likely to be provided. If full return on investment is likely, the remainder of the cost of the abandoned plant shall be recorded as a new asset. If partial or no return on investment is likely, the present value is to be recognized as a loss. A carrying charge will be accrued to increase the new asset. The new asset shall be amortized as if it were a rate-making asset when full return on investment is likely. When partial or no return is likely, the new asset shall be amortized in a manner to produce a constant return.

⊠ Phase-In Plans

As a result of increased costs in recent years, newly completed plants have had greater costs incurred than on those completed in the past. Based on the old rate-making methods, this can cause significant increases in rates when a newly completed plant goes into service. Therefore, regulators have gone to phase-in plans to increase rates more gradually than under old methods. Over time, the utility recovers all allowable costs and their return on investment. FASB issued SFAS 92 in August 1987, which required capitalization of allowable costs under a phase-in plan related to plants either completed or on which substantial physical construction has been performed before Jan. 1, 1988, if all the following conditions are met:

1. The plan has been agreed to by the regulator.
2. The plan specifies when recovery will occur.
3. Allowable costs deferred under the plan are scheduled for recovery within 10 years of the date when deferrals begin.
4. The percentage increase in rates scheduled for each future year under the plan is not greater than the percentage increase in rates scheduled from each immediately preceding year.

CHAPTER NINE

Depreciation and Amortization Expense

Depreciation is of particular importance to water utilities because of the relatively large investment in the water utility plant required to produce each dollar of annual revenue. Amortization expense, similar in nature to depreciation expense, is also a significant item of expense for a typical water utility. This chapter deals with planning and accounting for depreciation and amortization expenses as elements in determining revenue requirements for rate-making purposes, determining income, and in analyzing and budgeting cash flow. For a further discussion of the subject of utility depreciation accounting, refer to the National Association of Regulatory Utility Commissioners' (NARUC) publication *Public Utility Depreciation Practices*.

⊠ Definitions and Concepts

Depreciation

NARUC defines depreciation as follows:

"Depreciation," as applied to depreciate utility plant, means the loss in service value not restored by current maintenance, incurred in connection with the consumption or prospective retirement of utility plant in the course of service from causes which are known to be in current operation and against which the utility is not protected by insurance. Among the causes to be given consideration are wear and tear, decay, action of the elements, inadequacy, obsolescence, changes in the art, changes in demand and requirements of public authorities.

For the purpose of clarifying the preceding definition and the remainder of this chapter, the following NARUC definitions are presented:

- *Service value* is the difference between the original cost and the net salvage of a utility plant.

- *Original cost*, as applied to a utility plant, is the cost of such property to the person first devoting it to public service.

- *Net salvage value* is the salvage value of property retired less the cost of removal.

- *Salvage value* is the amount received for property retired, less any expenses incurred in connection with the sale or in preparing the property for sale. If retained, salvage value is the amount at which the material recoverable is chargeable to materials and supplies, or other appropriate account.

- *Cost of removal* is the cost of demolishing, dismantling, tearing down, or otherwise removing the utility plant, including the incidental costs of transportation and handling.

- *Property retired*, as applied to a utility plant, is property that has been removed, sold, abandoned, destroyed, or for any cause has been withdrawn from service.

- *Service life* is the time between the date a utility plant is in service or leased to others, and the date of its retirement. If depreciation is accounted for on a production basis rather than on a time basis, then service life should be measured in terms of the appropriate unit of production.

In view of the NARUC definition of "depreciation," and the definitions of associated terminology, the term "depreciation" is limited to the accounting for original cost. Depreciation accounting for water utilities involves procedures whereby the original cost less net salvage value of the tangible utility plant (excluding land) is distributed over the estimated useful life of the assets in an orderly and rational manner. In addition, the depreciation expense for a particular period of time is the portion of the original cost (less net salvage value) of the tangible water utility plant that is allocated to that particular period.

It should be made clear that depreciation, from the standpoint of accounting, is defined in terms of cost. The economic concept of depreciation, on the other hand, involves the process of valuation. In this case, depreciation (or appreciation) is measured in terms of the loss (or gain) in value of property. The engineering concept of depreciation is established by comparing the present physical condition of a depreciated asset against the physical condition of the asset when new.

Amortization

The term "amortization" is defined by NARUC as follows:

> "Amortization" means the gradual extinguishment of an amount in an account by distributing such amount over a fixed period, over the life of the asset or liability to which it applies, or over the period during which it is anticipated the benefit will be realized.

This definition of amortization is very broad in scope, referring to the orderly extinguishment, over time, of amounts in balance-sheet accounts in general. Although the NARUC definition of amortization refers to both assets and liabilities, the discussion in this chapter emphasizes the process of amortizing amounts in asset accounts classified within the "utility plant" category. Nevertheless, the term "amortization" also applies to the distribution among accounting periods of amounts in other balance-sheet accounts, such as those associated with nonutility property, debt discount and expense, and debt premium.

Note that, from an accounting viewpoint, a broad definition of asset amortization encompasses the concept of depreciation. The term "depreciation" refers to a particular type of asset amortization — that associated with the allocation, among accounting periods, of the original cost of tangible utility plant (excluding land). In regard to the utility plant, amortization usually is employed more narrowly to describe the process of allocating, among accounting periods, the amounts in other accounts, including those commonly referred to as intangible assets.

Depreciation and Amortization Expense Accounts

The NARUC system of accounts for water utilities establishes a number of accounts for the purpose of recognizing depreciation and amortization. With regard to the income statement, and for the purpose of determining operating income, five accounts within the "operating expense" category are devoted to depreciation and amortization expense. A brief description of the five expense accounts (listed with their account numbers as shown in appendix A) is as follows:

> *Depreciation Expense (403).* This account includes the amount of depreciation expense associated with all classes of depreciated utility plant in service. However, depreciation expense applicable to transportation and work equipment, shop equipment, tools, and other general equipment may be charged to clearing distribution of expenses between construction and operation. In addition, depreciation and amortization expenses applicable to utility plant leased to others should be charged to account 413, "income from utility plant leased to other."

> *Amortization of Utility Plant Acquisition Adjustments (406).* When authorized by a state regulatory body, this account is charged or credited with amounts representing the periodic amortization of the balance in utility plant account 114, "utility plant acquisition adjustments." A utility plant acquisition adjustment is represented by the difference between (1) the cost to the acquiring water utility of utility plant acquired as an operating unit or system and (2) the original cost of such property less accumulated depreciation and amortization and less any related contributions in aid of construction.

> *Amortization of Limited-Term Utility Plant (407.1).* This account includes amortization charges applicable to utility plant accounts for limited-term franchises, licenses, patent rights, limited-term interests in land, and expenditures for improvements on leased property where the service lives of the improvements are less than the term of the lease (the cost of such improvements allocated to a particular accounting period is considered as depreciation expense).

> *Amortization of Property Losses (407.2).* This account includes the periodic charge for amortization of the balance in deferred debit account 182, "extraordinary property losses," when a state regulatory body authorizes such a balance to be amortized through charges to operating expense.

> *Amortization of Other Utility Plant (407.3).* When authorized by a state regulatory body, this account includes the periodic change for amortization of intangible or other utility plant in service that does not have a definite or terminable life and that is not otherwise subject to charges for depreciation expense.

Periodic depreciation and amortization expenses associated with nonutility operations and with nonutility rental properties should be excluded from the above accounts. Such amounts should be charged to other income and deductions account 426, "miscellaneous nonutility expenses."

Typically, the total amounts that are recognized over time for depreciation and amortization of a utility plant, and that represent accumulated write-offs of asset costs, are accounted for on the balance sheet through the use of contra-asset accounts. For this purpose, the NARUC system provides six "accumulated provision" accounts related to utility plant. These six accounts, together with account numbers, are as follows:

- accumulated provision for depreciation of utility plant in service (108.1)

- accumulated provision for depreciation of utility plant leased to others (108.2)

- accumulated provision for depreciation of property held for future use (108.3)

- accumulated provision for amortization of utility plant in service (109.1)

- accumulated provision for amortization of utility plant leased to others (109.2)

- accumulated provision for amortization of property held for future use (115)

For the same purpose, but with regard to nonutility property, the NARUC system establishes account 122, "accumulated provision for depreciation and amortization of nonutility property."

Alternative Methods for Recording Depreciation Expense for Governmental Entities

According to the *Governmental GAAP Guide,** two alternatives are available for recording depreciation expense. In the first alternative, depreciation expense on only the noncontributed assets is included with operating expenses and closed directly to retained earnings. This method is most like that of a commercial entity. In the second alternative, depreciation expense on contributed assets is closed directly to the contributed capital account that was created when the restricted grant, entitlement, or shared revenue was received and the noncontributed asset depreciation expense is closed directly to retained earnings. Depreciation expense on contributed assets is still included as an operating expense on the Statement of Revenues, Expenses, and Changes in Retained Earnings, but will be added to net income to determine the change in retained earnings for the period.

⊠ Nature and Significance of Depreciation

Depreciation of utility plant assets is an economic fact that must be given explicit and systematic recognition, by both investor-owned and municipally owned water utilities, as a cost of rendering water service. In order to plan

---

*Available from the US Government Bookstore, 1961 Stout St., Denver, CO 80204.

appropriate procedures for distributing the cost of a depreciated asset over its estimated service life, it is helpful to understand the forces that tend to limit the service life of the asset.

Causes of Depreciation

Both physical factors and functional factors affect the usefulness of water utility plant assets. Physical deterioration of an asset is due either to wear and tear resulting from use of the asset, or to decay, rot, rust, and corrosion resulting from the action of time and the elements. Physical deterioration generally can be observed. However, observation may sometimes be difficult, as in the case of water mains.

The physical lives of water utility plant assets are also related to the extent to which maintenance is carried out with regard to the assets. Maintenance limits depreciation by reducing the effects of the physical causes of depreciation. For example, failure to make even minor repairs on pumping equipment would quickly terminate the useful life of the equipment. A preventive maintenance policy will greatly prolong the physical life of many water utility plant assets. Therefore, the estimated physical life of plant assets is, to a large extent, a function of the maintenance policy discussed in chapter 8.

Functional or nonphysical causes of depreciation are external to the operation of a water utility plant. Functional depreciation occurs when utility plant assets are no longer usable as originally intended. Included among the functional causes of depreciation are obsolescence, inadequacy, and the actions of government authorities. Obsolescence indicates a lack of economic usefulness due to new designs, inventions, and other improvements. Inadequacy occurs when facilities are no longer large enough to meet the demand for water service. Actions of government authorities, including regulatory commissions, may require that water utilities make changes in serviceable property (affecting, for example, safety, convenience, or appearance) so that the welfare of the general public, water utility customers, or utility employees is improved. Property relocation due to urban renewal or highway construction projects are examples.

As the preceding discussion indicates, there are a number of factors that limit the useful life of a plant asset. To the extent that the factors can be forecast with a reasonable degree of accuracy, they should be given consideration in determining the service lives of plant assets.

Significance of Depreciation Expense to Interested Parties

Depreciation is important to a number of groups interested in the affairs of a water utility. The groups that are particularly interested in depreciation include public service commissions, management, customers, taxing authorities, and investors (bondholders and stockholders). Although the discussion in this section emphasizes the significance of depreciation expense associated with a utility plant, it is equally applicable to amortization expense.

Depreciation is of interest to public service commissions, management, and customers primarily because depreciation expense, as a cost of rendering water service, is an important factor in establishing the structure and level of rate schedules. The annual depreciation expense must be equitably apportioned among customer classes in order to develop a rate schedule based on the cost of supplying water service to each class (see the section in chapter 16 about planning rate schedules.) In addition, depreciation is important for establishing rates because accumulated depreciation is an element to be deducted from the original cost (or other value concept) of a utility plant in determining the rate base.

In the case of investors, appraisals of security values by bondholders and stockholders depend on the asset values and earnings information included in accounting reports, and on the maintenance of the capital invested in the water utility. Depreciation accounting helps to determine appropriate balance-sheet values for assets, to determine periodic earnings, and to maintain invested capital by allocating the costs of tangible plant assets over the service lives of the assets. The credit standing of a water utility, as well as future earnings, may be affected if current income measurement is based on incorrect depreciation charges.

Depreciation expense is of interest to management as an element in determining net income. It also is an important factor in the analysis and budgeting of cash flows. Depreciation charges are noncash expenses, thus must be added back to net income to determine cash flow resulting from operations. It should be emphasized that depreciation charges are not, by themselves, a source of cash. The accounting recognition of depreciation expense does not in itself directly produce additional funds. However, the recognition of depreciation expense by management does indirectly influence cash flows because it is a factor in setting rates. In addition, management recognition of depreciation expense indirectly influences cash flow to the extent that such recognition prevents disbursements for dividends (in the case of investor-owned water utilities) or to the general fund (in the case of municipally owned water utilities) that would otherwise be made from fictitious earnings resulting from inadequate depreciation charges. Further, depreciation expense, to the extent permitted by tax authorities, will influence cash flows by reducing the income tax liability of investor-owned water utilities. Because depreciation charges are allowable deductions in establishing an investor-owned water utility's liability for income taxes, procedures for calculating depreciation charges and the amount of such charges are necessarily of interest to tax authorities. The determination of depreciation charges for income tax purposes is discussed in a later section of this chapter.

⊠ Determining Depreciation Expense

Once the decision has been made to purchase or construct depreciable assets, management planning of annual depreciation charges is limited to determining the appropriate portion of the cost of the assets that should be allocated to each accounting period in the form of periodic depreciation expense. The determination of periodic depreciation charges involves the following four steps: (1) estimating the service lives of the depreciable assets, (2) estimating the net salvage value of the assets, (3) selecting a depreciation formula to distribute the cost of assets over their estimated service lives, and (4) applying the selected depreciation formula to the service value of the depreciable property.

In some instances, the water utility may not have sufficient retirement experience or sufficient records of asset retirements to estimate the service life of an asset or group of assets. In such cases, retirement experience of other water utilities, information concerning service lives provided by equipment manufacturers and regulatory commissions, and/or special engineering studies conducted by the utility may be used in making service-life estimates.

Estimated service life based on retirement experience or other information described in the preceding paragraph must be adjusted in light of available information regarding probable future conditions affecting the service life of the depreciable asset. Future conditions may alter the relative effect of causes (physical and functional) of depreciation that existed in the past. In brief, estimates of future service lives of assets are subjective and can reflect only the best informed judgement.

⊠ Estimating Net Salvage Value

Because the amount of a periodic depreciation charge is the function of the service value (original cost less the salvage value net of cost of removal) of the depreciable asset, it is necessary that the net salvage value also be estimated. Estimated net salvage value may be based on historical information and adjusted for probable future conditions affecting the salvage value and cost of removal.

⊠ Selecting a Depreciation Formula

There are a number of depreciation formulas that can be used to distribute the depreciable cost (or service value) of an asset over the estimated service life of an asset. Characteristics of the various methods are discussed below.

Straight-Line Method

The straight-line method of depreciation distributes the depreciable cost of an asset in equal amounts to each of the accounting periods comprising the total estimated service life of the asset. Under this method, the depreciation rate per period may be determined by dividing the depreciable cost or service value (original cost less net salvage value), expressed as a percentage of original cost, by the total number of estimated time periods (either months or years) in the service life of the asset. Figure 9-1 presents a simplified example of the application of the straight-line method; the example is in the form of an equipment ledger card. With regard to most depreciated water utility plant assets, the straight-line allocation method of recognizing depreciation is the predominant method used for reporting to water utility management and external groups (except the US Internal Revenue Service [USIRS]), and for determining annual depreciation expense and accumulated provisions for depreciation to be used in rate studies.

The straight-line method assumes that time expiration is the sole factor, other than asset cost and net salvage value, determining the depreciation charge. It is unlikely that the service value of an asset will expire uniformly throughout the service life of that asset; physical and functional factors that limit service life may cause more loss in service value of an asset in one period than in another. However, unless there is sufficient evidence that the rate of service value expiration differs substantially from one period to another (such as where service value expiration is due primarily to wear and tear from use), the assumption of uniform service life expiration is not unreasonable. In addition, the straight-line method is the easiest depreciation method to apply

Figure 9-1 ⊠ Application of straight-line method

PLANT ASSET AND ACCUMULATED DEPRECIATION
SUBSIDIARY LEDGER CARD

ITEM ____Accounting Machine____ PRIMARY ACCOUNT CLASSIFICATION ____Office Furniture and Equipment____

DESCRIPTION ____Excelsior, Model 140____ FROM WHOM ACQUIRED ____Excelsior Company____

SERIAL NUMBER ____R-1734____ ESTIMATED SERVICE LIFE ____10 years____

WHERE LOCATED OR STORED ____Office____ COST ____$2,000.00____

PERSON RESPONSIBLE FOR ASSET ____Office Manager____ SALVAGE VALUE ____$200.00 (10%)____

DEPRECIATION RATE (YEAR) ____$180.00 (9%)____ (MONTH) ____$15.00 (0.75%)____

Date	Description	Asset Account			Accumulated Depreciation			Net Book Value
		Dr.	Cr.	Bal.	Dr.	Cr.	Bal.	
July 1, 1964	Purchase of Asset	$2,000.00		$2,000.00				$2,000.00
Dec. 31, 1965	Annual Depreciation					$ 90.00	$ 90.00	1,910.00
Dec. 31, 1966	Annual Depreciation					180.00	270.00	1,730.00
Dec. 31, 1967	Annual Depreciation					180.00	450.00	1,550.00

Computations:*
Original Cost $2,000   (100%)
Net Salvage Value   200   (10% of original cost)
Depreciable Cost (Service value) $1,800   (90% of original cost)

Annual Depreciation Rate = $\dfrac{90\%}{\text{Estimated Service Life}}$ = $\dfrac{90\%}{10}$ = 9% of original cost (or $180 per year)

Monthly Depreciation Rate = 9% ÷ 12 = 0.75% of original cost (or $15 per month)

*Alternatively, the straight-line rate may be expressed as a percentage of depreciable cost or service value, an annual rate of 10% in this case (the annual depreciation charge is the same, 10% of $1,800, or $180).

and therefore the most acceptable from an administrative point of view. In contrast to other depreciation methods, the straight-line method readily permits the recalculation of depreciation charges based on changing estimates of service lives or net salvage values.

Method Based on Use

For some water utility plant assets, depreciation is more a function of actual use than of time expiration. As examples, depreciation of transportation equipment may be closely related to vehicle miles driven, and depreciation of pumping equipment may be closely related to hours operated. In such cases, a method that allocates depreciable cost among accounting periods based on asset use during each period may be considered appropriate. Such a method is commonly referred to as a unit-of-production method. Figure 9-2 presents an example of the application of a depreciation method based on use. For many types of assets, however, service life expiration is as much or more a function of time expiration as of actual use. In such cases, a depreciation method based on time is considered reasonable and appropriate.

Sum of the Years' Digits Method

The sum of the years' digits (SYD) method for recognizing annual depreciation charges is used by many investor-owned water utilities in determining taxable income. It is acceptable to the USIRS as a legitimate depreciation method for income tax purposes. However, this accelerated method may not presently be acceptable to public service commissions as an appropriate method for determining the depreciation expense portion of a utility's operating expenses for general financial reporting purposes or for rate determination purposes. Under the SYD method, annual depreciation expense is determined by applying a constantly declining fraction to the depreciable cost (service value) of an asset. The fraction to be applied in each year is determined as follows: (1) the years of service life of the asset are numbered in reverse order (1 for the last year, 2 for the next-to-last year, until all years in the service life are assigned a number); (2) the sum of the numbers thus assigned is determined; and (3) the applicable fraction for each year has as its numerator the number assigned to the year in question and as its denominator the sum of

Figure 9-2 ⊠ Application of a method based on use

End of Year	Miles Operated	Depreciation Charge	Accumulated Depreciation	Net Book Value
1	16,000	$640	$640	$3,360
2	12,000	480	1,120	2,880
3	18,000	720	1,840	2,160
4	20,000	800	2,640	1,360
5	14,000	560	3,200	800

Computations:

Cost of service truck	$4,000
Net salvage value	800
Depreciable cost (service value)	$3,200
Estimated Service Life	80,000 miles
Depreciation Rate ($3,200 ÷ 80,000 miles)	$0.04 per mile

the numbers assigned to all years. Figure 9-3 presents an example of the application of the SYD method.

Since the SYD method attributes a greater amount of cost to the early years of the service life of an asset than to the later years, there is a presumption that service value expires more rapidly in the early years than in the later years. Therefore, the method recognizes the fact that, in some cases, a plant asset makes a greater contribution to revenue when it is new than when it is old. Nevertheless, the fractional allocation to each year of the service life of the asset is rather arbitrary and, in most cases, will not match actual service value expiration.

Double Declining Balance Method

As an alternative to the SYD method, the double declining balance (DDB) method also is used by investor-owned water utilities to recognize depreciation on an accelerated basis for income tax determination purposes. As in the case of the SYD method, the DDB method may not presently be acceptable to public service commissions as an appropriate method for calculating the depreciation expense portion of a utility's operating expenses for general financial reporting purposes or for rate determination purposes. Under the DDB method, annual depreciation is determined by multiplying the undepreciated balance of asset cost by a percentage that is twice the annual rate (computed without adjustment for net salvage value) associated with the

Figure 9-3 ⊠ Application of the sum of the years' digits method

(1) Year	(2) Annual Depreciation Rate	(3) Depreciable Cost	(4) Charge to Depreciation Expense (2) × (3)	(5) Annual Credit to Accumulated Provision for Depreciation	(6) Balance in Accumulated Provision for Depreciation Account	(7) Net Book Value After Annual Charge
0						$1,800.00
1	5/15	$1,500.00	$500.00	$500.00	$500.00	1,300.00
2	4/15	1,500.00	400.00	400.00	900.00	900.00
3	3/15	1,500.00	300.00	300.00	1,200.00	600.00
4	2/15	1,500.00	200.00	200.00	1,400.00	400.00
5	1/15	1,500.00	100.00	100.00	1,500.00	300.00
		$1,500.00	$1,500.00			

Computations:
Cost of asset $1,800.00
Net salvage value   300.00

Depreciable cost (service value) $1,500.00

Service Life   5 years
Sum of the Years' Digits:
    Year 1 = 5
    Year 2 = 4
    Year 3 = 3
    Year 4 = 2
    Year 5 = 1

               15

straight-line method. Figure 9-4 presents an example. Like the SYD method, the DDB method serves rather arbitrarily to attribute a relatively greater portion of an asset's depreciable cost to the early years of the service life of the asset than to the later years.

There are two other methods of recognizing depreciation charges that make use of the "time value of money" concept. These two related methods

Figure 9-4 ⊠ Application of double declining balance method

(1) Year	(2) Annual Depreciation Rate	(3) Undepreciated Cost Before Annual Charge	(4) Annual Charge to Depreciation Expense (2) × (3)	(5) Annual Credit to Accumulated Provision for Depreciation	(6) Balance in Accumulated Provision for Depreciation Account	(7) Net Book Value After Annual Charge
0						$2,000.00
1	.20	$2,000.00	$400.00	$400.00	$400.00	1,600.00
2	.20	1,600.00	320.00	320.00	720.00	1,280.00
3	.20	1,280.00	256.00	256.00	976.00	1,024.00
4	.20	1,024.00	204.80	204.80	1,180.80	819.20
5	.20	819.20	163.84	163.84	1,344.64	655.36
6	.20	655.36	131.07	131.07	1,475.71	524.29
7	.20	524.29	104.86	104.86	1,580.57	419.43
8	.20	419.43	83.89	83.89	1,664.46	335.54
9	.20	335.54	67.11	67.11	1,731.57	268.43
10	.20	268.43	68.43*	68.43	1,800.00	200.00

Computations:
Cost of asset $2,000.00
Net salvage value $200.00
Service life   10 years

Annual straight-line rate† $= \dfrac{100\%}{\text{service life}} = \dfrac{100\%}{10} = 10\%$

Double straight-line rate = 10% × 2 = 20%

---

*Note that depreciation expense in year 10 is not the product of columns 2 and 3. The amount charged to depreciation expense in year 10 is an amount sufficient to reduce the cash value of the asset at the end of year 10 to an amount equal to estimated salvage value. In order to accomplish this, depreciation expense in year 10 is slightly higher than in year 9. To avoid the need for increasing depreciation expense in the last year, a formula is available for computing a fixed rate to apply each year to undepreciated asset cost. The computed rate, when applied annually to the undepreciated asset cost, will accumulate depreciation expense over the service life of the asset exactly equal to the depreciable cost of the asset. The fixed rate formula is:

$$r = 1 - \sqrt[n]{S/C}$$

Where

r = constant rate
n = number of periods in the estimated service life
S = net salvage value
C = cost of the asset

Applying the formula to our example results in the following fixed rate, which is slightly greater than the straight-line rate:

$$r = 1 - \sqrt[10]{\$200/\$2,000} = .2057$$

†Annual straight-line rate must be computed without adjustment for estimated net salvage value. Compare with Figure 13-1 where annual straight-line rate is computed after consideration of net salvage value.

are the compound interest and the sinking fund methods. While the two methods have some theoretical merit, they are more complex than the other depreciation methods discussed here and are infrequently employed in practice. A brief description of the two methods is presented in the following paragraphs.

Compound Interest Method

The compound interest method assumes that depreciation in any year will be the same in amount as the increase in the value of a sinking fund that is established for a period of time equivalent to the service life of the depreciable asset. Annual depreciation expense, therefore, is equal in amount to (1) an annuity that, at an assumed rate of interest compounded annually over the asset service life, will equal the depreciable cost plus (2) the annual interest on the compound amount of the accumulated annuities that are in the theoretical sinking fund during the year. The application of the compound interest method is shown in Figure 9-5.

As indicated by Figure 9-5, the compound interest method provides for increasing annual charges for depreciation. The compound interest method of computing depreciation results from a formula that usually has little or no relationship to the way in which the service value of an asset expires.

Figure 9-5 ⊠ Application of compound interest method

Year	(1) Balance of Theoretical Sinking Fund Beginning of Each Year	(2) Interest Assumed Earned on Fund Each Year	(3) Annual Contribution Made to Theoretical Sinking Fund at End of Year	(4) Depreciation Expense (2) + (3)	(5) Accumulated Provision for Depreciation	(6) Net Book Value After Current Charge for Depreciation
1	$0	$0	$758.68	$758.68	$758.68	$9,741.32
2	758.68	45.52	758.68	804.20	1,562.88	8,937.12
3	1,562.88	93.77	758.68	852.45	2,415.33	8,084.67
4	2,415.33	144.92	758.68	903.60	3,318.93	7,181.07
5	3,318.93	199.14	758.68	957.82	4,276.75	6,223.25
6	4,276.75	256.61	758.68	1,015.29	5,292.04	5,207.96
7	5,292.04	317.52	758.68	1,076.20	6,368.24	4,131.76
8	6,368.24	382.09	758.68	1,140.77	7,509.01	2,990.99
9	7,509.01	450.54	758.68	1,209.22	8,718.23	1,781.77
10	8,718.23	523.09	758.68	1,281.77	10,000.00	500.00
		$1,413.80	$7,586.80	$10,000.00		

Assumptions and Computations:
1. Total cost of asset $10,500.00
    Less: estimated net salvage value   500.00

    Depreciable cost $10,000.00

2. Estimated service life   10 years
3. Theoretical sinking fund assumed to earn 6 percent.
4. Amount of an annuity of 1 at 6 percent for 10 years equals 13.180795 (arrived at using annuity tables that employ the formula $[(1 + i)^n - 1]/i$ where n represents the number of years and i is the rate of interest). $10,000.00 (depreciable cost) ÷ 13.180795 (amount of annuity of 1) equals $758.68, which is the amount that must be contributed annually to a sinking fund for a period of 10 years in order to accumulate an amount equal to $10,000.

Sinking Fund Method

An alternative to the compound interest method is the sinking fund method. As in the case of the compound interest method, the sinking fund method employs the concept of establishing a hypothetical sinking fund in which a regular periodic deposit is made, and on which compound interest is earned at an assumed rate. The compound interest method and the sinking fund method are based on the same mathematical calculations, but the methods differ as to the amount recognized as depreciation expense. Under the sinking fund method, the annual depreciation expense would be equal in amount to the annuity (the amount shown in column 3 of Figure 9-5). The annual credit to the accumulated provision for depreciation account (which is the annual amount earned by the sinking fund) is charged to income (the amounts in column 2 of Figure 9-5) as a nonoperating expense item.

Using the sinking fund method has the same net effect on income as using the compound interest method. However, under the sinking fund method, operating income is greater by the amount of the annual interest earned by the sinking fund, which is charged to income as a nonoperating expense item. If the sinking fund method were to be required by a regulatory commission in a given jurisdiction, then an undepreciated rate base should be used for rate-making purposes. Based on the necessary assumption that amounts equal to the balance found in the accumulated provision for depreciation account are reinvested in plant assets, Figure 9-6 shows how the compound interest method and the sinking fund method can be reconciled for rate-making purposes. The data used in Figure 9-6 are based on those presented in Figure 9-5.

As in the case of the compound interest method, the sinking fund method results in increasing annual accruals to the accumulated provision for depreciation account. This pattern of increasingly greater accruals usually bears little resemblance to asset service-value expiration. In addition, the sinking fund method and the compound interest method both present more complex clerical problems than other methods described previously.

It may be observed that under the sinking fund method (as well as the compound interest method), the lower the interest rate used to determine the annuity and the hypothetical sinking fund earnings, the closer will be the results of the method to those of the straight-line method. At the limit, the use of either the sinking fund method or the compound interest method with an assumed interest rate of zero provides the same result as that determined by using the straight-line method.

⊠ Methods of Applying Depreciation Formulas

There are a number of ways depreciation formulas may be applied to the cost of depreciable assets. Depreciation expense and accumulated provision for depreciation may be accounted for by individual depreciable property items, groups of property items, functional groups of plant accounts, or the utility plant as a whole.

Accounting for Depreciation By Individual Property Items

Accounting for depreciation by individual property items requires that depreciation rates be fixed separately for each individual unit of property. Such a procedure is reasonable for large items of property, such as pumps and

Figure 9-6 ⊠ Reconciliation of compound interest method and sinking fund method for rate-making purposes*

```
Compound Interest Method:
  Revenue Requirement for Year 6:
    Depreciation expense for year 6                                    $1,015.29
    Return on rate base:
      Net book value of original asset at end of year 5    $ 6,223.25
      Reinvestment in plant assets of an amount equal
      to 5 years' accruals to the accumulated provision
      for depreciation account                                4,276.75

      Total rate base in year 6                             $10,500.00
      Rate of return allowed on rate base                       × 6%

    Return on rate base in year 6 ($10,500 × .06)                     $  630.00

  Revenue Requirement for Year 6                                      $1,645.29

Sinking Fund Method:
  Revenue Requirement for Year 6:
    Depreciation expense for year 6                                   $  758.68
    Return on rate base:
      Cost of original asset                                $10,500.00
      Reinvestment in plant assets of an amount
      equal to 5 years' accruals to the accumulated
      provision for depreciation account                      4,276.75

      Total rate base in year 6                             $14,776.75
      Rate of return allowed on rate base                       × 6%

    Return on rate base for year 6 ($14,776.75 × .06)                 $  886.61

  Revenue Requirement for Year 6                                      $1,645.29
```

*This example shows the calculation of revenue requirements (in the sixth year of the life of a depreciable asset costing $10,500) under the following two assumptions:
1. The compound interest depreciation method is used and the depreciated cost of plant assets serves as the rate base.
2. The sinking fund depreciation method is used and the undepreciated cost of plant assets serves as the rate base.

Operation and maintenance expenses, taxes, and the return on rate base resulting from other plant assets are ignored in determining revenue requirements; their inclusion would complicate the example and would not prohibit the reconciliation of the two depreciation methods.

vehicles. When an individual item is retired, the recorded cost of the item is credited to the primary plant account in which the cost of the item is included, and the accumulated provision for depreciation account is charged with the amount of accumulated depreciation related to the retired property item. Generally, a gain or loss from the disposal of the property item will result, measured by the difference between the net book value of the asset (original cost less accumulated depreciation) and the net salvage value. NOTE: Figure 9-1 presents an example of accounting for depreciation by individual property unit. In cases where many similar items of property are involved, accounting for depreciation by individual property items includes providing detailed information concerning accumulated depreciation related to the retired property item.

Accounting for Depreciation By Groups of Property Items

Classes of property consisting of numerous small units having the same or similar service life expectancies (such as meters) are generally accounted for by groups rather than individual units. In effect, each group is considered as one asset. Consequently, it is necessary to determine an average service life for each group. The aggregate cost of a group of property items having similar service life expectancies is represented by the balance in a primary plant account such as "services, meters or hydrants." Based on the average service life and the cost of the group of similar property items, periodic depreciation expense is determined for the group by applying one of the depreciation formulas described in the preceding section. Typically, straight-line depreciation is employed in conjunction with the group method, and a composite depreciation rate is determined for the group (or primary account). The amount of depreciation expense for any period is obtained by applying the composite depreciation rate to the balance in the primary account.

When an individual property item is retired, its cost is credited to the primary plant account in which the cost of the item is recorded and the accumulated provision for depreciation account is charged for the cost of the item less net salvage value. No recognized gain or loss will result from the disposal of individual property items when they are accounted for on a group basis. This procedure for accounting for retirements of depreciable property is basically the one required by the NARUC system of accounts. As discussed in chapter 7, this NARUC procedure avoids fluctuations in the rate base that would otherwise occur when property is retired and not immediately replaced.

The use of the group method is most logical when primary account balances consist of the cost of individual property items having similar service life expectancies. However, the use of the group method can be extended to other primary accounts, such as "structures and improvements," which have balances composed of the cost of a variety of property items that are not similar in nature and do not have the same estimated life.

Accounting for Depreciation By Functional Groups of Accounts and By the Utility Plant as a Whole

Use of the group method also can be extended to functional groups of primary plant accounts (source of supply pumping, water treatment, transmission and distribution, and general plant), and even to the depreciable cost of the utility plant as a whole. NARUC recommends that water utilities maintain subsidiary records showing the amount of accrued depreciation (as well as the book cost of property retired, the cost of removal, salvage, and such other items as recoveries from insurance) for each functional group plant account. Retirements of depreciable property would be handled in the manner described in the preceding section concerning accounting for depreciation by groups of property items.

Using the straight-line method, Figure 9-7 presents the calculation of a composite rate for a group of assets. Each asset may be considered as (1) an individual property item with the composite rate applicable to a primary plant account, (2) a primary account with the composite rate applicable to a functional group of primary accounts, or (3) a functional group of accounts with the composite rate applicable to the cost of depreciating utility plant as a whole.

Figure 9-7 ⊠ Computation of a composite depreciation rate

Asset	Cost	Net Salvage Value	Depreciable Cost	Estimated Service Life	Annual Depreciation Expense
A	$100,000	$10,000	$ 90,000	30	$ 3,000
B	50,000	1,000	49,000	10	4,900
C	60,000	4,000	56,000	16	3,500
D	200,000	0	200,000	40	5,000
	$410,000		$395,000		$16,400

Composite Rate on Cost: $16,400 ÷ $410,000 = 4 percent.

⊠ Reevaluating the Adequacy of Periodic Depreciation Charges

Because the service value and service life of an asset or group of assets are based on estimates of future conditions, the service value and service life chosen for use in the depreciation computation may prove inaccurate. Thus, service life estimates and net salvage value estimates should be reviewed periodically to determine their reasonableness in light of current knowledge and experience.

Depreciation Studies

The purpose of depreciation studies is to review a water utility's present depreciation rates in order to establish their adequacy and to recommend changes where appropriate. Depreciation studies, which may be conducted by water utility staff and/or outside consultants, represent an in-depth analysis of plant depreciation policies and procedures. Typically, the studies make use of accounting records of a utility, including historical service-life evidence, field inspections of selected properties, consultations with utility personnel, and information concerning conditions expected to exist in the future that will influence physical and functional depreciation.

The primary component of depreciation studies is the estimate of average service lives of property groups. Such estimates of future service lives, which necessarily require some degree of judgment, typically are founded on a study of past retirement experience. In the ideal situation, the continuing property records of a water utility provide the information concerning installation and retirement dates. However, since a large part of a water utility plant is long-lived, there often is an insufficient quantity of retirement data available to make a meaningful study. In such cases, a technique using survivor curves may be employed. In general, this technique involves a comparison of the water utility's own retirement experience with more complete known data (survivor curves) in order to project estimates of service lives. The determination of reliable projections ordinarily is accomplished through the use of a computer. Under this approach, information concerning the water utility's own retirement history is required, but not on as detailed a basis as in the ideal situation.

Remaining-Life Method

The remaining-life method serves to update depreciation charges with respect to a depreciable asset or group of assets. The method is particularly useful in cases where it is difficult to determine with any degree of exactness the service lives of utility properties at the time of their purchase or construction.

The remaining-life method emphasizes estimated remaining service life as opposed to the estimate of total service life. Under this method, an estimate of the remaining service life of an asset or asset group is made periodically. The new estimate of service life is then applied against the undepreciated cost less estimated net salvage value of the asset to determine an appropriate depreciation expense figure applicable to future periods. The depreciation expense computed by the remaining-life method is compared with the depreciation expense computed in accordance with the method currently in use in order to determine (1) an appropriate depreciation expense figure applicable to future periods and (2) whether current charges are reasonable or if adjustments need to be made.

⊠ Depreciation Based on Replacement Cost

Conventional depreciation accounting for water utilities reflects a process of historical or original cost allocation. In recent years, due largely to the presence of substantial inflation, concern over the adequacy of historical cost-based depreciation charges has increased. At issue is the question of whether or not current depreciation practices can ensure maintenance of the original capital invested in a water utility. In connection with the concern over maintenance of invested capital, it has been suggested that depreciation charges should be based on the cost of replacing the water utility plant as opposed to the original cost of the plant.

In December 1986, the Financial Accounting Standards Board (FASB) issued Financial Accounting Standards Number 89 (SFAS 89), "Financial Reporting and Changing Prices." This statement encourages (but does not require) a business enterprise to disclose supplementary information on the effects of changing prices. Entities are not discouraged from experimenting with other forms of disclosure.

The practical justification for measuring depreciation in terms of replacement cost can be appreciated by water utility treasurers and controllers who have had to secure funds for plant replacement, improvement, and expansion in the face of constantly rising price levels. One purpose served by depreciation accounting based on replacement cost is to permit a more meaningful calculation of actual water utility operating expenses and income in order to establish realistic rate schedules and to permit capital maintenance. Depreciation accounting based on replacement cost is not at present generally accepted for financial reporting purposes in the United States or Canada, nor is it accepted by tax authorities or regulatory authorities in either country. Nevertheless, it is a concept that should be considered by water utility management, regulatory authorities, and other interested groups, if a high rate of inflation persists.

⊠ Determining Amortization Expense

The determination of periodic amortization expense related to assets and deferred debits generally presents little problem. The service lives of the assets and deferred debits are established by law or contract (as in the case of limited-term interests in land and improvements on leased property where the service life of the improvements is terminable by action of the lessee) or are established by regulatory commissions (as in the case of utility plant acquisition adjustments and extraordinary property losses). The straight-line depreciation method generally is employed to compute the amortization expense.

Utility Plant Acquisition Adjustments

NARUC recommends that water utilities acquiring properties from another utility record such property at the original cost to the first utility devoting it to public service. If the purchase price differs from the original cost, the difference is recorded separately in account 114, "utility plant acquisition adjustments." As approved or directed by state public service commissions, the "utility plant acquisition adjustments" account balance may be amortized over a period of time (generally as recovered through rates) with a corresponding charge to an amortization expense account.

Extraordinary Property Losses

Account 182, "extraordinary property losses," is provided by NARUC to record extraordinary losses on property abandoned or otherwise retired from service, losses that could not be reasonably anticipated (and therefore could not be avoided through greater accumulated provisions for depreciation or amortization), and that are not covered by insurance. The amounts to be included in this account are authorized or directed by state public service commissions. The period over which the extraordinary property loss is to be amortized or otherwise disposed of is also subject to the approval or direction of the regulatory commission.

⊠ Depreciation Expense for Income Tax

Under certain circumstances, the US Internal Revenue Code permits investor-owned water utilities to use accelerated depreciation methods for income tax purposes. The accelerated methods, which were originally authorized as a result of the 1954 revision of the federal income tax laws, may be applied to the cost of water utility property purchased, constructed, or reconditioned after 1953. The accelerated methods provide for the depreciation of a particular item of property at a faster rate than under the straight-line allocation method, thus resulting in larger deductions for tax purposes during the early years of the service life of the property and smaller deductions during later years. The accelerated depreciation methods permitted include the sum of the years' digits method (see Figure 9-3 and related discussion) and the double declining balance method (see Figure 9-4 and related discussion).

In addition, the federal tax law provides guidelines for determining depreciate lives to be used for income tax purposes. These tax lives may differ from the service lives used by the water utility for purposes other than tax determination. It should be apparent that depreciation charges for tax purposes may differ from depreciation charges for other purposes if (1) an accelerated depreciation method is used for tax purposes and the straight-line method is used for other purposes and/or (2) the depreciate lives employed for tax purposes differ from the estimated service lives of assets used for determining depreciation expenses for other purposes.

Effect of "Tax" Depreciation on Cash Flows

The use of accelerated depreciation methods for tax purposes has implications both from the standpoint of increasing cash flows (assuming normalization) and from the standpoint of rate determination. With regard to an individual property item, the use of accelerated depreciation for tax purposes (as opposed to the straight-line method) will result in lower income taxes in the early years of the property life and higher taxes in later years. This will result in additional funds for working capital or plant investment during the early years of the life of the property. In later years, however, cash flows will decrease due to the smaller deduction for depreciation and the resulting increase in taxes. Therefore, accelerated depreciation results in a tax deferral as opposed to a tax saving. From the standpoint of the water utility as a whole, accelerated depreciation will result in a permanent tax saving only if the utility experiences a continual growth in plant investment sufficient to permit high depreciation charges on new plant investment to offset the lower depreciation charges on older plant investment.

Flow-Through Method

For rate-making purposes, actual income taxes paid are considered as the income tax expense and are included in the cost of service; however, depreciation expense for rate-making purposes is based on the straight-line method. This approach to the treatment of income taxes resulting from accelerated depreciation is known as the "flow-through" approach. The benefits received from electing to use accelerated depreciation methods for tax purposes are allowed to flow through to water customers as reduced rates resulting from the reduction in income taxes.

Normalization

Considered as a tax deferral, if accelerated depreciation methods are employed for tax purposes, the actual income tax paid must be adjusted or "normalized" by recomputed income tax expenses on the basis of the straight-line depreciation. The amount of income tax computed by using the straight-line method represents the income tax figure for financial statement and rate-making purposes. The difference between the income tax computed using the straight-line method and the actual tax liability as determined using accelerated depreciation methods is credited to a balance-sheet account for accumulated deferred income taxes (see account 282, "accumulated deferred income taxes — liberalized depreciation," in appendix A). The accumulated deferred income tax account balance is increased or decreased each year as necessitated by the difference between the normalized tax expense and the actual income tax liability.

Alternative Methods for Recording Depreciation Expense on Contributed Assets for Governmental Entities

According to the Governmental GAAP Guide, two alternatives are available for recording depreciation expense on contributed assets. In the first

Figure 9-8 ⊠ Statement of revenues, expenses, and changes in retained earnings

San Antonio Water System Schedule of Funds — Revenues, Expenses, and Changes in Retained Earnings
For the period of May 19, 1992, through May 31, 1993

	System Fund	Internal Service Fund	Debt Service Fund	Reserve Fund	Renewal and Replacement Fund	Project Fund	Combined Total
Operating Revenues							
Water System Revenues	$ 60,325,527	—	—	$ —	$ —	$ —	$ 60,325,527
Wastewater System Revenues	78,126,058	—	—	—	—	—	78,126,058
Chilled Water and Steam System	2,925,532	—	—	—	—	—	2,925,532
Reuse System Revenues	1,978,235	—	—	—	—	—	1,978,235
Total operating revenues	143,355,352	—	—	—	—	—	143,355,352
Operating Expenses							
Personal Services	32,834,823	—	—	—	—	—	32,834,823
Contractual Services	33,573,293	—	—	—	—	—	33,573,293
Materials & Supplies	8,666,993	—	—	—	—	—	8,666,993
Other Charges	17,028,833	—	—	—	—	—	17,028,833
Interfund Transfers	(11,009,752)	—	—	—	—	—	(11,009,752)
Internal Service Fund — Net (gain)	—	(702,280)	—	—	—	—	(702,280)
Total operating expenses before depreciation	81,094,190	(702,280)	—	—	—	—	80,391,910
Depreciation Expense	37,452,499	1,020,291	—	—	—	—	38,472,790
Total operating expenses	118,546,689	318,011	—	—	—	—	118,864,700
Operating income	24,808,663	(318,011)	—	—	—	—	24,490,652

Figure continued next page

Figure 9-8 ⊠ Statement of revenues, expenses, and changes in retained earnings (continued)

San Antonio Water System Schedule of Funds — Revenues, Expenses, and Changes in Retained Earnings
For the period of May 19, 1992, through May 31, 1993

	System Fund	Internal Service Fund	Debt Service Fund	Reserve Fund	Renewal and Replacement Fund	Project Fund	Combined Total
Nonoperating Revenues							
Interest Earned and Miscellaneous	$ 2,800,378	$ —	676,153	1,973,146	153,519	1,079,142	6,682,338
Total nonoperating revenues	2,800,378	—	676,153	1,973,146	153,519	1,079,142	6,682,338
Nonoperating Expenses							
Amortization of Refunding Bond Expense	48,192						48,192
Write-off of Capital Project	168,108						168,108
Interest Expense:							
Revenue bonds	(1,044,045)	—	39,008,326	—	—	—	37,964,281
Installment notes	3,651	—	—	—	—	—	3,651
Loss (Gain) on Sale of Fixed Assets	35,352	—	—	—	—	—	35,352
Amortized Discount Expense	595,713	—	—	—	—	—	595,713
(Gain) on Sale of Investment	—	—	—	(6,915)	—	—	(6,915)
(Gain) on Escrow Account Reorganization	(1,239,222)	—	—		—	—	(1,239,222)
Total nonoperating expenses	(1,432,251)	—	39,008,326	(6,915)	—	—	37,569,160
Income (loss) before operating transfers	29,041,292 (	318,011)	(38,332,173)	1,980,061	153,519	1,079,142	(6,396,170)
Operating transfers in (out)	(36,352,112)	—	38,332,173	(1,980,061)	—	—	—
Net Income (Loss) — Carried Forward	($ 7,310,820)	($ 318,011)	$ —	$ —	$153,519	$1,079,142	($ 6,396,170)

Figure continued next page

Figure 9-8 ⊠ Statement of revenues, expenses, and changes in retained earnings (continued)

San Antonio Water System Schedule of Funds — Revenues, Expenses, and Changes in Retained Earnings
For the period of May 19, 1992, through May 31, 1993

	System Fund	Internal Service Fund	Debt Service Fund	Reserve Fund	Renewal and Replacement Fund	Project Fund	Combined Total
Retained Earnings, May 19, 1992	159,342,198	10,807,960	3,717	41,200,687	42,820,207	21,493,697	275,668,466
Residual Equity Transfers In (Out)	(34,069,660)	—	15,481,102	2,574,495	16,014,063	—	—
Transfers to the City of San Antonio	(2,470,142)	—	—	—	—	—	(2,470,142)
Contributions in Aid of Construction	(16,508,002)	—	—	—	16,508,002	—	—
Retirement of Revenue Bond Principal	15,375,000	—	(15,375,000)	—	—	—	—
Expenditures for Plant Additions	63,087,955	—	—	—	(44,991,898)	(18,096,057)	—
Retained Earnings, May 31, 1993	$177,446,529	$10,489,949	$ 109,819	$43,775,182	$30,503,893	$ 4,476,782	$266,802,154

alternative, depreciation expense on only the noncontributed assets is included with operating expenses and closed directly to retained earnings. This method is most like that of a commercial entity. In the second alternative, depreciation expense on contributed assets is closed directly to the contributed capital account that was created when the restricted grant, entitlement, or shared revenue was received and the noncontributed asset depreciation expense is closed directly to retained earnings. Depreciation expense is still included as an operating expense on the Statement of Revenues, Expenses, and Changes in Retained Earnings, but will be added to net income to determine the change in retained earnings for the period. See Figure 9-8 for an example.

CHAPTER TEN

General and Income Taxes

Planning and controlling tax expense is of greater concern to investor-owned water utilities than to government-owned water utilities since the latter are exempt from the payment of federal income taxes and, in most cases, from the payment of state and local taxes. Tax expenses of investor-owned water utilities average 18 percent of revenues, making a thorough knowledge of taxes important.

In the case of a government-owned water utility, direct payments for taxes may not serve as the real measure of the tax burden placed on the utility. In measuring the extent of the tax burden of a government-owned water utility, "payments in lieu of taxes" may be applicable in addition to any direct tax payments.

The US Internal Revenue Code is very complex; therefore, this chapter will only present an overview of federal income taxes as it relates to water utility operations.

⊠ Types and Descriptions of Taxes

Water utilities, particularly investor-owned utilities, are subject to a wide variety of taxes. Income taxes usually get the most attention because of their complexity and regulatory accounting problems. However, in total dollar amounts, other taxes represent a larger portion of the utility's total tax expense.

Federal Income Taxes

Government-owned water utilities are exempt from federal income taxation. Further, government-owned water utilities are exempt from most state and local taxation. As a result, tax reporting requirements faced by government-owned water utilities generally are small in comparison with requirements faced by investor-owned water utilities, which are subject to federal, state, and local taxes. Government-owned water utilities may be required to provide free water service to other departments of government as an alternative to payment of local taxes, or they may be required to transfer cash to the general fund as a "payment in lieu of taxes."

The preparation and filing of returns involves more than merely reporting taxable income and the tax liability thereon. It is necessary that the return be accompanied by supporting information or statements required by regulations or instructions. The net income as shown in the financial statements of an investor-owned water utility may differ from the taxable income shown on the federal income tax return because the accounting treatment of certain income and expense items differs from the tax treatment. Income tax laws are written with feasibility of collection and enforcement in mind and are not necessarily in agreement with sound accounting principles. Tax payments made during a particular accounting period usually do not coincide with the tax expense for that period. Some payments, for example, are properly classified as prepaid taxes allocable to a future period; other payments, for taxes properly classified as expenses of the current period, are not made until a future period. The National Association of Regulatory Utility Commissioners (NARUC) account classification provides for prepaid and deferred taxes and for accrued taxes.

In the case of investor-owned water utilities, the recognition of revenues and expenses for financial reporting purposes on a basis different than income tax purposes may give rise to differences between the income tax liability for a particular period and the amount considered as income tax expense for the same period. For example, the use of an accelerated depreciation method for tax purposes and the straight-line method for financial reporting purposes may cause such a "timing" difference. These differences are accounted for on the balance sheet by establishing accumulated deferred income tax accounts.

Federal tax laws are extremely complex and change frequently in response to new or amended federal tax legislation. The water utility should employ qualified specialists in tax law and accounting. Even though the utility has a staff specialist, the use of consultants on a part-time basis may be necessary.

State and Municipal Income Taxes

State and municipal income taxes are becoming increasingly important as a source of revenue for state governments and municipalities. Investor-owned utilities should verify the tax filing requirements for each locality in which it generates income. Some state and municipal income tax returns correspond to the federal income tax return and, in such cases, state and municipal income tax returns usually can be prepared from the federal return and supporting schedules. In other cases, even though the state and municipal income tax is patterned after the federal tax, income subject to taxation and deductions allowed may differ somewhat from that reported on the federal return. In such a situation, the income tax return for the state or municipal government may still use the taxable income figure derived from the federal return, with adjustments being made on the return itself or on a separate schedule for the difference between federal, state, or municipal taxable income.

Property Taxes

Taxes based on the value of property are a major source of revenue for state and municipal governments. Property taxes are not levied by the federal government. A water utility may be liable for payment of several different types of property taxes and may pay property taxes to many different tax authorities, including states, counties, school districts, cities, or any other tax districts. The expression "property tax" generally means an ad valorem (that is, in proportion to the value) levy on real and personal property. In general, a property tax in its true form is a tax on all property not specifically exempt. All property is valued uniformly and taxed at a uniform rate. In many instances, property is classified as real property, or tangible and intangible personal property. Each class of property is individually valued and a tax rate (which may be the same or may be different for each class of property) is applied to each class. The basis for valuing real property and tangible and intangible personal property varies widely among various taxing jurisdictions. The basis for valuation may be established by law or regulation as original cost less depreciation, reproduction cost less depreciation, cash value, or some other value.

Frequently, the tangible and intangible personal property of a water utility is valued on a going-concern basis, as opposed to a piecemeal assessment of specific items of property. In some instances, the assessed value may be determined by the total market value of securities outstanding or by capitalizing utility net income. Once the value of all property subject to tax is assessed, the tax rate per unit value of property, such as per $100 or per $1,000, is fixed. Property tax returns typically include information concerning the class of property subject to the tax, a listing of such property, the assessed value of the taxable property, and the tax liability on the assessed valuation.

Gross Receipts Taxes

These taxes are levied on the revenue or receipts of the water utility. They may be based on all operating revenue; on revenue from sales to particular classes of customers, such as residential and commercial; or on all revenues, both operating and nonoperating. Taxes actually levied on revenue or receipts may carry different descriptive titles among different tax jurisdictions. For example, they may carry the title of franchise taxes, privilege taxes, occupational taxes, or license taxes. A gross receipts tax return may include data on total receipts, sales originating in the taxing jurisdiction, and sales by class of customer.

Sales Taxes

Sales taxes are based on sales of utility services to customers. They usually are levied on retail sales (sales to final water customers). A tax also may be levied on sales for resale in some instances. Whereas gross receipts taxes are levied on water utilities, sales taxes are levied on utility customers, with utilities serving as collecting agencies. Sales taxes are normally stated as separate items on bills for service and are neither expenses nor revenues to the utility. Water utilities must collect the taxes, maintain appropriate records, and make periodic reports and payments to the tax authorities. A sales tax return typically includes data concerning gross receipts from taxable sales to customers, as well as data regarding sales for resale and to governmental authorities, which are usually exempt from taxation.

Payroll Taxes

Payroll taxes include Federal Insurance Contribution Act (FICA) taxes, Federal Unemployment Tax Act (FUTA) taxes, State Unemployment Tax Act (SUTA) taxes, and possibly local taxes.

FICA taxes are taxes on employees' salaries to finance the federal social security program, which provides for old age, survivor, disability, and medical benefits. The employees of an investor-owned water utility are covered by the federal social security program. Government-owned water utilities also are subject to payment of FICA taxes if the employees of the utility have been brought into the social security program through agreements with the US Secretary of Health, Education and Welfare.

The purpose of the FUTA and SUTA taxes on wages and salaries is to finance a fund for the joint federal–state unemployment insurance program. The federal tax is levied on the employer but not on the employee. In a few cases, state employment taxes are levied on both employers and employees.

Investor-owned water utilities generally are subject to FUTA and SUTA taxes. The federal act establishing unemployment compensation insurance excludes employees of government-owned water utilities from coverage on a mandatory basis since, under the US Constitution, the federal government cannot tax state and local governments or their instrumentalities. Nevertheless, a majority of the states participate in the unemployment compensation program through legislation that affords some form of unemployment insurance coverage for employees of government-owned water utilities, either on a compulsory or voluntary basis.

Other Taxes

There are many other types of corporate taxes levied on water utilities by state governments and municipalities. These include franchise taxes based on flat annual fees and capital stock taxes.

The utility also pays a Workers' Compensation *insurance premium* either to a state fund or a private insurance company. This premium is computed on payroll dollars, but *is not a tax* and should be included in the appropriate operating expense account that includes the cost of insurance or reserve accruals to protect the utility against injuries and damage claims of employees or others.

⊠ Accounting for General Taxes

The total amount of taxes applicable to a given accounting period is not always charged immediately to expense, because a portion of the tax liability may be assigned to various asset accounts. Any tax payments that are capitalized become expenses when the assets are subsequently amortized and their costs charged as expenses of the appropriate accounting periods. Examples of tax payments properly charged to asset accounts include the following:

- taxes, including payroll taxes, specifically applicable to construction work should be considered as a cost of construction and charged to the applicable plant account

- special assessments for street and similar improvements should be included in the appropriate utility plant account

- gasoline and other sales taxes should be charged as far as practicable to the account that includes the cost of the materials on which the tax is levied

Only those taxes assessed directly against the water utility are accounted for as part of the utility's own tax expense. There are some taxes levied against customers and employees for which the water utility collects the tax and remits the amount collected to the appropriate tax authorities. Examples of taxes remitted by the water utility but not classified as tax expense include the following:

- sales taxes, which are levied against customers and which are collected from customers on the basis of separate charges designated on the bills for service

- amounts withheld from employees for federal and state income tax liability

- amounts withheld from employees' wages as the employees' contribution for FICA taxes

Property taxes have been charged against the revenues of various periods, including (1) the year in which paid (the cash basis method of accounting), (2) the fiscal year of the taxpayer during which the assessment date falls, and (3) the fiscal year of the governmental body levying the tax. The Committee of Accounting Procedure of the American Institute of Certified Public Accountants (AICPA) took the position that the most acceptable procedure is for the tax to be accrued over the fiscal period of the taxing authority even though the amount of the property tax has to be estimated for a considerable part of each period. However, the committee indicated that special circumstances may suggest the use of alternative accrual periods. They stated that the important consideration is consistency from year to year and that the selection of any one of a number of periods over which property taxes may be accrued is a matter of judgement.

In some cases, the final determination of a tax liability cannot be made until after the end of the accounting period in which the tax expense is assignable. In such cases, the tax expense and tax liability must be estimated for financial statement purposes. If estimates are used for the purpose of making periodic charges to the tax expense accounts and periodic credits to a liability account, "accrued taxes," or debits to an asset account, "deferred taxes," then when the actual tax liability becomes known, adjustments will be required in order to account for any differences between estimated and actual taxes payable. In addition to the use of estimates of tax expense in the preparation of periodic statements of income, tax expense estimates must be made to complete the operating expense budget.

⊠ Anticipating Tax Implications

The tax implications of each alternative course of action must be considered by the management of an investor-owned utility. It must be emphasized that not even the chairperson of the board of directors should commit the water utility to any course of action until the tax implications of each practicable method of implementing a decision have been considered.

Decisions regarding expenditures for utility plant assets will affect the amount of property tax paid (by increasing the assessed valuation) and the amount of income tax incurred (because depreciation is a deductible expense for income tax purposes). When evaluating whether to lease or purchase property, proper recognition must be given to the tax advantages and disadvantages associated with each alternative. In addition, evaluating financing alternatives must give due recognition to the tax effects associated with each alternative. For example, interest payments on debt are tax deductible whereas dividend payments on stock are not. For rate-making purposes, decisions regarding the revenue requirement will also depend on the anticipated tax rates (since taxes are a cost of rendering water service). The estimated tax expense will also depend on decisions regarding financing and capital expenditure projections.

Management cannot make proper decisions regarding the activities of the water utility without knowledge of the tax implications associated with alternative courses of action. Management may be kept aware of these tax implications through the use of a capable staff of tax experts whose duty it is to give advice concerning the tax effects associated with the proposed alternatives.

For operating budget purposes, forecasting the liability and expense associated with any particular type of tax requires the application of an estimated tax rate to estimated taxable income in order to obtain estimated tax liability and estimated tax expense. Forecasting the major types of taxes incurred by water utilities is discussed in the following sections.

⊠ Estimating Taxes

Federal Income Taxes

Estimating federal income tax expense for the budget period requires that taxable income be forecast. The appropriate tax rates expected to be in effect during the budget period are then applied to estimated taxable income in order to determine the estimated federal income tax expense for the period.

Taxable net income has no particular relationship to book net income as defined by the NARUC Uniform System of Accounts or to net income as shown in financial reports to stockholders or regulatory commissions. Taxable net income is a legal concept that may be defined as gross income (revenue) not specifically exempt from taxation, less deductions (expenses) permitted by law. Revenue and expense items as described in the Uniform System of Accounts do not necessarily coincide with revenue and expense items includable for federal income tax purposes.

Estimating gross income. The major sources of gross income as defined for income tax purposes include operating revenues, nonoperating revenues, and gains and losses from the sale or exchange of property and investments. Nonoperating revenues includable in gross income typically are small in relation to operating revenues. Historical data, adjusted for anticipated changes in revenue levels during the tax period, serve as a basis for estimating taxable nonoperating revenues.

As noted in the preceding paragraph, gains and losses from the sale or exchange of property and investments also are factors in determining gross income for income tax purposes, and thereby influence the utility's income tax liability. However, for financial accounting purposes, the tax implications associated with these gains and losses may not influence operating income. If these gains and losses are considered to be extraordinary, the associated tax effects should be classified with the extraordinary items in the utility's income statement, in accordance with the NARUC Uniform System of Accounts.

The correct income tax treatment of gains and losses from the disposition of assets, as well as the amount of gains and losses resulting from asset dispositions, may be difficult to determine. The advice of qualified tax consultants (certified public accounts, lawyers, or members of the tax staff of the utility) should be obtained before any decision is made regarding the sale or exchange of assets.

Estimating deductions. Allowable expenses for income tax purposes, as specified by the Internal Revenue Code, occasionally differ from expenses as determined for general accounting purposes. To the extent that property losses and injury and damages claims not covered by insurance are estimated, no permissible deduction from gross income is allowed. (Deductions are limited to those amounts representing the actual losses during the tax year that are not covered by insurance.)

In general, budgeted operation and maintenance expenses serve as the basis for forecasting deductions from gross income for tax purposes. Expense estimates included in the operation and maintenance expense budget will require adjustment in cases where the basis for estimating a particular expense item is inconsistent with the basis employed for federal income tax purposes.

The amount of depreciation expense included as a deduction from gross income for tax purposes may differ substantially from that computed for book purposes. Factors that may give rise to this difference include the following:

- A depreciation method, such as straight-line, may be used for financial accounting purposes, whereas an accelerated depreciation method, such as double declining balance or sum of the years' digits, may be used for income tax purposes.

- Estimated service life of depreciable assets for financial accounting purposes may differ from depreciable lives used for tax purposes.

- Depreciation of the utility plant for financial accounting purposes is based on original cost (cost of property to the person first devoting it to public service), whereas depreciation for tax purposes is based on cost to the taxpayer.

It is apparent that two separate estimates of annual depreciation expense may be required — one estimate for financial accounting purposes and one for tax purposes.

For tax purposes, depreciation expense may be accounted for by individual property items, by groups of property items, or by total depreciable property as a single asset. Depreciation by individual property items requires that individual depreciation rates be established for each asset. Depreciation by asset groups requires that group rates be established and applied to the cost of each group of assets. Depreciation of property as a single asset requires that a composite rate be developed and applied to the total cost of utility property.

The amount of income taxes determined to be payable for a period does not necessarily represent the appropriate income tax expense determined for financial accounting purposes for that same period. The problem of properly matching income tax expense with accounting income is resolved through an accounting process known as "interperiod" tax allocation or most commonly referred to as accrued or deferred income tax accounting. Generally accepted accounting principles require that accrued or deferred income tax accounting be used to account for the tax effects of transactions that involve timing differences. This practice is referred to as "normalization." If the differences between book and tax income are ignored and there is no provision for deferred income tax to be paid in the future, this accounting method is referred to as "flow-through accounting." Accrued or deferred income tax entries may arise from book and tax differences other than depreciation, although depreciation usually is the largest difference between book and tax income.

The earlier discussion concerning the components of gross income and the types of allowable deductions from gross income provides only an overview of forecasting taxable income; it is not a comprehensive study of all the considerations involved in estimating or determining taxable income. Federal tax laws and procedures for determining taxable income are extremely complicated and subject to frequent change. The advice of qualified tax consultants or members of the utility's tax department is required for planning and control of taxable income.

Estimating tax rates and determining tax liability. The estimated income tax liability is a product of estimated income tax rates and estimated taxable income (gross income less allowable deductions) less any permissible tax credits. Federal income tax rates are set by the US Congress and may vary from year to year. Normally, the best guide as to rates of the budget period is to use rates in effect at the time of budget preparation. However, when legislative bodies are contemplating revisions in income tax rates, the best available information concerning the revisions should be used in estimating tax rates to be applied.

Estimating the investment tax credit. Although the Tax Reform Act of 1986 repealed the investment tax credit as of Dec. 31, 1985, a discussion of that credit is appropriate because most utilities that received the investment tax credit prior to that time now have a deferred federal income tax on the balance sheet that must be amortized over future periods. Also tax credits could again be established in future years, in which case this discussion would be relevant in analyses of potential credits. The investment tax credit (ITC) provided for a reduction in the income tax liability in the year in which the related asset was placed in service. For financial reporting purposes, the manner of recognizing the benefits associated with the ITC varies. In some cases, the ITC was accounted for on a deferral basis in which the benefits of the ITC were reflected in net income over the estimated service life of the asset to which the credit applied. In other cases, the flow-through method was used, which reflected the benefits in income during the year the asset was placed in service.

In the past, some state public service commissions required that water utilities under their jurisdiction account for the ITC on a flow-through basis, thereby reducing the revenue requirements of the water utilities and passing the benefit of the ITC on to customers. Alternatively, but with a similar effect, the ITC was sometimes required to be accounted for on a deferral basis, with the associated deferred ITC deducted from the rate base or otherwise treated as a zero-cost element of the rate base.

However, as a result of the Revenue Act of 1971, the scope of nonfederal regulatory control in this area is now limited by the requirement that the benefit of the ITC be handled in a manner that will allow the utility to share in the benefit arising from the ITC, unless an affected utility requests a continuation of the flow-through approach. Further, the Tax Reduction Act of 1975 provided for an increase from 4 to 10 percent in the ITC for utilities. In order to qualify for this 6 percent increase, the 1975 act specified that the utility must account for the increased benefits on a deferral basis, unless the utility elects not to; but no pressure can be applied by regulatory bodies to force the use of the flow-through method. The Economic Recovery Tax Act of 1981 (ERTA) prohibited the flow-through of the ITC. Thus, after the enactment of ERTA, utilities that had been using a flow-through accounting method were required to follow the normalization rule.

Investor-owned water utilities generally did not consider the entire allowable ITC in any tax year to be solely applicable to that year. Instead, at least a portion of the allowable investment credit is reflected in net income over the estimated service life of the property to which the credit applies, not in the year in which the property is placed in service. As a result of this treatment, the actual income tax liability in any year was less than the recognized income tax expense, and the difference was accounted for by establishing a deferred credit account for the unamortized investment tax credit. The amount in the deferred credit account was then amortized to income over the life of the property receiving the tax credit.

State and Municipal Income Taxes

The discussion of estimating income taxes has been primarily targeted at the federal level. In many locations, state and municipal income taxes are patterned after the federal income tax. Taxable income estimated for federal tax purposes generally can be used as a basis for income subject to state and municipal income taxes. The estimated state and municipal income taxes depend on the tax rates expected to be in effect for the budget period. Current state and municipal tax rates, adjusted for anticipated changes in the rates, serve as the basis for estimating rates applicable to the budget period.

Property Taxes

Because a water utility has a large investment in plant facilities, property taxes typically comprise a large portion of the utility's tax burden.

Property taxes are based on the assessed valuation of property held as of a given date. (Property not held on that assessment date is not subject to property taxes.) The assessed value is multiplied by the tax rate per unit of assessed value (such as per $1,000 of assessed value) to obtain the property tax liability.

Estimating assessed valuation. The bases for valuing property vary widely among the various taxing jurisdictions. Assessment of public utilities may be done by state agencies or by local assessors.

Typically, not all property of a water utility is reassessed on an annual basis. Rather, property is valued once as a whole, then adjusted on an annual basis to account for additions and retirements.

In estimating the valuation to be assigned to properties owned in order to arrive at an estimated property tax liability, assessed value from the preceding year serves as a beginning point. Utility management must adjust the prior year's assessed value for anticipated additions and retirements of properties owned during the budget period.

Utility management may take or time certain actions to minimize property taxes. For example, management may plan to accomplish retirements of property items before the assessment date while delaying property acquisitions until after the assessment date. To the extent practicable, management may also save taxes by minimizing inventories of materials and supplies held on the assessment date.

Estimating property tax rates. Property tax rates often vary from year to year. Nevertheless, the best guide to the property tax rate for the budget year is the rate in effect during the current period. Utility management must be aware of new rates being considered by governmental bodies that might be enacted during the budget period. If historical data show a trend line of increasing taxes, the budget period might be based on this historical trend.

Other Taxes

Other major taxes to which a water utility may be subject are the revenue tax, or gross receipts tax, and payroll taxes.

Revenue taxes. The revenue tax is easy to administer in comparison with the property tax, and for that reason it is sometimes levied in lieu of the property tax. Revenue taxes may be levied on all operating revenue or on a particular class of operating revenue, such as residential sales or commercial sales. Forecasted operating revenues for the budget period serve as the basis for determining estimated revenue or gross receipts taxes. In addition to the estimate of operating revenues subject to the tax, revenue tax rates must be estimated. Although rates may vary from year to year, revenue tax rates applicable to the current period serve as the basis for estimating tax rates during the budget period. Adjustments in current rates may be called for if there is evidence that revenue tax rates will be changed by the legislative body imposing the tax.

Payroll taxes. The major types of payroll tax expenses are social security taxes and unemployment insurance taxes. Under the federal social security program, FICA taxes are levied on both employee and employer. Only that portion of the tax levied on the water utility is treated as a tax expense. The FICA tax expense is determined by the number of employees, the FICA tax rate, and the amount of each employees's wages or salary subject to the tax. However, the FICA rate and the wage base to which it applies are subject to periodic and frequent upward revisions.

Under the FUTA, a tax on the employer is levied based on each employee's income. States have similar taxes, but the wages subject to the tax and the rates differ in most instances from the federal wages and rates. However, a credit against the FUTA is allowed for employer contributions to a state plan. State unemployment tax laws contain a merit rating provision under which a reduction in the state contribution rate is allowed to employers who show a favorable and steady employment record.

The estimated payroll as forecast serves as the base against which the unemployment tax rate is applied to forecast unemployment tax expense applicable to the budget period. This forecast payroll is reduced by the amount of salaries and wages that exceed the taxable base for federal and state for each employee. The product of the estimated taxable payroll and the estimated tax rates for the budget period (consistent with the anticipated merit rating for the utility) results in the budget estimate for the tax expense.

Other taxes. There are many other varieties of taxes to which a water utility may be subjected, such as franchise taxes based on a flat annual fee or other basis. These taxes must also be forecast for inclusion in the annual operating budget. For minor taxes, historical data may act as a sufficient guide in estimating for the budget period.

⊠ Summary

The number and variety of taxes levied on water utilities, as well as the financial impact taxes have on operating expenses, requires that water utility management maintain effective control over the determination and incurrence of tax expense. The existence of a tax department within the utility organization is typical of large water utilities. The tax department is responsible for the efficient planning and control of tax expense.

The tax department of the utility must ensure that managers are aware of the tax implications of operating and capital budgeting decisions. The tax department is responsible for keeping abreast of current tax developments in order to minimize tax payments within the context of existing tax regulations and requirements. In addition, the tax department is responsible for meeting tax reporting and tax payment deadlines in order to avoid the incurrence of legal penalties associated with noncompliance. It is important that appropriate tax records be maintained for use in justifying the amount of tax payments made, disputing deficiency assessments, and settling tax claims with tax authorities.

If the utility does not have qualified tax experts within the organization, tax consultants should be retained to advise the utility staff as required.

Periodic reviews comparing actual taxes with budget estimates may prove helpful in discovering errors in tax computations. Further, such reviews may reveal areas requiring additional or more effective tax planning.

CHAPTER ELEVEN

Utility Plant Investment

Water utility property having an expected life of one year or more and employed for the primary purpose of delivering water to customers (for example, mains, standpipes, and pumps) is classified as the utility plant. To aid in understanding the problems involved in planning and controlling investment in the utility plant, review the National Association of Regulatory Utility Commissioners' (NARUC) account classification and nature of the cost elements included in the utility plant accounts. Refer to appendix A to examine the relationship of utility plant accounts to other balance-sheet accounts and to income accounts.

⊠ Control Accounts

The NARUC classification of accounts segregates utility plant cost into general categories, which serve as control or summary accounts. The categories are as follows:

Utility Plant in Service (101)

This account includes the original cost of the utility plant owned and used by the water utility. This account includes the cost of additions to, and betterments of, property leased from others that is used to provide water service to customers. The cost of property is subclassified in primary (detailed) accounts 301–399.

Utility Plant Leased to Others (102)

This account includes the original cost of the utility plant owned by the utility, but leased to others as operating units or systems. The cost of property is subclassified into primary accounts.

Property Held for Future Use (103)

This account includes the original cost of property owned and held for future use in utility service under a definite plan for such use. The cost of property is subclassified into primary accounts.

Utility Plant Purchased or Sold (104)

This account contains the cost of the utility plant acquired as an operating unit or system by purchase, merger, consolidation, liquidation, or otherwise, and is credited with the selling price of utility property transferred to others. The balance in this account is only temporary and is ultimately cleared by appropriate charges and credits to other accounts, including the other seven utility plant control accounts.

Construction Work in Progress (105)

This account includes the cost of a utility plant in the process of construction but not yet completed. The balance in this account is supported by work orders. (Work orders are discussed later in this chapter.)

Completed Construction Not Classified (106)

This account includes the cost of a utility plant that has been completed but not yet subclassified into primary (detailed) accounts. The balance in this account is supported by work orders for construction that has been completed.

Utility Plant Acquisition Adjustments (114)

This account contains the difference between

- the cost of the utility plant acquired as an operating unit or system by purchase, merger, consolidation, liquidation, or otherwise
- the original cost of such property, estimated if not known, less the amount credited by the utility at the time of acquisition to accumulated provisions for depreciation and amortization and to contributions in aid of construction with respect to such property

Other Utility Plant Adjustments (116)

This account includes the difference between the original cost, estimated if not known, and the amount at which property is recorded in other utility plant control accounts, to the extent that such difference is not properly includable in the "utility plant acquisition adjustments" account.

⊠ Construction Costs

Direct Construction Costs

The costs of assets constructed by outside contractors ordinarily may be determined on the basis of payments to the contractors. If, as is often true, a single contract covers the construction and acquisition of a number of different kinds of assets, then proper detail must be secured from the contractor to permit the determination and recording of costs by continuing property record (CPR) units or retirement units.

If assets are constructed partially or completely by the utility's own personnel, then labor and materials costs may be assigned to the project. The costs are assigned from labor time records and materials requisitions. Other items of cost, as discussed in the following section, are properly capitalizable but it is generally impossible or not clerically feasible to trace them directly to specific CPR units or to retirement units. Costs that cannot be so assigned are called "indirect" costs.

Indirect Construction Costs

Examples of indirect construction costs include salaries and wages of utility employees whose time is not assignable to specific construction projects, labor-related costs commonly called "fringe benefits," transportation costs, the cost of special machine service, shop service costs, engineering and supervision costs, general and administrative costs, and the cost of taxes and interest during construction. Some of these, particularly engineering and supervision costs, general and administrative costs, and the cost of taxes and interest during construction, are incurred for the benefit of the utility in its entirety and are only partially assignable to the construction activity. Such costs must be allocated between construction work and operating expense.

Indirect construction costs should be charged to individual projects, plant assets, and property units on the basis of amounts reasonably applicable to each. Each asset should bear an equitable proportion of indirect costs. Therefore, valid bases must be found for allocating the several kinds of indirect costs between construction work and operating expense and for allocating indirect construction costs among construction projects, plant assets, and property units.

Regarding indirect costs incurred by a utility in its entirety, two alternative methods are commonly used to determine the amounts that should be allocated to construction work. One method is called the "incremental cost" method. Under this method, only the costs specifically incurred for construction — costs that would not be incurred by the utility if construction were not undertaken — are chargeable to construction. Under an alternative method, called the "benefits-realized" method, costs incurred by the utility are allocated to construction work in proportion to the construction activities performed by various divisions (such as the administration and general division) of the utility organization.

Using the benefits-realized method, the indirect labor component of costs incurred by the utility in its entirety is allocated to construction work on the basis of studies made to determine the proportion of time spent by such personnel as administrators, supervisors, and engineers, on construction work and on operations. Where expenditures made by the utility relate to things other than compensation for personal services, special studies are needed to determine that the expenditures have a beneficial relationship to construction and to determine a reasonable basis for capitalizing a portion of the expenditures.

The use of the benefits-realized method has the effect of reducing expenses and increasing net income during periods of heavy construction activity. The use of the incremental cost method avoids the effect of showing greater net income merely because of increased construction activity.

Administrative and General Costs

A portion of administrative and general activities usually is associated with construction work. That portion of the general officers' and administrators' pay, and other general expenses applicable to construction work should be capitalized. The portions capitalized should have a provable relationship to construction work. As in the case of engineering and supervisory costs, the amount of administrative and general costs associated with construction work typically is determined by special studies. The portion of administrative and general expenses must then be allocated to construction projects, plant assets, and property units in an equitable and clerically feasible manner.

Interest During Construction

Interest costs during the period of construction of a utility plant asset are included as a cost of the asset by the utility industry. The recognition of interest as a cost of construction is based on the theory that the use of money to finance construction activities involves an opportunity cost. The cost of using money to finance investment in plant assets during the period of construction is equal to the income foregone by being unable to invest the money in some immediately productive asset. Therefore, interest during construction is properly considered as a cost of constructing the productive asset. As soon as the completed plant is placed in service, interest is treated as an expense to be matched against the revenues that presumably result from the use of the productive asset. The cost of the completed asset becomes a part of the rate base.

Interest during construction is measured by the net cost (for the period of construction) of borrowed funds used for construction purposes and a reasonable cost for other funds when so used. Because a number of different sources of money are available to finance construction projects, the weighted average cost of capital is generally the preferable measure of an interest rate to use in determining the cost of money during construction.

Transportation and Special Machine Service Costs

The labor costs associated with transporting equipment operators and special machine equipment operators generally can be identified with construction projects, plant assets, and property units through the use of labor time sheets; therefore, such costs are "direct construction" costs. Other costs of operating equipment (gasoline, lubricants, depreciation of equipment and garage, taxes on equipment, and other garage overhead expenses) and the costs of maintaining equipment (maintenance labor or maintenance materials and supplies) customarily are allocated to construction projects on the basis of a predetermined rate based on expected costs of operation and maintenance for each piece of equipment. After the cost of operating and maintaining transportation equipment and special machine equipment is allocated to construction projects, it must be distributed among plant assets and property units involved in the project. The cost must be allocated to plant accounts and property units on an equitable and clerically feasible basis.

Shop Service Cost

The cost of materials used or fabricated by a central shop may be charged to construction projects, plant assets, and property units on the basis of the cost of actual materials used plus an allowance for labor and overhead. The allowance is generally determined on the basis of a rate sufficient to absorb budgeted shop costs.

Engineering and Supervision Costs

A portion of engineering and supervision costs may be directly identified with construction projects, plant assets, and property units. However, if engineering and supervisory personnel are used jointly for construction and operating purposes, the associated costs must be appropriately allocated.

Unless time sheets are kept by engineering and supervisory personnel, special studies will be required to determine the portion of costs allocable to construction work. After the portion of indirect costs of engineering and supervision is allocated to construction work, this portion must be distributed to individual projects, plant assets, and property units. This distribution must be made in an equitable and clerically feasible manner, for example, it may be in proportion to direct labor hours incurred with respect to the projects, plant assets, or property units.

Taxes During Construction

Payroll taxes should be included as part of the direct and indirect labor costs distributed to construction projects, plant assets, and property units. Sales taxes on construction materials and supplies should be included as part of the cost of materials and supplies distributed to construction projects, plant assets, and property units. The capitalization of property taxes generally is limited to substantial projects to which actual tax payments can be directly identified.

⊠ Funding Sources

At the time this publication was being prepared, the Governmental Accounting Standards Board (GASB) issued a Discussion Memorandum (Oct. 15, 1993) on "Reporting Contributions, Subsidies, Tap Fees, and Similar Inflows to Enterprise and Internal Service Funds and to Entities Using Proprietary Fund Accounting." The memorandum indicates such issues are being discussed, and the user may want to further verify the issue's status.

Donated Utility Plant

The recommendations of NARUC and the National Council on Governmental Accounting (NCGA) vary somewhat with regard to accounting related to donated assets. NARUC states that plant assets contributed to a water utility, or constructed by a utility from contributions, are to be charged to utility plant accounts at the cost of construction. The costs can be estimated if not known. The accounts for accumulated depreciation and amortization should be credited for the estimated amount of depreciation and amortization expense applicable to the property at the time the property is donated to the utility. The difference between the amounts included in the utility plant accounts and the accumulated depreciation and amortization accounts is to be credited to account 271, "contributions in aid of construction." The remaining depreciated or unamortized balances associated with donated assets should then be depreciated or amortized, as appropriate, over the remaining estimated service lives of the donated properties.

NCGA recommends that a donated fixed asset be recorded in utility plant accounts at its estimated fair market value at the time received. The offsetting credit for the recorded value should be to an appropriately labeled contributed capital account within the equity capital (fund/equity) section of the balance sheet of the water utility (enterprise fund). NCGA also states that operating expenses associated with an enterprise fund should include depreciation on all depreciable fixed assets, including those donated to a utility (i.e., credits to accumulated depreciation on the contributed asset would be recorded as operating expenses that are closed to the contributed capital–equity account).

It should be noted that, under special circumstances, NCGA does permit depreciation charges associated with assets acquired through certain resources to be treated as a reduction of contributed capital as opposed to retained earnings, although the depreciation charges are recognized in the determination of net income. In turn, the income figure, unaffected by depreciation charges on capital assets so acquired, would be closed to retained earnings. These special circumstances arise when grant, entitlement, or shared revenue resources (as defined by NCGA) are restricted for the acquisition or construction of capital assets. As an alternative, NCGA permits the entire amount of net income to be closed to retained earnings, leaving the contributed equity balance unaffected.

Federal

Funding from the federal government typically comes in the form of a grant to construct a specific project. Nonmunicipal utilities are not likely to receive grants from the federal government. The federal government may also be a customer who is required to contribute facilities in the same manner that other customers make contributions.

When the utility applies for and receives a grant from the federal government, the requirements of the granting agency should be examined in detail. Federal governmental agencies require the utility to file periodic reports and have the grant funds audited. They may also require the transfer of the property acquired with the grant when the facility is no longer deemed useful.

State

Funding from the state government typically comes in the form of a grant or loan to construct a specific project. The state government may also be a customer who is required to contribute facilities in the same manner that other customers make contributions.

When the utility applies for and receives a grant from the state government, the requirements of the granting agency should be examined in detail. State governmental agencies generally require the utility to file periodic reports and have audits of the grant funds performed. State government agencies may require the transfer of the property acquired with the grant when the facility is no longer deemed useful.

Developers

As a matter of policy, either the public utility commission or the utility may require that developers needing extensions or additions to the water system contribute the costs of such extensions or additions. The intent of the policy is that the new development will not be subsidized by the customers currently on the system.

Bonds

The utility may at times pledge future earnings to fund additions to the water system. The pledge is done through the issuance of bonds. The bond and interest will be repaid over the life of the asset from the income generated by the asset acquired with the bond proceeds.

The utility is not required to specifically identify the asset acquired when recording an asset acquired with bond proceeds.

A utility using bond proceeds to generate funds for plant expansion will acquire cash and expend the cash for the assets.

Internally Generated Funds

Retained earnings are a source of funds the utility can use to acquire assets. The utility may build into its rate base a factor for the replacement of assets. The revenue derived from rates will be reflected as net income to the utility. Net income will be transferred to retained earnings representing the internally generated funds.

The utility using retained earnings to generate funds for plant expansion will acquire cash through operations and expend the cash for the assets.

Proceeds From the Sale of Assets

Sometimes a utility will dispose of an asset and use the funds provided from the disposal for the acquisition of additional assets. This method is infrequently used because a depreciated asset normally will not provide the funds necessary to acquire a new asset.

The utility may find it advantageous to trade one asset for another. When this type of transaction is concluded, the utility will transfer the cost of the original asset to the cost of the new asset. Any additional payments will be additions to the cost.

Proceeds From the Sale of Equity Securities

Corporate utilities have the ability to issue stock to fund the acquisition of assets. The stock is sold and the utility acquires cash from the sale. The cash is then used to acquire the asset.

Partnerships and proprietorships can have their ownership interests changed by the contribution of cash or assets to the organization. The owner's interests may subsequently change with additional contributions.

Retirement Units of Property

Proper accounting for the cost of plant assets requires that a distinction be made between expenditures that should be classified as maintenance expenses and expenditures that should be capitalized (charged to the utility plant accounts). In order to facilitate this distinction, the concept of "retirement unit" of property has been developed. "Retirement units" are defined by NARUC as "those items of utility property which, when retired, with or without replacement, are accounted for by crediting the book cost thereof to the utility plant account in which included."

In general, any item of property that is readily separable, and separately useful, from a larger assembly of which it forms a part should be treated as a retirement unit. A retirement unit usually consists of an assembly of items that, as assembled, perform a single function and are customarily installed or removed together. For example, a meter is a retirement unit. The cost of replacing any property item smaller than a retirement unit is accounted for, except for any substantial betterment involved, by charging such cost to maintenance expense.

List of retirement units of property. NARUC and certain regulatory agencies provide lists showing the composition of retirement units for each kind of utility plant asset. Such lists furnish useful guides to the proper classification of expenditures. In the case of water utilities subject to the jurisdiction of a state public service commission, the commission customarily prescribes the list of retirement units to be used by the water utilities. The use of a prescribed list produces greater uniformity among utilities in accounting for replacements of property. If the list of retirement units is extensive and includes many small items, then maintenance expense will be less than if the list includes only relatively large items. Therefore, the cost of assets included in the utility plant accounts, and the related depreciation expense, depend on the size of the retirement units included in the list. When a prescribed list of retirement units is furnished by a public service commission, the list may be expanded by any water utility within the jurisdiction of the commission, but the list cannot be condensed. A prescribed list includes retirement units for each of the structures and improvements accounts and for each of the equipment accounts making up the primary or detailed utility plant accounts.

Minor items of property. Minor items of property include all parts or elements that make up a retirement unit of property. If a minor item of property is retired and not replaced, then the accounting treatment of costs involved is the same as when a retirement unit of property is retired — the cost of the minor item retired is credited to the utility plant account in which the cost is recorded, and the cost-less-net-salvage-value of this item is charged to accumulated provision for depreciation. If the cost of a minor item of property will be accounted for by its inclusion in the cost of the retirement unit of property of which it is a part, then no entry is made until the retirement unit itself is retired.

If minor items of property are replaced, then the cost of replacement is charged as maintenance expense to the activity in which the item of property is used. As noted previously, if the replacement of a minor item of property constitutes a betterment, then the replacement cost should be capitalized, the cost of the minor item retired should be credited to the appropriate plant account, and the cost-less-net-salvage-value of the replaced item should be charged to the accumulated depreciation account. However, even if the replacement of a minor item of property does constitute a betterment, then the cost of the replacement normally should not be capitalized unless the replacement exceeds an established minimum (such as $100). If the replacement involves a cost of less than the established minimum, then the expenditure is treated as maintenance expense.

Relationship between retirement units and continuing property records. As mentioned earlier in this chapter, a CPR system involves the maintenance of a separate record for each unit of utility property (CPR unit). Generally, each CPR unit is composed of one or more retirement units. For a relatively large CPR unit, such as that representing structures (or major components thereof) and large items of equipment, the CPR unit may be composed of a number of retirement units. In the case of a smaller CPR unit, such as that representing a meter or hydrant, the CPR unit generally corresponds to a retirement unit.

For a further discussion of continuing property records, see National Association of Regulatory Utility Commissioners, Subcommittee on Valuation and Plant Costs of the Committee on Engineering (1975).

The National Committee on Governmental Accounting's *Governmental Accounting, Auditing, and Financial Reporting* (1968) defines a betterment as follows: "An addition made to, or change made in, a fixed asset which is expected to prolong its life or to increase its efficiency over and above that arising from maintenance (q.v.) and the cost of which is therefore added to the book value of the asset."

NARUC, in *Uniform System of Accounts for Class A Water Utilities* defines a "betterment" as making "the property affected more useful, more efficient, of greater durability, or of greater capacity."

A list of retirement units is published by NARUC. See National Association of Regulatory Commissioners, Committee on Accounts and Statistics (1962).

⊠ Value of Plant Defined

Original Cost

Historical accounting records record the cost of assets at the cost the utility incurred in acquiring the asset. Generally accepted accounting principles require the recording of the cost incurred in acquiring the asset. Under the historical cost principles, the asset is depreciated during its life as an estimate of the deterioration of the asset.

Replacement

Replacement cost is the estimate of cost the utility would incur to replace the asset. Reporting of replacement cost is optional in the utility's financial statements.

Identification by Function and Property Account

Level of detail. The detail to which property accounting records are retained is a function of the requirements of the utility's management and the body that approves the utility's rates. Management may prescribe that all assets be identified for control purposes, while the rate-making body may require a lower level of capitalization and record keeping.

Rate-making needs. To develop rates the utility must be able to identify which assets are used to provide service to their customers. The cost of providing service is an integral factor used in setting rates for a class of customers. To determine the cost of service related to assets, the cost of operating, maintaining, and depreciating such assets should be considered.

Recommended functions. The National Association of Regulatory Utility Commissioners' edition of the *Uniform System of Accounts for Class A Water Utilities* defines water utility plant accounts. The NARUC classification of accounts shown in appendix A provides for the segregation of the cost of the utility plant into general categories, which serve as control or summary accounts. The categories are as follows:

Organization (301). All fees expended during organization or incorporation of the utility.

Franchises (302). Fees paid to governmental agencies or political subdivisions that allow the utility to operate in certain jurisdictions in perpetuity or for a specified term. Annual or other periodic payments under franchises shall not be included.

Land and land rights (303). The cost involved in acquiring and placing land in a condition in which it can be used by the utility. The land or land rights will be identified for all uses in this account. The account can be subdivided for source of supply, pumping, water treatment, transmission and distribution, and general plant.

Structures and improvements (304). This account will include the cost of all structures and improvements connected with the utility plant. The account can be subdivided for source of supply, pumping, water treatment, transmission and distribution, and general plant.

Collecting and impounding reservoirs (305). The cost of the structure used to collect and store water.

Lake, river, and other intakes (306). All costs associated with the construction of intakes that will be a source of the water supply.

Wells and springs (307). All costs associated with the installation of wells and springs that will be a source of the water supply.

Infiltration galleries and tunnels (308). All costs associated with the construction of infiltration galleries and tunnels used as a source of the water supply.

Supply mains (309). The cost associated with the installation of mains, canals, aqueducts, tunnels, and their appurtenances used to transport water from the source to the water treatment facility.

Power generation equipment (310). The cost incurred with the installation of power generation equipment. Normally, the equipment will be used for the production of power used in pumping operations.

Pumping equipment (311). The cost of pumps and motors used to move water. The equipment may be driven by electric power, diesel engines, steam engines, or hydraulic water methods.

Water treatment equipment (320). The cost of apparatus and equipment used during the treatment of water.

Distribution reservoirs and standpipes (330). The cost associated with the construction of facilities used to store treated water.

Transmission and distribution mains (331). The cost incurred in the installation of the mains and appurtenances used to move treated water to the customer's service line.

Services (333). The cost associated with installing service pipes from the distribution main to the customer.

Meters and meter installation (334). The cost incurred in the installation of meters used to measure the quantity of water delivered to the customer.

Hydrants (335). The cost associated with the installation of fire hydrants that the utility owns.

Other plant and miscellaneous equipment (339). The cost of intangible source of supply, water treatment, pumping or transmission, and distribution plant not properly classified in another account.

Office furniture and equipment (340). All costs of office furniture and equipment devoted to utility service. Normally these items will not permanently attach to buildings.

Transportation equipment (341). The cost associated with vehicles used for transportation of equipment, material, and personnel.

Stores equipment (342). Cost of all equipment used for receiving, shipping, handling, and storing of materials and supplies. Each location that the utility has for storage will have the assets maintained separately.

Tools, shop, and garage equipment (343). The cost of tools, implements, and equipment used in construction and maintenance not includable in other accounts.

Laboratory equipment (344). All costs associated with the laboratory equipment used for general laboratory purposes.

Power-operated equipment (345). The cost of power-operated equipment used for the construction and maintenance of the various assets of the utility.

Communication equipment (346). The cost associated with telephone, telemetry, and wireless communication equipment.

⊠ The Capital Expenditures Budget

The capital expenditures budget is a plan for all changes to the existing utility plant, including both additions and retirements. In order to facilitate coordination of long-range and short-range plans, the capital expenditures budget should be prepared for a period of at least five years. The process of developing a five-year capital expenditures budget should integrate all aspects of the planning function, including design, financing implications, and the impact the facilities would have on assignment of personnel and the use of material. The effect of the capital expenditures budget on personnel and material requirements serves as the basis for planning the operating and construction activities to be performed by a utility. The capital expenditures budget enables management to develop a financing program to meet the cash requirements of the budget and allows management to time its activities in money markets in order to minimize the cost of money. In addition, the capital expenditures budget serves as a management control mechanism over capital expenditures.

To be useful as a planning and control mechanism, a summary of budgeted capital expenditures, such as that shown in Figure 11-1, should be based on a carefully prepared and detailed analysis of individual projects. It is useful to classify capital expenditure projects as "major projects" and as "blanket projects." Major projects include proposed additions to and retirements of the utility plant that involve relatively large outlays and are of a nonroutine nature. Examples of major projects include the construction or retirements of a water treatment plant, a pumping station, a standpipe, transmission mains, and other similar large additions or retirements of a water utility plant. Each of these projects is of sufficient size to warrant individual attention and consideration by top management and policy-making groups (the city council or board of directors).

Blanket projects include proposed additions to and retirements of the utility plant that are routine in nature. Examples of blanket projects include the installation and retirement of customer meters and hydrants. The individual items included in blanket projects are so numerous, so similar in character, and so small in cost relative to major projects, that individual attention and consideration by management is unwarranted.

The summary of budgeted capital expenditures is supported by individual project budgets, for both major projects and blanket projects. Typically, each individual project budget includes a project number, a description of the project, the purpose and necessity of the project, scheduled starting and completion dates for the project, estimated cost of the project, estimated

Figure 11-1 ⊠ Five-year capital expenditures budget summary

The Willing Water Utility Five-Year Capital Expenditures Budget Summary
19B1 to 19B5

Project Number	Brief Description of Projects	Estimated Expenditures or Retirements*	Expenditures or Retirements as of Dec. 31, 19CY	Expenditures or Retirements Required to Complete	Budgeted Expenditures or Retirements				
					19B1	19B2	19B3	19B4	19B5
	Source of Supply Plant								
307	Purchase of Reservoir Land — Expenditures	$ 41,000		$ 41,000	$ 41,000				
308	Extension of Roadway on Reservoir Land — Expenditures	20,000		20,000		$ 15,000	$ 5,000		
309	Replacement of Bridges and Culverts Expenditures	37,000	$ 17,000	20,000	20,000				
	Retirements	(20,000)	(10,000)	(10,000)	(10,000)				
310–313	Construction of Wells — Expenditures†	200,000	20,000	180,000	40,000	40,000	40,000	$ 40,000	$ 20,000
	Total Expenditures — Source of Supply Plant	$ 298,000	$ 37,000	$ 261,000	$ 101,000	$ 55,000	$ 45,000	$ 40,000	$ 20,000
	Total Retirements — Source of Supply Plant	($ 20,000)	($ 10,000)	($ 10,000)	($ 10,000)				
	Pumping Plant								
314	New Booster Pumping Station (Structure & Parts) — Expenditures	$ 275,000	$ 10,000	$ 265,000	$ 85,000	$ 180,000			
315	Replacement of Pumps at Clear River Pumping Station — Expenditures	475,000		475,000		160,000	$ 315,000		
	Retirements	(375,000)		(375,000)		(175,000)	(200,000)		
	Total Expenditures — Pumping Plant	$ 750,000	$ 10,000	$ 740,000	$ 85,000	$ 340,000	$ 315,000		
	Total Retirements — Pumping Plant	($ 375,000)		($ 375,000)		($ 175,000)	($ 200,000)		

*Expenditure figures include the cost of removal less salvage value of assets being retired as well as the cost of new assets. Retirement figures indicate the book cost of assets being retired.

†In order to conserve space these categories have not been classified by individual projects.

Figure continued next page

Figure 11-1 ⊠ Five-year capital expenditures budget summary (continued)

The Willing Water Utility Five-Year Capital Expenditures Budget Summary
19B1 to 19B5

Project Number	Brief Description of Projects	Estimated Expenditures or Retirements*	Expenditures or Retirements as of Dec. 31, 19CY	Expenditures or Retirements Required to Complete	Budgeted Expenditures or Retirements				
					19B1	19B2	19B3	19B4	19B5
316–321	**Water Treatment Plant†**								
	Total Expenditures — Water Treatment Plant	$ 540,000		$ 540,000				$ 270,000	$ 270,000
	Total Retirements — Water Treatment Plant	($ 290,000)		($ 290,000)				($ 200,000)	($ 90,000)
	Transmission and Distribution Plant								
322	New Distribution Tank — Expenditures	$ 75,000		$ 75,000			$ 75,000		
323	Landscaping Around Standpipes — Expenditures	10,000		10,000	$ 10,000				
324–355	Extension and Replacement of Mains†								
	Expenditures	6,790,000	$190,000	6,600,000	1,130,000	$1,400,000	1,180,000	$1,440,000	1,450,000
	Retirements	(340,000)	(40,000)	(300,000)	(60,000)	(40,000)	(70,000)	(70,000)	(60,000)
356	Services‡								
	Expenditures	250,000		250,000	50,000	50,000	50,000	50,000	50,000
	Retirements	(10,000)		(10,000)	(2,000)	(2,000)	(2,000)	(2,000)	(2,000)
357	Meters‡								
	Expenditures	525,000		525,000	100,000	100,000	100,000	110,000	115,000
	Retirements	(5,000)		(5,000)	(1,000)	(1,000)	(1,000)	(1,000)	(1,000)
358	Meter Installations‡								
	Expenditures	105,000		105,000	20,000	20,000	20,000	20,000	25,000
	Retirements	(6,000)		(6,000)	(1,000)	(1,000)	(1,000)	(1,000)	(2,000)

*Expenditure figures include the cost of removal less salvage value of assets being retired as well as the cost of new assets. Retirement figures indicate the book cost of assets being retired.

†In order to conserve space these categories have not been classified by individual projects.

‡These categories of expenditures and retirements are considered as "blanket projects" as opposed to "major projects."

Figure continued next page

Figure 11-1 ⊠ Five-year capital expenditures budget summary (continued)

The Willing Water Utility Five-Year Capital Expenditures Budget Summary
19B1 to 19B5

Project Number	Brief Description of Projects	Estimated Expenditures or Retirements*	Expenditures or Retirements as of Dec. 31, 19CY	Expenditures or Retirements Required to Complete	Budgeted Expenditures or Retirements				
					19B1	19B2	19B3	19B4	19B5
359	**Hydrants‡**								
	Expenditures	420,000	20,000	400,000	80,000	80,000	80,000	80,000	80,000
	Retirements	(35,000)	(5,000)	(30,000)	(6,000)	(6,000)	(6,000)	(6,000)	(6,000)
	Total Expenditures — Transmission and Distribution Plant	$ 8,175,000	($210,000)	$ 7,965,000	$1,390,000	$1,650,000	$1,505,000	$1,700,000	$1,720,000
	Total Retirements — Transmission and Distribution Plant	($ 396,000)	($ 45,000)	($ 351,000)	($ 70,000)	($ 50,000)	($ 80,000)	($ 80,000)	($ 71,000)
360–384	**General Plant†**								
	Total expenditures — general plant	$ 1,050,000	$ 50,000	$ 1,000,000	$ 150,000	$ 200,000	$ 200,000	$ 250,000	$ 200,000
	Total retirements — general plant	($ 400,000)	($ 20,000)	($ 380,000)	($ 80,000)	($ 70,000)	($ 80,000)	($ 70,000)	($ 80,000)
	Total Expenditures — Water Utility Plant	$10,813,000	$307,000	$10,506,000	$1,726,000	$2,245,000	$2,065,000	$2,260,000	$2,210,000
	Total Retirements — Water Utility Plant	($ 1,481,000)	($ 75,000)	($ 1,406,000)	($ 160,000)	($ 295,000)	($ 360,000)	($ 350,000)	($ 241,000)

*Expenditure figures include the cost of removal less salvage value of assets being retired as well as the cost of new assets. Retirement figures indicate the book cost of assets being retired.

†In order to conserve space these categories have not been classified by individual projects.

‡These categories of expenditures and retirements are considered as "blanket projects" as opposed to "major projects."

incremental operating revenues and expenses associated with the project, and estimated return on the investment. Individual project budgets should be prepared for uncompleted major projects (carryover projects from the prior and/or current years) as well as for new projects.

Therefore, the work order system with the capital expenditure budget, serves as an instrument to assist management in planning and controlling capital expenditure activities. Separate work orders may be prepared for additions to and retirements of the utility plant, or retirements may be included with additions on the same work order, provided that all items related to retirements are kept separate from those relating to additions.

Planning Capital Expenditure Activities

Construction activities may be performed either by a utility itself or by outside contractors. Within a large water utility organization, specialized skills and services may be available that can be used for both operating and construction activities. The use of a utility's personnel resources to conduct construction activities may be more economical than construction by outside contractors if the special resources, such as engineering services, can be jointly applied to operating and capital expenditure activities. However, the performance of construction activities by the utility itself generally requires that special construction equipment be purchased, and that employees who are skilled in construction work be employed on a permanent basis. Construction equipment and personnel are expensive and, if such resources cannot be used fully throughout the year (either for construction purposes or for operating purposes during periods of reduced construction activity), then it may be uneconomical for a utility to construct plant assets. The use of outside contractors permits more flexibility because resources for carrying out construction activities are hired and paid for only when needed. Therefore, the appropriate procedure for conducting capital expenditure activities depends on whether it is more economical for the utility or for an outside contractor to construct the asset. The best solution to the problem of choosing between self-construction and construction by outsiders may be to employ the utility's own equipment and personnel resources to complete relatively small and/or routine construction projects (replacement or extension of distribution mains and service, and meter installations, for example), and to contract with outsiders to complete relatively large and/or nonroutine construction projects.

Consistent with the level of construction activity indicated by the capital expenditures budget, a determination must be made as to whether particular construction projects included in the budget are to be completed by an outside contractor or by the utility itself. The personnel and equipment resources of the utility should be allocated to those projects for which they are best adapted. Projects should be matched with the capabilities and skills of the equipment and personnel resources available to the utility. The amount of equipment and personnel resources allocated to individual projects also must be sufficient to permit scheduled completion dates (or required completion deadlines) to be met. In some cases, construction work necessitated by a particular project may be partly performed by outside contractors and partly performed by the utility itself.

Effective planning requires that, for construction projects to be undertaken by outside contractors, the process of advertising and awarding bids (or by otherwise negotiating contracts) be initiated soon enough to permit the process to be completed prior to the scheduled date on which construction is to begin. Further, the purchase of construction materials and supplies, or the purchase of such utility plant assets as equipment (either through competitive bidding or by negotiating contracts), should be initiated and completed in time to permit the delivery of the materials and supplies, or the delivery of the utility plant assets, as needed to meet scheduled completion dates.

With regard to costs in excess of a specified amount, municipally owned water utilities are frequently bound by laws that require competitive bidding for construction contracts, contracts for the purchase of construction materials and supplies, and contracts for the purchase of items of the utility plant. Normally, a contract will be awarded to the "lowest and best" bidder, but it should be kept in mind that the lowest bidder is not necessarily the best. The ability of the bidder to furnish goods and services promptly as needed, and the quality of goods and services furnished, as evidenced by past performance and current financial capability, are important factors in determining the best bid.

Comparing Budgeted and Actual Expenditures

Actual capital expenditures usually differ to some extent from budgeted capital expenditures. Budgeted capital expenditure estimates serve as useful standards only to the extent that they are valid and reasonable. Minor variations from budgeted expenditures are to be expected. Significant variations should be investigated in order to determine necessary management action. In some cases, variations arise from faulty capital budgeting procedures. In other cases, managers or employees fail to follow appropriate procedures for conducting capital expenditure activities. Variations between budgeted and actual capital expenditures also may result from other causes, such as unanticipated changes in construction materials and supplies prices or labor wage rates.

If significant variations between budgeted and actual expenditures exist for individual projects, then management should be informed of the variations and the reasons for them, so that proper control action can be taken for the remainder of the project and for subsequent projects.

The amount of capital expenditures and the status of capital expenditure projects should be reported to management on a periodic basis, typically at monthly or quarterly intervals. Capital expenditure control reports usually consist of a listing of major projects and blanket projects. In cases in which total costs to complete a given project are expected to exceed budget authorization by a substantial amount, authorization to make additional expenditures should be required. In the case of a municipally owned water utility subject to a legally binding capital expenditures budget, it may be necessary for utility management to obtain a supplemental appropriation in order to issue commitment documents and make expenditures beyond original authorizations.

Expenditure Authorization

The capital expenditures budget is an advance estimate of requirements for additions to, and retirements of, the water utility plant. The expenditures are limited to those items approved by management and policy-making groups and included in the budget as necessary to meet the demands of customers for water service. The construction budget usually has its origin in requests from division heads to the general manager of a utility for approval of specific projects, presented in the form of individual project budgets. It is the responsibility of the general manager and his or her staff to evaluate individual project requests and to consolidate those projects approved by the general manager. The consolidation of individual projects aids the general manager in coordinating the activities of the individual departments of the water utility so as to best meet the demands of customers for water service. The budget is then submitted to the policy-making group (city council or board of directors) for final approval.

In the case of municipally owned water utilities, the capital expenditures budget may become a legally binding document on approval by the city council or other policy-making group. The approved capital expenditures budget serves as the authorization to issue commitment documents and to incur expenditures in the amount appropriated (approved) by the city council or other policy-making group. In the case of investor-owned water utilities, the capital expenditures budget, although ordinarily requiring approval by the board of directors, is not a legally binding document. It is generally agreed that appropriations for capital expenditures should be stated in broad terms to provide reasonable latitude for water utility management consistent with the broad control needs of the policy-making group.

In addition to the approval of the capital expenditure budget, specific management approval is customarily required in order to begin work on each individual project. A work order, when approved, serves as the authorization to commence a specific unit of work, places responsibility for the execution of the work, and serves as a review of a proposed expenditure at the time the request for authorization to make expenditures is received by management. In addition, the work order is the basis for accumulating costs, which are later transferred to appropriate plant accounts and continuing property records when the work is completed. A separate work order is sometimes issued for each primary plant account that will be affected by a particular capital expenditure project. Other utilities may provide only one work order for each project, even though a project may affect the total in more than one primary plant account.

In some cases, the individual project budgets that support the summary of budgeted capital expenditures serve as work orders. Frequently, however, there is a substantial time lag between the time a proposed capital expenditure project is tentatively approved and included in the capital expenditures budget and the time work is to begin on the project. Prior to the time project work is to begin, various factors may develop that affect management's plans and that make it undesirable to start or to complete a project previously approved. As a result, work orders permit management to review previously approved projects and either give final authorization to begin work or to cancel projects. In the case of blanket projects, each individual item of work, such as a customer service or meter installation, also may be supported by a work order.

⊠ Property Records

Owners

The property-records requirements for utility owners will differ from those of other users of financial information. The owner's requirements for information regarding the utility's assets are that they be properly identified so that they may be properly accounted for. Management in following the owner's conditions will develop the asset control system that meets the needs of owners and management.

Regulatory Agencies

Regulatory agencies may be able to dictate methods of capitalization and depreciation that effect the utility's manner of recording assets. Each regulatory agency will have requirements based on their need to allocate costs and assets to classes of customers.

Continuing Property Records

Proper accounting for utility plant assets includes the maintenance of a continuing property record (CPR) system. As discussed earlier, a CPR system involves the maintenance of a separate record for each unit of utility property. A "unit of property" (or CPR unit) is defined as an item of property that can be readily identified and accounted for by itself. A single record may, however, be used for a group of small items, such as meters. The property record card for each unit of utility property should contain complete details on the unit, such as

- any information that will identify the unit of property (for example, name of property item, brief description of the property item, and manufacturer's identification number)

- location

- administrative custody

- from whom acquired

- when acquired

- where taxed (investor-owned utility)

- information as to the cost of the asset, estimated service life, net salvage value, and any other factors that are useful for determining depreciation

- recorded depreciation (if depreciation is charged by individual property units)

- any date, such as that taken from an account number, that will tie the record in with the proper utility plant account

The CPR for each unit of property also must provide for recording changes in the cost of the property unit as a result of additions, replacements, and retirements. The recording of such changes is based on information contained in investment or construction work orders and retirement work orders. Completed work orders that have not been transferred to account 101, "utility plant in service," provide supporting data for account 106, "completed construction not classified"; and incomplete work orders provide supporting data for account 105, "construction work in progress." Account 106, "completed construction not classified," includes the total balances of work orders for the utility plant that have been completed and placed in service but for which work orders have not been entered in the CPRs as of the balance-sheet date. Account 105, "construction work in progress," includes the total balances of work orders for the utility plant in process of construction but not ready for service as of the balance-sheet date. Most public service commissions require that water utilities under their jurisdiction maintain adequate work order systems to record all changes in the water utility plant. Many public service commissions also prescribe the use of CPR systems for the larger water utilities under their jurisdiction.

In summary, investment or construction work orders serve as a basis for accumulating charges for construction work in progress. Ultimately, when the construction work is completed, the accumulated charges are transferred to the primary utility plant accounts. The continuing property records support the balances in the primary or detailed utility plant accounts. The primary utility plant accounts, in turn, support the balances in utility plant control accounts, principally account 101, "utility plant in service."

Normally, control account 106, "completed construction not classified," also would be supported by detailed accounts. However, the detailed accounts employed may differ from those presently recommended by NARUC, since such a difference is one reason for categorizing the assets as completed construction not classified. The "utility plant in process of reclassification" account represents a clearing account until audit and analysis permits the asset costs to be reclassified in a manner consistent with NARUC classifications.

The Work Order System

In addition to the capital expenditure budget, the work order system provides an accounting procedure to check the relationship between actual capital expenditures and the approved budget. The costs, accumulated through the use of a work order system, should be reported in detail sufficient to show the number and cost of the various CPR units involved in the capital expenditures project covered by the work order. A work order system operated in this manner permits management control of detailed capital expenditures for individual projects through comparison with authorizations.

In order to provide management with information concerning the costs associated with each project, or for each primary plant account and property unit involved in the project, a "work order record" is customarily maintained. In the case of an investment work order, costs included on the work order record include direct and indirect labor costs, the cost of contract work, the cost of materials and supplies, transportation expense, and all other indirect (or overhead) costs. In the case of a retirement work order, costs included on the work order record are the cost of property retired and the cost of removal and salvage value. By using work orders and work order records, the capital expenditures for, and retirements of, utility plant assets are identified, classified, and traced from the authorization stage, through the construction or retirement stage, to the continuing property records in support of the primary utility plant accounts. The cost of work in progress included on a work order record permits immediate reference to the corresponding work order estimate in order to determine the amount of variation between actual and budgeted expenditures for a particular project.

The CPR System

It has been noted previously that additions to, and retirements of, the water utility plant customarily are made under the authority of work orders (in the case of the construction or retirement of plant) or by purchase requisitions (in the case of the purchase of plant). In turn, charges and credits to the plant accounts and to the continuing property records in support of the plant accounts are based on cost information shown on (1) the work order records (in the case of the construction or retirement of plant) or (2) on invoices (in the case of the purchase of plant).

A CPR system can be an elaborate and detailed system for matching property units (CPR units) with their costs. The CPR system supports the plant accounts with a perpetual inventory of the property represented by the plant accounts and shows the portion of total plant cost associated with each individual unit of property or with each aggregate unit composed of similar small items of property.

Uses of a CPR system. In general, public service commissions require that water utilities under their jurisdiction maintain CPR systems. A CPR system is a tool of regulation and a way to compile a complete record of the original cost of property owned by the water utility. The CPR system is a useful tool not only for regulatory commissions' purposes but also for management purposes. Some of a CPR system's uses are as follows:

- provides a record of plant costs for use in rate studies. Although the CPR system customarily shows the original cost of property units, the system also facilitates the computation of other kinds of property values. The reproduction or replacement costs of plant assets can be determined by applying price indexes to the historical cost or original cost of property units.

- as a record of the dates of property additions and retirements, provides historical information about the service lives of different property units. This facilitates service life studies to determine appropriate depreciation rates.

- provides cost data that may be useful to management in the preparation of capital expenditure budgets.

- assists in determining the cost of property retired.

- substantiates the costs included in the plant accounts. The cost of property as shown by the CPR system should be in balance with the cost of property shown by the plant accounts.

- provides a useful tool for internal control of utility property. A physical inventory of utility property should agree with the inventory records generated by the CPR system.

Selecting appropriate CPR units. The development of a CPR system begins with selecting CPR units relating to which physical inventory records are maintained and which plant costs are allocated. The selection of CPR units also should be guided by reasonable limits of detailed property classification, since the cost of establishing and maintaining records increases with the degree of detail involved. The selection of appropriate CPR units should be guided by cost considerations as well as by anticipated usefulness of more detailed classification. Property records should be established and maintained in the degree of detail required to ensure a reasonably close relationship between recorded cost and the actual cost of utility property in use (NCGA 1968). NARUC defines a retirement unit for a main as two or more standard lengths of main, including fittings, or one continuous run of 24 ft or more.

In the case of land, each separate parcel of land constitutes a CPR unit. In the case of land rights, each land right having a useful life of more than one year constitutes a CPR unit. A CPR unit of depreciable property generally is composed of one or more retirement units.

In the case of structures and improvements, and major items of equipment (such as those equipment items comprising source-of-supply plant, pumping plant, water treatment plant, transmission plant, and general plant), CPR units typically are relatively large in size. Each structure and improvement, or each major item of equipment, sometimes is treated as a CPR unit; however, a particular structure, improvement, or major equipment item may be composed of a number of retirement units. Distribution facilities are in large part composed of many small, similar items of property (such as mains, services, meters, meter installations, and hydrants). Each item of property (for example, a given length of main, a service, a meter, a meter installation, or a hydrant) typically is chosen as a CPR unit. Each CPR unit is relatively small in size and generally corresponds to a retirement unit.

It was noted earlier that a major purpose or use of a CPR system is to permit tracing the cost of a particular property unit so that its cost can be eliminated from the plant accounts when that property unit is retired. However a CPR system does not eliminate cost estimates in connection with the retirement of property items constituting less than a CPR unit or retirement unit. It would be impractical to establish and maintain cost records in detail sufficient to eliminate all cost estimates and to provide actual cost information for all property items retired.

Establishing a CPR system. For relatively large CPR units (such as those representing land, land rights, structures and improvements, or major components thereof) it is advisable to provide a separate cost record for each unit.

In the case of relatively small CPR units (such as those representing mains, services, meters, meter installations, and hydrants), a single cost record may be provided for groups of similar CPR units. For example, a single cost record may represent the aggregate cost of CPR units of the same size and the same year of installation. The average cost of similar units installed in each year can then be determined by dividing the aggregate cost by the number of CPR units represented by the aggregate cost. In the case of meters owned by the utility, it also is desirable to have a card showing the history of each meter, including its cost, date purchased, addresses at which used, and number of times repaired.

When a CPR system is first established, an inventory of property must be made in accordance with the selected CPR units. This inventory can be prepared from existing utility records (such as maps and engineering reports) to the extent that such records exist. To the extent that records are unavailable or incomplete, a physical inventory of property units must be made.

After the inventory of property has been prepared, the cost of CPR units must be established. In the initial establishment of a CPR system, direct and indirect costs (original cost in the case of commission-regulated water utilities) associated with inventoried CPR units should, if possible, be based on accounting entries and supporting documents, such as work order authorizations and records, purchase requisitions and invoices, vouchers, and contracts. When accounting records are unavailable or incomplete, costs of inventoried property units must be estimated by referring to labor wage rates, material costs, and other historical information relevant to the period when property units were constructed or purchased.

Maintaining the CPR system. After the CPR system has been established, subsequent additions to, and retirements of, the utility plant must be reflected in the property records in terms both of costs and quantities. To the extent possible, physical inventory tests also should be conducted periodically to establish the existence of property reflected by the CPR system.

The direct and indirect costs associated with additions to the water utility plant are based on investment work order records and purchase invoices. These costs, which are transferred to property record cards, represent either the cost of individual CPR units (in the case of relatively large units) or the aggregate cost of CPR units (in the case of relatively small, similar units) installed during a given period of time.

The direct and indirect costs associated with retiring water utility plant assets are based on retirement work order records. The cost of retirements credited to property record cards represents either the cost originally assigned to the individual CPR units being retired (in the case of relatively large units) or the average cost of CPR units being retired (in the case of relatively small, similar units, where the original cost is represented by the aggregate cost of similar units installed during a given period of time).

If depreciation is accounted for by individual CPR units (which might be the case for relatively large property items), rather than by treating each plant account, functional group of accounts, or total depreciable property as a single account, then accumulated depreciation charges should also be reflected by the property record cards.

In summary, the elaborate procedures involved for allocating costs among property units in a CPR system permit the immediate determination of costs of property items being retired to the extent that the costs are recorded at the time of purchase or construction of property. In addition, the CPR system assists management in ensuring that recorded costs correspond closely to the actual cost of property in service. This is important from the standpoint of establishing an appropriate rate base value to use in determining water rates. Further, the CPR system facilitates the placing of insurance by identifying the items of property that are insurable and by identifying the costs associated with insurable property items. The recorded cost of individual items of property frequently serves as the starting point for determining insurable value. Insurable value will determine the amount of premium payments required to obtain full (or adequate) insurance coverage. Finally, the CPR system functions as an important tool of internal control by serving as a perpetual inventory record of utility property.

⊠ References

National Committee on Governmental Accounting. 1968. *Governmental Accounting, Auditing, and Financial Reporting*. Chicago, Ill.: Municipal Finance Officers Association.

National Association of Regulatory Utility Commissioners. 1977. *Uniform System of Accounts for Class A Water Utilities 1976*. Washington, D.C.: National Association of Regulatory Utility Commissioners.

National Association of Regulatory Utility Commissioners, Committee on Accounts and Statistics. 1962. *List of Retirement Units for Property for Water Utilities 1962*. Washington, D.C.: National Association of Regulatory Utility Commissioners.

National Association of Regulatory Utility Commissioners, Subcommittee on Valuation and Plant Costs of the Committee on Engineering. 1975. *Model Valuation. Plant Costs and Continuing Property Records Manual*. Washington, D.C.: National Association of Regulatory Utility Commissioners.

CHAPTER TWELVE

Current and Other Assets

As discussed in chapter 11, the greatest portion of the total assets of a water utility is the utility plant. Other classes of assets, however, are also of major importance to a utility. Among the more important classes are current assets and restricted assets (or special funds). The National Association of Regulatory Utility Commissioners (NARUC) defines "current and accrued assets" as follows:

> Current and accrued assets include cash, those assets which are readily convertible into cash or are held for current use in operations or construction, current claims against others, payment of which is reasonably assured, and amounts accruing to the utility which are subject to current settlement, except such items for which accounts other than those designated as current and accrued assets are provided. There shall not be included in the group of accounts designated as current and accrued assets any item, the amount of collectability of which is not reasonably assured, unless an adequate provision for possible loss has been made therefor. Items of current character but of doubtful value may be written down and for record purposes carried in these accounts at nominal value.

Asset items classified by NARUC as current and accrued assets may be broadly grouped into the following four categories: (1) cash or cash equivalents, such as special deposits with fiscal agents, and temporary cash investments; (2) notes and accounts receivable; (3) materials and supplies; and (4) prepaid expenses and other receivables. A complete list of current and accrued assets is provided in appendix A.

Restricted assets (or special funds) are comprised of cash and investments that have been segregated in special accounts and restricted for use for such special purposes as bond debt service, replacement or construction of plant assets, and employee pension and other benefits. Special funds are not classified under current assets according to NARUC, but instead are shown under the balance-sheet asset category, "other property and investments." This chapter is concerned with the planning and control of major kinds of current assets and restricted assets.

⊠ Liquid Assets

Cash

Current assets that are cash or cash equivalents are called "liquid assets." Assets customarily included in the liquid asset category include cash, temporary cash investments, and accounts receivable (primarily those from customers). In general, inventories of materials and supplies are not considered to be liquid assets.

Nature of cash. Cash includes demand deposits in banks, monies, checks (and other similar credit instruments that function as money) held by the utility for deposit, and petty cash (or working funds). Bank demand deposits generally comprise the greatest portion of cash. In order to be classified as cash, deposits with banks or other institutions must be available for use for general purposes. The deposits must be free and their use must not be restricted either by contract or special trust agreement. The fact that water utility management may intend to use cash for the discharge of a particular obligation is not material if there is no legal compulsion to use the particular cash for that obligation. On the other hand, special deposits with fiscal agents or others for the payment of interest, dividends (in the case of investor-owned water utilities), and for other special purposes are not considered to be cash.

Sources of cash. The sources of cash available to a water utility are many and varied. Most of the sources are described elsewhere in this book and are only briefly summarized here. The two major sources of cash for a water utility are (1) cash received from the sale of water service to customers and (2) cash received from creditors and investors in return for evidences of debt or ownership.

Other important sources of cash may include cash received from the rent of utility and nonutility plant assets leased to others, interest or dividends on securities owned, sale of property and investments, customers' deposits, and advances and contributions for construction from customers, subdividers, and governmental authorities.

Uses of cash. The disposition of cash falls into the following four major categories:

1. Operations — payment of expenses incurred in the conduct of utility and nonutility operations, primarily operation and maintenance expenses and taxes.
2. Financing — interest payments and repayment of principal amounts to creditors (and dividend payments to stockholders in the case of investor-owned water utilities).
3. Capital expenditures.
4. Repayment of customers' meter deposits and repayment of advances for construction.

In general, the cash generated from the sale of water service and from the conduct of other miscellaneous utility and nonutility operations is the source for payment of expenses incurred in the conduct of utility and nonutility operations. It is also the source for payment of interest and, in the case of investor-owned water utilities, dividends. During periods when cash from operations is generated at a rate less than that required to discharge obligations, short-term borrowings may be required to supplement cash resources.

To the extent that retirement of long-term debt is not financed by new security issues, cash generated from sale of water service is used to repay long-term debt obligations. For example, in the case of revenue bonds issued by a municipally owned water utility, a portion of cash generated from operations typically is transferred periodically to asset accounts restricted for revenue bond debt service. The restricted funds are then used to pay interest and to repay debt principal. Debt service on general obligation bonds of municipally owned water utilities typically is payable from utility revenues. If operating revenues are insufficient, then a general property tax levy may be required to meet debt service requirements.

Cash generated from the sale of water service (in excess of cash required to pay operation and maintenance expenses, taxes, interest, and dividends, and to repay debt principal) can be used to finance current capital expenditures. Cash received from creditors and investors, and advances and contributions in aid to construction, provide the other major sources for financing capital expenditures. In some cases, particularly in the case of municipally owned water utilities, cash proceeds from a securities issue are segregated in a restricted asset account (or construction fund) to be used solely for capital expenditures.

In some jurisdictions, cash received as customers' deposits must be segregated in a restricted asset account. The restricted assets sometimes serve as the source for repayment of deposits to customers. If cash received from customers' deposits is not segregated, then cash generated from the sale of water service normally serves as the source for repayment of the deposits. Repayment of advances from customers or others for construction typically is also made from cash generated from the sale of water service.

If, during a given period of time, the cash accumulated by a water utility is in excess of needs for cash, then the excess can be used to purchase investments, such as short-term government securities. This procedure permits the temporary use of idle cash to purchase earning assets with little risk of loss of principal when the investments are sold. Temporary investments are liquidated as required to meet obligations.

Although special deposits with fiscal agents or others for the payment of interest or dividends and for other special purposes are considered current assets by NARUC, the National Council on Governmental Accounting (NCGA) considers such deposits restricted assets. NCGA recommends use of the term "restricted assets" to describe cash and investments that have been segregated for use for specific purposes. NARUC uses the term "special funds."

Controlling cash. Cash is perhaps the easiest asset to lose through theft, therefore, rigid control over cash should be practiced. Proper internal control of cash requires that persons handling cash should not be given the responsibility of accounting for cash, and vice versa. The work of every employee concerned with cash should be reviewed by other employees so that a continuous check and audit is made of all cash receipts and disbursements.

In the case of cash receipts, an adequate system of internal control is required for the preparation of a receipt document at the time cash is received by the utility. The receipt document then passes through bookkeeping channels while the cash itself passes through cashier channels for deposits intact in bank accounts. Personnel responsible for receiving cash should not be given duties involving the keeping of accounting records. In addition, persons receiving cash should have no duties involving the preparation of customer bills.

Cashiers should be required each day to turn over to the head cashier the amount of cash collected through payments made in person by customers or received from other sources. The reports of individual cashiers summarizing cash receipts, together with the receipt stubs, should be reconciled by the head cashier with the amount of cash received from each cashier. Copies of the cashiers' reports, together with the receipt stubs, should be turned over to the bookkeeping personnel.

Remittances received by mail should be handled by employees under effective supervision, and each remittance should be accompanied by a bill. Remittances by mail should be turned over daily to the head cashier, and a report summarizing remittances by mail, together with bill stubs as verified by the head cashier, should be turned over to bookkeeping personnel. Each day's cash receipts should be deposited intact in a bank and a copy of the deposit slip should be reconciled with the daily cashiers' reports and the daily mail receipts report by an employee having no other connection with the accounting records or the handling of cash. Figure 12-1 presents a summary diagram of the flow of cash received by a water utility and of the accounting for cash receipts so as to obtain effective internal control over the receipts.

All cash disbursements, except for minor expenditures made through the petty cash fund or working fund, should be made by check. Invoices received should be properly vouchered after comparison with receiving reports or other documents to ensure that value has been actually received by the utility. Cash disbursements should be authorized by the treasurer of the utility or his or her properly designated representative. It should be required that all checks be signed by an authorized person who is responsible for examination of the voucher and other documents supporting the disbursement. Persons responsible for the check-signing function should not be the same as those responsible for the bookkeeping function.

Disbursements from the petty cash fund (or working fund) should be supported by sales receipts or other memoranda. Petty cash on hand should be defined as some nominal sum of money such as $50 or $100, depending on the size and needs of the utility. At the time it is reimbursed, the petty cash fund should be examined by someone other than the person in charge of the fund to verify that the amount of the reimbursement check (properly vouchered) corresponds to the amount by which the petty cash fund is depleted. Figure 12-2 presents a summary diagram of the flow of cash disbursed by a water utility and of the accounting for cash disbursements so as to obtain effective control over the disbursements.

For proper control, it is also necessary that the bank balance according to the bank statement be reconciled monthly with the bank balance according to the utility's books. This reconciliation should be performed by an employee having no other connection with the accounting records or the handling of cash. In addition to maintaining adequate internal control over cash in order to prevent theft, it is important that water utility management maintain close and continual control over cash balances in order to ensure that sufficient cash is available to meet maturing obligations. The general manager and/or treasurer customarily receives a daily cash report that summarizes cash receipts and disbursements and the cash balance. The report is similar in nature to that shown in Figure 12-3.

Figure 12-1 ⊠ Accounting control of cash receipts

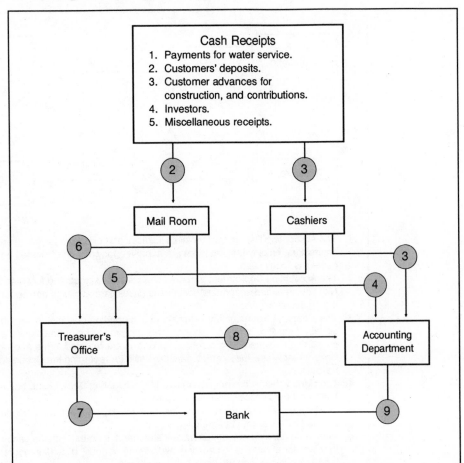

Cash Receipts
1. Payments for water service.
2. Customers' deposits.
3. Customer advances for construction, and contributions.
4. Investors.
5. Miscellaneous receipts.

1. Payments from customers or other sources are made in person. Cashiers prepare a list of receipts showing customer account numbers or other sources of payment, and the amounts received.
2. Payments are received by mail. Mail clerks prepare a mail remittance list showing customer account numbers or other sources of payment, and the amounts received.
3. A copy of the list of receipts, together with receipt stubs, is routed to the Accounting Department where it is used as the basis for recording the receipt transactions as an increase in cash and a decrease in accounts receivable or an increase in liabilities or equities.
4. A copy of the mail remittance list, together with receipt stubs, is routed to the Accounting Department where it is used as the basis for recording the receipt transactions as an increase in cash and a decrease in accounts payable or an increase in liabilities or equities.
5. Cash received by cashiers, together with a list of the cash receipts is forwarded to the Treasurer's Office.
6. The mail remittances, along with a copy of the remittance list, are forwarded to the Treasurer's Office.
7. The Treasurer's Office deposits cash receipts intact in the bank on a daily basis.
8. A copy of the bank deposit slip is sent to the Accounting Department. It is compared with the list of receipts from cashiers and the mail remittance list to see that all cash receipts were deposited in the bank.
9. At month-end, the bank renders a bank statement showing the opening cash balance, the daily bank deposits, the checks drawn against the account and the closing cash balance. The Accounting Department prepares a reconciliation of the bank balance of cash with the book balance of cash.

Figure 12-2 ⊠ Accounting control of cash disbursements

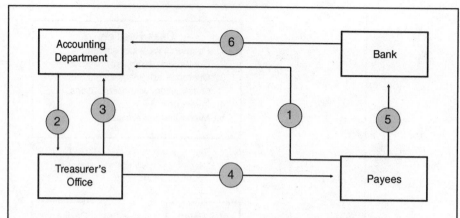

1. The Accounting Department receives invoices and bills from payees (vendors, contractors, employees, etc.) that are approved for payment. Included among the payees is "petty cash."
2. The Accounting Department prepares checks to be signed and forwards them, together with vouchers and supporting documents (invoices and bills approved for payment), to the Treasurer's Office.
3. The Treasurer examines the vouchers and supporting documents, and the checks to be signed. If satisfied that the disbursements are proper, he or she signs the checks. The supporting documents are stamped "paid" and are returned to the Accounting Department where they are used as the basis for recording the disbursement transaction.
4. The signed checks are not returned to the Accounting Department, but are sent from the Treasurer's Office directly to the payees.
5. The payees present the checks to the bank for payment and the bank balance is reduced by the amount of the checks.
6. At month-end, the bank sends a bank statement, together with the canceled checks, to the water utility. The Accounting Department or auditing department reconciles the bank balance with the book balance of cash.

The daily cash report permits management to observe the present cash position of the utility and to compare the actual cash position with the position forecast by the cash budget. If the actual cash position differs substantially from the forecast position, a revision of the forecast may be required. In addition, reports of actual cash positions may indicate that financing plans should be altered, both from the standpoint of seeking additional sources of cash and from the standpoint of making revisions to planned borrowing and debt repayment schedules.

Cash flow statements. Information concerning the sources and uses of cash funds frequently is presented to water utility management in the form of cash flow statements. An example is illustrated in Figure 12-3. Preparing the statement shown there requires that cash receipts from operations and cash disbursements for operations be enumerated. This procedure is akin to the cash basis of accounting (as opposed to the accrual basis of accounting).

An alternate format for a cash flow statement is presented in Figure 12-4. The preparation of the statement shown there is founded on information contained in other statements, such as the income statement and balance sheet. The statement begins with the net income of the water utility (as determined under the accrual basis of accounting), together with necessary adjustments to

Figure 12-3 ⊠ Statement of sources and uses of cash

The Willing Water Company Statement of Sources and Uses of Cash For the Year Ended Dec. 31, 19CY

Cash Balance, Jan. 1, 19CY		$ 250,000
Cash Received From:		
Collection on customer accounts receivable	$8,932,000	
Rent of utility and nonutility property	37,000	
Interest and dividends on investments	14,000	
Net cash inflow — advances and contributions in aid of construction	125,000	
Net cash inflow — customer meter deposits	10,000	
Sale of property and investments (including liquidation of special funds)	157,000	
Net short-term borrowings	973,000	
Issuance of long-term debt	2,947,000	
Other	15,000	
Total Cash Receipts During 19CY		$13,210,000
Total Cash Available During 19CY		$13,460,000
Cash Used For:		
Payments for salaries and wages	1,638,000	
Purchase of materials and supplies	2,947,000	
Purchase of property and investments	920,000	
Payments to contractors for construction	4,107,000	
Interest payments	540,000	
Dividend payments	1,312,000	
Tax payments	1,283,000	
Repayment of debt	300,000	
Other	142,000	
Total Cash Disbursement		$13,189,000
Cash Balance, Dec. 31, 19CY		$ 271,000

reflect cash generated from operations. For example, depreciation and amortization expense must be added to net income because these expense items do not involve a current disbursement of cash. Other expense items, such as operation and maintenance expenses, taxes, interest, and the purchase and construction of assets during the accounting period, do not fully reflect cash disbursements; therefore, changes during the accounting period in the balances of current asset accounts other than cash, and in current liability accounts must be considered in order to determine actual cash disbursements. For example, an increase in current liabilities generally indicates that cash disbursements are less than the amount indicated by expenses and by the purchase and construction of assets during the period; therefore, an increase in current liabilities can be considered as a source of cash. Similarly, an increase in current noncash assets generally indicates a use of cash. For example, an increase in inventories of materials and supplies would be considered as a use of cash. Revenues as shown in the income statement and the sale of plant

Figure 12-4 ⊗ Statement of sources and uses of cash

```
┌─────────────────────────────────────────────────────────────────────┐
│                                                                       │
│      The City Water Department Statement of Sources and Uses          │
│            of Cash For the Year Ended Dec. 31, 19CY                    │
│                                                                       │
│   Cash Balance, Jan. 1, 19CY                              $  274,000  │
│                                                                       │
│   Cash Was Provided By:                                               │
│     Utility operating income before depreciation                     │
│        and amortization expense              $  614,000               │
│     Interest income from investments             23,000               │
│     Sale of utility plant assets                 56,000               │
│     Increase in advances and contributions in aid                     │
│        of construction                          376,000               │
│     Increase in customer meter deposits           9,000               │
│     Revenue bond issue                        1,927,000               │
│     Decrease in noncash current assets           32,000               │
│     Increase in current liabilities              78,000               │
│     Other                                        14,000               │
│                                                                       │
│   Total Cash Provided During 19CY                         $3,129,000  │
│                                                                       │
│   Total Cash Available During 19CY                        $3,403,000  │
│                                                                       │
│   Cash Used For:                                                      │
│     Interest charges                         $  306,000               │
│     Retirement of long-term debt                208,000               │
│     Increase in restricted assets — bond debt service  47,000         │
│     Additions to utility plant                1,482,000               │
│     Increase in restricted assets — revenue bond                      │
│        proceeds                               1,102,000               │
│     Increase in restricted assets — customer meter                    │
│        deposits                                   9,000               │
│     Other                                        37,000               │
│                                                                       │
│   Total Cash Used During 19CY                             $3,191,000  │
│                                                                       │
│   Cash Balance, Dec. 31, 19CY                             $  212,000  │
│                                                                       │
└─────────────────────────────────────────────────────────────────────┘
```

assets and investments also will not fully reflect cash sources to the extent that there is a change in receivable during the accounting period. Therefore, an increase in receivables can be considered as a use of cash.

For further discussion of cash flow analysis, see Mason (1961) and National Association of Accountants (1961).

Determining appropriate cash balances. Perfect synchronization between cash realization from operations and the disbursement of cash in the discharge of obligations is impossible. Cash may be realized more rapidly than needed to discharge obligations, resulting in an excess of cash; or cash realization may not be adequate and borrowing may be required in order to discharge obligations. Cash held in checking accounts and cash on-hand are nonearning assets. To the extent that cash balances are excessive, water utility management is withholding resources from possible profitable employment or is paying interest on borrowed money that is not needed by the utility to finance operations.

The amount of cash to be retained in bank accounts depends in part on the amount to be held as minimum balances to compensate banks for services rendered, lines of credit or other credit agreements, and bank loans. In addition to minimum balances, cash in banks must be sufficient to permit a utility to conduct normal activities (both operating and capital expenditure activities). The amount held in banks for normal activities depends on the seasonal requirements of a utility for cash needed for transactions. A utility also may wish to maintain cash to meet contingencies. The amount of cash held as a safety factor to meet contingencies depends on the subjective feelings of utility management toward risk. Contingencies should be interpreted as minor unforeseen requirements for cash. The amount of cash required to conduct normal utility activities and to meet contingencies, plus minimum balances required by banks, determines the appropriate amount of cash to be retained in bank accounts.

It should be noted that lines of credit and other credit agreements with banks may serve to reduce the appropriate amount of cash to be retained in bank accounts by reducing the amount of cash needed as a safety factor to meet contingencies. On the other hand, the use of lines of credit or other credit agreements will increase the appropriate amount of cash to be retained in bank accounts to the extent that additional compensating balances are required by banks under the terms of the credit arrangement. Lines of credit or other credit agreements are not for the purpose of meeting long-run cash needs; rather, they serve as a quick source of money to meet cash deficiencies that arise in the normal course of utility operations.

For further discussion of the determination of the appropriate level of cash on hand, see Bierman (1963).

Forecasting cash balances. Although it is important that a water utility earn an adequate return, it is also important that the utility maintain an adequate cash position in order to discharge obligations as they mature. It is essential to sound financial planning and to the maintenance of an adequate cash position that forecasts of cash receipts and disbursements be made. Cash flow forecasts permit water utility management to anticipate future cash deficiencies and to augment cash balances by short-term borrowing or by issuing long-term securities. Likewise, cash flow forecasts permit management to formulate debt repayment plans and to plan the investment of excessive cash balances.

Forecasts of cash receipts and disbursements may be made for a year, a quarter, a month, or even a week. A one-year forecast of cash receipts and disbursements may be developed by months (or by quarters) and updated each month (or quarter) by dropping the elapsed month (or quarter) and adding the next month (or quarter). If a one-year cash flow forecast is made by quarters, the earliest quarter forecast should be made for each of the three months in that quarter. Figure 12-5 presents an example of a one-year forecast of cash receipts and disbursements by quarters, with the earliest quarter forecast by months. The forecast anticipates the need for short-term and long-term borrowing in order to meet cash deficiencies and to maintain a minimum cash balance. In general, the longer the period covered by a cash flow forecast and the more distant in time the period covered, the less reliable are the estimates. Therefore, periodic revisions in cash flow estimates are required in order for the estimates to serve as useful financial planning guides.

The forecast of cash receipts and disbursements during the budget period is based in part on past experience and in part on anticipated changes in the

Figure 12-5 ⊠ One-year cash flow forecast

The City Water Department Cash Flow Forecast For the Year 19BY

	First Quarter — 19BY			2nd Quarter —19BY	3rd Quarter —19BY	4th Quarter —19BY
	January	February	March			
Estimated Cash Balance, Beginning of Period	$250,000	$174,000	$ 69,000	$ 142,000	$ 96,000	$ 75,000
Estimated Cash Provided By:						
Sale of water service	$500,000	$500,000	$ 570,000	$1,630,000	$1,720,000	$1,790,000
Rent of property	3,000	3,000	3,000	9,000	9,000	9,000
Interest on investments	1,000	2,000	3,000	12,000	15,000	10,000
Sale of plant assets and other property	12,000	5,000	18,000	25,000	30,000	10,000
Advances and contributions in aid of construction (net of repayment of customer advances)	10,000	12,000	14,000	50,000	60,000	60,000
Customer meter deposits (net of repayments)	1,000	1,000	1,000	3,000	3,000	3,000
Use of restricted assets — revenue bond proceeds				380,000	420,000	200,000
Short-term borrowings				300,000		
Issuance of bonds			1,972,000			
Other	5,000	5,000	5,000	15,000	15,000	15,000
Estimated Total Cash Provided During Period	$532,000	$528,000	$2,586,000	$2,424,000	$2,272,000	$2,097,000
Estimated Total Cash Available During Period	$782,000	$702,000	$2,655,000	$2,566,000	$2,368,000	$2,172,000
Estimated Cash Disbursements:						
Salaries and wages	$ 80,000	$ 80,000	$ 75,000	$ 250,000	$ 255,000	$ 235,000
Materials and supplies	160,000	165,000	150,000	670,000	540,000	450,000
Payments to outside contractors for construction	200,000	250,000	150,000	930,000	870,000	530,000
Purchase of plant assets and other property	75,000	60,000	65,000	225,000	210,000	100,000
Interest (payments from other than restricted assets)	15,000	10,000	25,000	50,000	75,000	60,000
Taxes	8,000	10,000	20,000	75,000	32,000	98,000
Repayment of short-term borrowings	15,000	5,000	10,000	20,000	60,000	310,000
Transfers to restricted assets — bond debt service	40,000	40,000	35,000	200,000	195,000	190,000
Transfers to restricted assets — customer meter deposits	1,000	1,000	1,000	3,000	3,000	3,000
Transfers to restricted assets — proceeds from sale of bonds			1,972,000			
Other	14,000	12,000	10,000	47,000	53,000	32,000
Estimated Total Cash Disbursements During Period	$608,000	$633,000	$2,513,000	$2,470,000	$2,293,000	$2,008,000
Estimated Cash Balance, End of Period	$174,000	$ 69,000	$ 142,000	$ 96,000	$ 75,000	$ 164,000

activities of a water utility during the budget period. Forecast monthly or quarterly cash receipts from the sale of water service are based on the revenue budget, adjusted for differences between the revenue estimates as determined on the accrual basis and revenues as determined on the cash basis. This adjustment may be made by applying a ratio, based on past experience, of cash receipts to revenues. Forecasting other sources of cash, such as the rental of utility property, interest and dividends on securities owned, customers' deposits, and advances and contributions for construction, can be based on past experience adjusted for anticipated change during the budget period. Cash receipts from sales of utility property and investments generally are more difficult to estimate. To the extent possible, such estimates must be based on management's plans to dispose of property and investments and on prospective market prices for such property and investments.

Forecasts of monthly or quarterly cash disbursements for operations are based on the operating budget, adjusted for differences between expense estimates as determined on the accrual basis and expenses as determined on the cash basis. For example, cash disbursements for wages and salaries in any given month or quarter may vary depending on the number of "paydays" falling within the period. Since monthly or quarterly labor expense included in the operating budget reflects expenses incurred (but not necessarily paid), an adjustment is necessary to place labor expense on a cash basis.

In addition, monthly or quarterly materials and supplies expense included in the operating budget ordinarily differs from cash outlays for operating materials and supplies. Particular material and supply items used are usually included in expenses at the average unit costs of the material and supply items on hand during the accounting period. Therefore, to the extent that materials and supplies are on hand at the beginning of the budget period, the cost of such items will influence the expense estimates included in the operating budget. On the other hand, cash disbursements for operating materials and supplies depend on actual outlays during the budget period, regardless of whether or not such materials and supplies are actually used during the period. Therefore, it may prove helpful in estimating cash outlays for operating materials and supplies to base such estimates on a separate materials and supplies budget (discussed later in this chapter) rather than the estimate of materials and supplies expense included in the operating budget. The materials and supplies budget is based on requirements for materials as reflected in the operating budget.

Cash outlays for taxes also differ from tax expense. Monthly or quarterly cash outlays for taxes depend on the scheduled tax payment dates falling within each period. The operating budget reflects accrued taxes and is not affected by dates on which the taxes are actually paid.

Cash management. Monthly or quarterly cash outlays for interest payments, repayment of debt principal, and dividend payments (in the case of investor-owned water utilities) must also be anticipated. Interest payment dates for short-term borrowings depend on the terms of existing borrowing agreements. Dividends on capital stock typically are paid quarterly. Monthly or quarterly cash disbursements for repayment of debt principal depend on existing repayment schedules as determined by debt agreements. Repayments of principal amounts of serial bond issues typically are made semiannually or annually. Cash disbursements for repayment of term bond issues also must be included in the cash budget if such issues mature during the budget period. Cash disbursements for repayment of debt principal (or for both the payment of interest and the repayment of debt principal) may be based on a schedule of payments to asset accounts (for example, special funds) restricted for bond debt service.

Monthly or quarterly cash outlays for capital investment projects (both additions and retirements) are an important component of estimated monthly or quarterly cash disbursements. The capital expenditures budget, together with the construction work schedule and the schedule for purchasing plant assets during the budget period, serves as the basis for forecasting these disbursements. To the extent that the capital expenditures budget reflects accrued costs, as opposed to actual payments, the budget must be adjusted to a cash basis. In the case of contracts with outsiders, progress payment dates and final payment dates as provided by existing or proposed contracts determines when cash outlays will occur. In addition, monthly or quarterly outlays for the payroll of construction workers must be estimated. The cost of construction materials and supplies as included in the capital expenditures budget may differ substantially from actual outlays for such items. (See the preceding discussion in this section concerning cash outlays for operating materials and supplies.) Therefore, in estimating cash outlays for construction materials and supplies, it may prove helpful to base the estimates on a separate materials and supplies budget (discussed in a later section of this chapter).

To the extent the capital investment projects are paid for from assets (for example, special funds) restricted for construction or replacement of the utility plant, disbursements from general cash for capital investment are reduced. Therefore, total disbursements for capital investment, as shown in the cash budget, may be reduced by the amounts to be paid from restricted assets. As an alternative, the assets that are restricted for construction or replacement of the utility plant, and that are to be expended during a budget period, may be considered separately as a source of cash rather than subtracted from total cash disbursements for capital investments. Similarly, scheduled payments to restricted asset accounts during a budget period (for future expenditure for construction or replacement) must also be included among cash disbursements.

Past experience, adjusted for anticipated changes during the budget period, serves as the base for estimating repayments of customers' deposits and advances for construction. Estimated cash outflows resulting from repayment of customers' deposits and advances for construction may be offset against estimated cash inflows from customers' deposits and advances and contributions. Accordingly, estimated net cash inflow from customers' deposits and advances and contributions for construction should then be included as a source of cash.

After cash sources and uses (including interest and repayment of principal amounts on existing debt) are estimated for each month or quarter of a budget period, the resulting net cash balance for each month or quarter will indicate the need for, and the timing of, additional financing through borrowings (and/or through the issuance of stock, in the case of investor-owned water utilities). The cash forecast included in Figure 12-5 includes anticipated borrowings during the budget period. A monthly or quarterly cash forecast, including the cash flows resulting from additional financing during a budget period, also permits management to plan for temporary investment of excessive cash balances that are forecast to develop during the budget period.

Other Liquid Assets

Temporary investments represent a short-term use of cash that is temporarily in excess of needs. These excess amounts of cash might develop from such sources as seasonal or other periodic excesses of cash inflows from the sale of water service over cash outflows for operating expenses, or cash received through contributions or from investors (other than amounts transferred to restricted asset accounts) that is held temporarily pending more permanent investment in plant assets. Cash also may be accumulated from a number of sources in anticipation of future outlays for general utility purposes, such as payment of taxes, interest (if not paid from restricted assets), and dividends (in the case of investor-owned water utilities). Unless invested temporarily, pending future cash needs for ordinary utility purposes, or pending a more permanent investment decision, the excess cash would lie idle in a checking account rather than making a contribution to net income.

Temporary investments ordinarily consist of readily marketable securities. Municipally owned water utilities usually are limited by statute or charter as to the types of securities in which cash can be invested. Such investments may include bank certificates of deposit, or federal, state, and municipal securities. Investor-owned water utilities may invest in certificates of deposit, stocks, bonds, or other debt instruments. In some cases, the utility's board of directors may limit the type of securities eligible for investment. In all cases, the general manager or other members of top management should approve specific investments in temporary securities. An attempt should be made to invest in securities that will bring a reasonable return, but safety of principal should receive primary consideration. Certificates of deposit, government securities, and other debt instruments customarily offer a small risk of loss (or gain) of principal and offer a relatively safe investment; they provide interest income for whatever period they are held. Even among debt instruments there are variations in risk. For example, short-term government securities are less risky than long-term government securities, in the sense that the price of short-term securities may be expected to change less during the period of investment than would the price of long-term securities. In addition to differences in risk due to differences in maturities, risk among debt instruments differs depending on the issuing body. For example, investment in government securities generally are considered to involve less risk of loss (or gain) of principal for a given maturity than investment in corporate debt instruments. Of course, the income from investment in high-grade debt instruments may not be as great as it would if investment were made in such securities as stocks or low-grade debt instruments.

General guidelines concerning the type of securities that can be purchased and the composition of the securities portfolio should be provided by the board of directors, city council, state legislature, or other policy-making group. The guidelines should not, however, render management incapable of taking advantage of market conditions that permit the improvement of returns from temporary securities consistent with reasonable risk. Within the limits set by law and by the board of directors, city council, or other policy-making group, it is reasonable for a water utility to invest in long-term securities or non-US government securities and to bear the accompanying risk if management believes the increase in income over short-term US government securities is such that the risk is outweighed by the expected return. Water utility management may also have a policy of buying securities that mature on a date close to the time when cash from the liquidation of securities is expected to be needed. However, utility management may desire to invest in securities that mature after the time cash is needed, but that can be readily converted into cash when needed.

From the standpoint of internal control, detailed inventory records regarding securities acquired should be maintained and should include information regarding description, purchase price, maturity date, and income of the securities. Securities should be kept so that there will be no possibility of theft or mishandling. Only responsible officials should have access to them, and, whenever possible, securities should be registered. If they cannot be registered, then they should be endorsed so as to prevent their negotiation without proper authorization.

⊠ Receivables

Receivables expected to be paid to the utility within a year are customarily classified as current assets. Included within the classification "receivables" are receivables from associated companies (in the case of investor-owned organizations), customer accounts receivable, receivables from officers and employees, and amounts due from other municipal departments (in the case of municipally owned water utilities). Typically, accounts receivable from customers comprise the major portion of receivables (unless customers are billed in advance, as is done in many flat-rate territories).

Types of Receivables

Customer. Receivables, together with cash and temporary investment represent purchasing power in suspense. As such, the utility is primarily interested in the market or cash value of the receivables. Therefore, the utility must provide for possible losses from uncollectible notes and accounts receivable. The appropriate amount to be included in the "accumulated provision for uncollectibles" account will depend on the credit and collection policies of the utility, the existing economic conditions of the locality served by the utility, and the length of the meter reading and billing period used by the utility. The total investment in customer accounts receivable also depends on the length of the meter reading and billing period — the longer the period, the greater the investment in accounts receivable. Control of customer accounts receivable is discussed in other portions of this book, particularly in connection with controlling and accounting for revenues (chapter 7) and in connection with the preceding discussion in this chapter dealing with the control of cash.

Employee. Receivables due from employees may come in many forms. Examples are travel advances and loans and taxes paid for the employee. As with other receivables, employee receivables must be classified as current or long term depending on the term in which the payment of the debt will be made. Most employee receivables will be classified as current.

Travel advances and taxes paid by the employer have income tax implications to the employee and employment tax consequences to the employer. Under the current Internal Revenue Code Regulations, travel advances must be accounted for within a reasonable period and any excess repaid to the employer. If the employee has an outstanding advance at the end of the year, the outstanding amount is taxable income to the employee and the employee will have federal income and social security taxes withheld. The employer will incur social security taxes on the outstanding travel advance.

An employer may remit the taxes due for an employee to the federal government. When this occurs, the employee has until April 1 of the next year to reimburse the employer for the taxes paid. If the taxes are not reimbursed, the employer must recalculate the employee's earnings for the previous year, including the taxes paid as income to the employee.

Associated companies. The corporate water utility may have several affiliated companies that receive service. The affiliated companies may either be those that the utility owns or a company that owns the utility and other companies. In either case, the utility may provide service to these companies.

Receivables from affiliated companies must be segregated from other receivables, whether or not the receivable is current or long term. The segregation is required to allow consolidation of the balance sheets and income statements of affiliated companies. Without the segregation, the receivables must be analyzed individually to determine those of affiliated companies.

Other municipal departments. The municipal water utility may have several other municipal departments that receive service. Receivables from other municipal departments must be segregated from other receivables, whether or not the receivable is current or long term. The segregation is required to allow consolidation of the balance sheets and income statements of other municipal departments. Without the segregation, the receivables must be analyzed individually to determine those of other municipal departments.

Classifications of Receivables

Short term. Accounting for receivables presents two types of problems to the utility. The first is the classification of the receivable on the balance sheet. The second problem area is the valuation of the receivable. The utility's receivables are classified similarly to payables. A receivable must be classified by the time period in which payment for the amount due is expected. If the payment is expected to be paid within a one-year period or the current operating cycle, then the receivable is classified as current. Most of the utility's receivables will relate to the furnishing of water to the customers. These receivables will be trade receivables. All other types of receivables are nontrade or special receivables.

Long term. The utility's receivables are classified in a similar manner as the payables. A receivable must be classified by the time period in which the payment for the amount due is expected. If the receivable is not expected to be paid within a one-year period or the current operating cycle, then the receivable is classified as a long-term receivable.

Valuation. Utilities will normally not have the valuation problem with trade accounts receivable that other organizations have. The utility has the power to withhold service when the receivable has not been paid. Utilities that have a turn-off policy will find that most receivables will be paid prior to the service being disconnected.

Customers filing bankruptcy and those accounts that are disconnected will be accounted for as uncollectible receivables. The utility's historical record of uncollectibles will determine the method used in recognizing the bad debt expense. Utilities with immaterial amounts of bad debt expense can use a direct write-off method. The direct write-off method does not allow the utility to match the bad debt expense to the period in which the revenue has been recorded.

The allowance method for recognizing bad debt expense is the theoretically preferred method. In this method, the utility will recognize an amount of bad debt expense based on an estimate in the period in which the revenue is recorded. Examples of the allowance method are the percentage of sales or percentage of outstanding receivables.

The utility should use an acceptable method of recognizing bad debt expense on nontrade receivables. Nontrade receivables have a higher probability for the utility to become a bad debt than the trade accounts due the inability of the utility to curtail service when the receivable has not been paid.

Customer Accounting

The utility has a choice of two methods of customer accounting — the invoice method and the open-account billing method.

If the utility bills on an invoice basis, each payment received should identify the invoice where the payment should be applied. The utility should prepare a policy for application of payments that do not have the invoice identified. Normally the oldest outstanding invoice will have the cash applied to it. Using the invoice method may require the separation of a payment among several invoices.

Utilities billing on an open-account basis will increase the amount due for each customer at each billing. The customers' payment will reduce the amount due by the amount of the payment. With an open-account billing method, the customers' account could have a credit balance if overpayments have been made to the account or payments have been credited to an incorrect account.

The invoice method of billing requires more detailed information when applying payments than the open account method.

A history of the customer's account should be maintained from the application for the service to the cut off of the tap at the main. Some utilities require payments for all services performed, from processing the application for service, installation of the tap, through disconnection of service. Each of the transactions will be recorded on the customer's account history.

Customers with no meter will be billed based on anticipated requirements the customer will place on the utility. The number of water-using devices and the area that is irrigated will be factored together in determining the amount to be billed. Some utilities bill these customers in advance, while others may bill after the service has been performed. The utility should periodically inspect each account that is billed under the flat-rate method to determine that factors for the basis of billing have not changed, for example through the addition of a swimming pool.

Metered customers require more labor in preparing the billing. Each customer's meter must be read at a recurring period. Some utilities may read the meter monthly, others bimonthly or another regular period. Larger utilities may have automated the meter reading process through inquiry through telephone lines or hand-held computers. Once consumption has been determined by comparing the previous reading to the current reading, the customer's bill can be calculated.

The bills should contain statements concerning the due date of the payment from the customer for the service provided. The utility can estimate the cash flow based on an historical record of billings during a similar period in previous years.

The depositing and recording of the cash received should be separated. The separation of these duties will aid the internal control of cash receipts.

⊠ Materials and Supplies

Water utility inventories are not the type accounted for in a manufacturing concern. The utility maintains an inventory in order to provide service to the customers. Items in the water utility's inventory may remain in the stock account for many years before the item is issued. Regardless of the historical manner in which the utility maintains its inventory, the inventory is recorded as a current asset.

The materials and supplies inventory of a water utility is comprised of many items, including fuel stocks, chemicals for the treatment of water, materials and supplies used in the operation of utility plant facilities, maintenance materials and supplies, construction materials and supplies, and materials and supplies held primarily for merchandising, jobbing, and contract work. In general, all material and supply items, regardless of their purpose, are considered as current assets. The NARUC classification of accounts (see appendix A) provides a number of current asset accounts to be used to record the cost of materials and supplies. These accounts provide for the cost of supervision, labor, and other expenses incurred in purchasing, storing, handling, and distributing material and supply items, as well as the invoice price of the items.

Particular material and supply items may be held in stock for a relatively short or relatively long period of time depending on the nature of, and frequency of need for, the item. For example, fuel stocks and chemical stocks may be maintained in amounts sufficient for operating requirements for an extended period of time. The turnover of some operating material and supply items may be quite rapid because the items are continually used in operation and maintenance activities. The turnover of other operating items may be extremely slow because such items are held to meet emergency requirements.

The costs of materials and supplies purchased by a water utility are charged to the appropriate materials and supplies account and the items placed in stores until required for use by the utility. The cost of material and supply items is charged to expense accounts or investment work orders when the items are issued from stores for a specific purpose. Typically, the cost of material and supply items is charged to expense accounts or investment work orders and credited to inventory accounts on the basis of actual cost, average cost, first-in/first-out, or such other method of inventory accounting as conforms with accepted accounting standards consistently applied.

For further discussion of stores accounting, see Matz and Usry (1977) and Neuner and Deakin (1977).

Cost Basis

Actual cost. Ideally an inventory would be valued at the historical cost for each item in the stock account. Valuation using this type of accounting would be through a specific identification methodology. When using this valuation method, the utility records the cost of each item as it was acquired and charges the issuance of the item with the acquisition cost.

The cost included in the acquisition of the materials for stock are similar to those found in chapter 11. The cost of transportation and other incidental costs required to acquire the item should be included as a cost of the stock item.

Specific identification is the theoretically preferred method of valuing the inventory, although it is probably the most impractical. If the utility maintained a small inventory of expensive items, the cost to maintain this valuation method might be justified. But when the utility maintains stock ranging from nuts and bolts to large butterfly valves, using the specific identification valuation method is impractical.

Organizations that use the specific identification valuation method invite manipulation of the issues when more than one item of a group is held in stock. The inventory manager may cause net income to fluctuate by allowing the issuance of a lower priced or higher priced item from stock. The utility may also find it difficult to identify costs of a specific item when the costs involve transportation, storage, trade or cash discounts. When it becomes difficult to identify costs of specific items, the utility will find it more practical to allocate the costs. When allocation begins, the theoretical basis diminishes as the value of the item in stock is now not specific.

Average cost. The average cost method or the more frequently used weighted average cost method of valuing stock allows the utility to maintain the valuation without the enormous record-keeping nightmares found in the specific identification method.

When using the weighted average cost method, the utility will recalculate the costs at the end of a specific period. With the advent of computerization, the recalculation can occur as frequently as every day. With high-use items, such as gasoline, the utility should consider the calculation of the average cost daily. This will allow the utility to issue the item from stock and value the item at the current value.

Theoretically, the use of a weighted average cost would not be preferred. The use of this method is founded on a practical, not a theoretical basis. Advocates of this method argue that it is impossible to measure the specific identification of an item of inventory and, logically, it follows that the average weighted cost is more practical and representative of the value of the inventory.

First in/first out. Another acceptable method of inventory valuation under generally accepted accounting principals is first in/first out or FIFO. The valuation assumption under this method is that the first products purchased are also the first products used. The remaining inventory represents the last purchases of the utility.

The inventory system required for a FIFO inventory will track all receipts into the inventory account and apply the issues against the receipts. FIFO requires a more sophisticated system than used in a weighted average cost system.

The FIFO system more accurately represents the specific identification method of valuing the inventory than the average weighted cost valuation method. FIFO also has the advantage of reducing the ability of management to cause a fluctuation of the net income with the issues from stock.

The inventory value under FIFO approximates the current replacement cost of the stock. However, FIFO does not allow current costs to be matched against current revenue as the costs of issues are the oldest stock cost.

Conformity to generally accepted accounting standards. Generally accepted accounting principals have identified other acceptable valuation methods. Other methods available to utilities include standard costs, last in/first out (LIFO), dollar value LIFO, and the base stock method.

The LIFO method assumes that the cost to acquire the inventory in the current period should be the cost that is assigned to items issued from stock. The valuation of inventory under LIFO requires that the stock on hand be valued at a base-year layer. The quantity on hand in the base year must be maintained or the utility will be required to adjust the base year to the appropriate period in which the quantity was on hand. The issues from stock are made at the most recent cost.

A variation of the LIFO is dollar value LIFO. With dollar value LIFO, the utility adjusts the base year value of the inventory based on an appropriate price index. The use of the dollar value LIFO method allows the utility to record the value of the inventory at a cost that more closely represents the current cost of acquiring the inventory.

Standard costing of inventory is used by management to identify the variances between actual costs and expected costs. This method is acceptable when the utility revalues the inventory to one of the other acceptable valuation methods at periodic intervals, not less than one year or the current operating period. Typically this method would be used by a manufacturing concern and not a utility providing services.

The base stock method is also a variant of the LIFO method of inventory valuation. It is assumed that the utility retains a fixed base of stock that in fact represent a fixed asset. This method is not allowed for income tax purposes and is rarely used.

Planning for Inventory Levels

Planning investment in materials and supplies. Investment in material and supply inventories for a water utility is substantial and requires careful planning. Such planning takes the form of a materials and supplies budget, which is a plan for the purchase of materials and supplies during the budget period. This budget is developed after considering the material and supply requirements from the operating and capital expenditures budgets, the existing inventories of material and supply items, and the desired inventory level at the end of the budget period. The greater the construction work performed by the utility itself (as opposed to work by outside contractors), the greater will be the materials and supplies budget.

The materials and supplies budget should show material and supply requirements in terms of dollars, as well as a detailed listing of material and supply items required for stock. A time schedule for the purchase of such items during the budget period should be prepared. This will permit management to plan the purchase of material and supply items so as to avoid the cost of maintaining higher-than-necessary levels of inventories (resulting from premature purchases) while at the same time ensuring that adequate levels of material and supply items are on hand to meet operating and construction requirements.

The materials and supplies budget in terms of dollars, together with the time schedule of purchases, facilitates the determination of cash disbursements resulting from the purchase of materials and supplies and provides information for the development of the cash budget (as discussed earlier in this chapter). The listing of material and supply items included in the budget, together with the proposed time schedule of purchases, permits stores personnel to plan their operations during the budget period.

The operation and maintenance budget and the capital expenditures budget are the foundation for the preparation of the materials and supplies budget. The operating and construction requirements for material and supply items are adjusted for items already on hand and for planned reductions or increases in existing levels of inventory items during the budget period. Inventories should be maintained at levels that minimize cost. In the language of operations researchers, a proper inventory level for a particular item is one that minimizes the cost of not carrying a given inventory level plus the cost of not carrying enough inventory. The cost of carrying inventory includes the risk of obsolescence, interest on investment, handling and storage cost, property taxes and the property insurance, and clerical costs. The cost of not carrying enough inventory includes the costs incident on an interruption of services supplied by the utility (loss of revenues, loss of customer goodwill, and the extra cost of making emergency purchases). In determining the amount of purchases during the budget period, utility management also should consider the benefits of quantity discounts, transportation conditions, and possibilities of changes in market prices of material and supply items.

Delivery time. Manufacturers attempt to have their additions to stock delivered just in time for the items to be issued, this allowing the company a minimal amount of inventory on hand at any one point in time. Utilities have a different requirement for inventory, as the inventory is required to be at a level that will allow the utility to meet emergency requirements.

Utilities review usage and delivery times to determine the order point for the items in stock. Most water utilities will have a policy that the inventory for certain stock items used in emergency repairs will never have a quantity of zero.

With this policy, the purchasing agent will set order points for each item in stock. When the order point is reached, the agent will request quotations from vendors able to supply the item. The vendor that can supply the item at the most favorable price and delivery terms will be selected for the purchase. The agent will review the delivery status of the item periodically to determine that the vendor will meet the promised terms. If the vendor does not deliver as promised, the purchasing agent will contact the vendor to determine the delivery date. If the delivery date is not acceptable, the agent may cancel the order and reorder with a vendor capable of meeting the required delivery schedule.

Quantity discounts. The utility should consider quantity discounts for all purchases. The amount purchased may satisfy the utilities needs for a specific time period, but a larger purchase may afford an economy of scale.

Type of material and identification. Items carried in inventory must be properly classified and identified so that they can be accounted for and located when needed. A large water utility may, for example, have 20,000 separate items in its inventory. Clearly, proper classification and identification of inventory items is a requisite to efficient operation of the store's activity. As an example, pipe must be classified by type and diameter. In addition, a unit of issue must be chosen (feet of pipe, for example) and a stock number assigned to each item.

Record keeping. The inventory requires record keeping that materials and supplies purchased for direct use do not require. Inventory requires that usage patterns, location of the material, economic order quantities, and other pieces of information be retained on the inventory stock.

Each receipt and issue of inventory stock must be recorded. The inventory will be maintained in a perpetual inventory system, which allows the access and determination of the status of each stock item as needed.

Physical storage. The inventory stock must be kept in a secure location. As issues and receipts of the stock must be maintained, the stock can only be placed into the storage location or removed from the location by authorized personnel.

Purchasing procedures. Although the size of a water utility will determine the complexity of its purchasing organization, the purchasing activity should be centralized. In some municipalities, a separate working capital fund handles purchasing, storing, and issuing. Centralized purchasing permits the realization of quantity discounts from combined purchases (as opposed to losing such discounts as a result of having each segment of the organization make its own purchases); it allows the elimination of overstocking or duplications of materials and supplies inherent in a system of decentralized purchasing; and it permits the use of personnel who are skilled or specially trained in purchasing activities.

The two major decisions required in placing a purchase order for a particular item are (1) when to place an order and (2) the size of the order. When to place an order depends on the lead time (the time interval between placing an order and receiving delivery) and the rate of usage of an item. For example, if the lead time is 20 days and the average rate of use of an item is 4 units per day, then a purchase request should be initiated when the inventory level for the item reaches 80 units (the "order point" for that item). A safety factor normally would be included to allow for fluctuations in usage of an item. This would increase the order point for the item.

The size of the order depends on such factors as the quantity of an item used per unit of time, the incremental cost of placing an order, the cost of carrying one unit of an item in stock per unit of time, the cost of being out of stock one unit, and quantity discounts. The optimum size of order or economic order quantity (EOQ) is the quantity that minimizes the cost enumerated above. A number of mathematical techniques and formulas have been developed to determine the EOQ for an item of inventory. For an extended discussion of the optimum order point and the EOQ, together with the associated mathematical formulas, see Horngren (1977), Killough and Leininger (1977), and National Association of Accountants (1964).

It is apparent that a decrease in the order point and/or a decrease in the order size will decrease the carrying cost of inventory and increase the cost of being out of stock. An increase in the order point and/or an increase in the order size will increase the carrying cost of inventory and decrease the cost of being out of stock.

Physical receiving. When materials are received in the storeroom, they should be inspected, counted, and recorded by the storekeeper. A copy of the purchase order should be on hand so that the storekeeper can verify that the goods received are in compliance with the specifications. A receiving report should then be prepared by the storekeeper for comparison with the vendor's invoice and with the purchase order, to ascertain that the prices, quantities, and terms are in agreement. Any irregularities between amounts ordered, amounts received, or amounts billed for by vendors should be resolved before payments are made to vendors. Figure 12-6 presents a diagram that summarizes the flow of information and documents related to the purchasing and

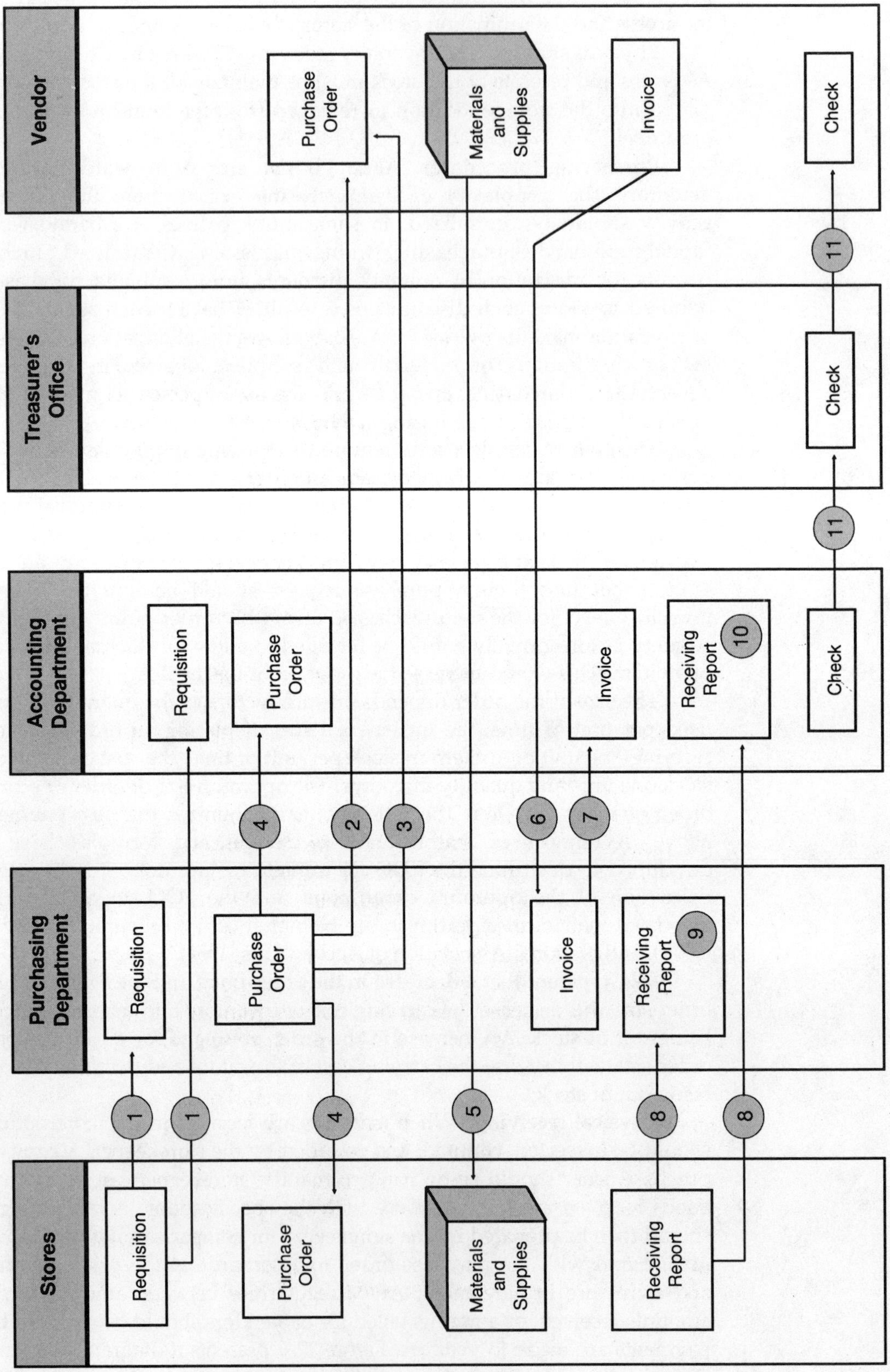

Figure 12-6 ⊠ Flow of information and documents related to the purchasing and receiving of materials and supplies

Figure 12-6 ⊠ Flow of information and documents related to the purchasing and receiving of materials and supplies (continued)

1. The purchase requisition is prepared by stores personnel indicating the item to be purchased and the quantity to be purchased (EOQ). Copies are forwarded to the purchasing department and accounting department.

2. A purchase order is prepared by the purchasing department indicating the desired items to be purchased, the quantities to be purchased, and the desired time and place of delivery. Typically, the order is placed with a supplier on the basis of competitive bidding.

3. Receipt of purchase order is acknowledged by vendor.

4. A copy of the acknowledged purchase order is forwarded to the accounting department for the purpose discussed in item 10 below. A copy of the purchase order also is sent to stores as notification of the status of the order and expected delivery date.

5. Materials and supplies shipped by vendor and received by stores.

6. Invoice (showing description and quantity of items shipped, date shipped, carrier, prices the utility is being billed, and payment terms) is forwarded from vendor to purchasing department.

7. Copy of invoice forwarded from purchasing department to accounting department.

8. On receipt of the purchased goods from suppliers, stores personnel count, weigh, or otherwise measure the quantity of goods received; the quality of the goods also is determined. A receiving report is prepared by stores personnel indicating the quantity, conditions, and description of all items received. Copies of the receiving report are forwarded to the purchasing department and to the accounting department.

9. The purchasing department compares the receiving report with the sales invoice and purchase order to determine any discrepancies that require settlement with vendors.

10. The accounting department also compares the receiving report with the purchase order and the sales invoice. If the three documents agree (if the utility is being billed for the quantities actually received and at the agreed prices), then the invoice can be approved for payment. The accounting department then records the acquisition of the materials and supplies and the related liability to the supplier.

11. A check, properly vouchered and supported by the sales invoice and other documents, is prepared by the accounting department and forwarded for signature to the treasurer's office. The signed check is then mailed to the vendor (see Fig. 12-2).

receiving of materials and supplies. This diagram also reflects the segregation of duties necessary for effective internal control.

Requisitions of materials. When the level of a particular material or supply item approaches the order point, a purchase requisition should be prepared by stores personnel and forwarded to the purchasing department. The ordering procedure depends on the amount to be ordered and the requirements of law. For contracts with outsiders for construction, municipally owned water utilities typically are required by law to obtain competitive bids for purchases in excess of a stated amount. Even if not required by law, it may be desirable for a utility to request formal bids before placing an order. Before selecting vendors, the purchasing department should obtain information regarding prices, payment terms, reliability of vendors with respect to meeting delivery dates, and quality of products.

In addition to selecting vendors, the purchasing department is also responsible for obtaining proper authorization to make purchases. The approved materials and supplies budget may serve as authorization. If the budget is a legally binding document for municipally owned water utilities, then the purchasing department must ensure that limits on committing funds are not exceeded. In cases where budgeted amounts are inadequate, additional authorization to commit funds must be obtained.

Physical Inventories

It is necessary for several reasons to supplement the maintenance of the perpetual inventory records with an actual physical count of the materials and supplies on hand. A physical count will verify the inventory records and will substantiate the figures that appear in the utility's financial reports. It is also necessary to take the physical inventory regularly in order to adjust the records because of any errors that may have occurred in the preparation or recording of the material documents. All materials and supplies in stores should be physically inventoried at least once a year. The physical inventory can be conducted by counting all stores items at the end of a fiscal or calendar period, at a time of minimum activity, or when minimum quantities of stores items are on hand. Further, the physical count can be made on a piecemeal basis by inventorying only certain items at one time, since separate records are available for each category of materials and supplies. The responsibility for the physical inventories should be vested in a different individual, or department, from the one responsible for maintaining the storerooms and inventory records. This segregation of responsibility helps to ensure that inventory shortages are discovered instead of being covered up (by falsifying inventory counts) by those persons responsible for the maintenance of stocks.

Any materially significant differences between the inventory records and the physical count should be investigated to determine whether or not they are due to shrinkage, breakage, counting errors, recording errors, or theft. After this is completed, and the proper steps taken to correct the situation, the inventory records should be adjusted to the figures disclosed by the physical count.

Status Reports of Material on Hand

To facilitate the operation of the stores control system, and to obtain benefits from the system, periodic reports showing the status of materials and supplies should be prepared weekly, monthly, or as otherwise needed. Reports on materials and supplies should show, for the period covered by the reports, information regarding the activity of each major type of material and supply item. For each type of item, activity information includes the balance at the beginning of the period, quantities of the item received and issued during the period, the balance at the end of the period, and amount of the item on order but not yet received.

In addition, it is desirable to indicate in the status report the order point and maximum inventory level for each type of material and supply. The maximum inventory level typically should be equal to the order point quantity plus the economic order quantity (as discussed earlier in this chapter). For example, if the order point is 200 units of an item and the EOQ is 800 units, then the maximum inventory level should be set at 1,000 units for that item. Normally, the maximum inventory level for a particular item will not be reached, since units comprising the order point will be issued during the time interval between placing an order and receiving delivery.

If, for a particular item, the inventory on hand is less than the order point and no action has been taken to reorder, an explanation should be sought to explain the lack of reordering. Likewise, if units of a particular item on hand plus amounts ordered but not yet received are in excess of the maximum inventory level, an explanation of the excess should be sought by management. In summary, status reports on materials and supplies permits management and personnel of the purchasing department to observe the status of inventory levels and to initiate corrective action when necessary to increase or reduce inventory levels of particular items of materials and supplies.

Reconciliation of Inventory Records to General Control Account

The inventory records maintained on a perpetual basis will represent the actual stock on hand at any particular date. Accounting for the receipts and issues through the general ledger may not correspond to the stock records. Timing differences between the methods that record the receipts and issues will cause the differences between the general ledger and the stock records.

Reconciliation of the general ledger and the stock records requires review of receipts and issues. Receipts in the stock records may be recorded when the material is placed on the stock floor while the receipts on the accounting records may be delayed until the invoice for the item has been paid. Timing differences in issues may not be as obvious as those with receipts. The issue may be posted a day later than the actual issue. Adjustments may also be required in the stock records for price variances that are not known at the time of the receipt. These variances will include freight and price changes.

⊠ Restricted Assets

Planning and Controlling Restricted Assets

As discussed earlier in this chapter, restricted assets consist of money and investments that have been segregated and that are to be used for specific purposes, such as debt service, replacement or construction of plant assets, and employees' pensions. The restriction of assets may be voluntary or in compliance with the provisions of a contract. A balance in a restricted asset account is established through the transfer of cash from the general cash account or through the direct transfer of cash to the restricted asset account at the time the cash is originally received by the utility (proceeds from the sale of bonds, for example). When the money in restricted asset accounts is to be held for extended periods of time, it is commonly invested in interest-bearing securities administered by the utility or a trustee. These securities should not be classified as temporary investments (since temporary investments are current assets, the proceeds from which, on liquidation, are available for general utility purposes).

A distinction can be made between restricted assets classified as current assets and restricted assets classified as noncurrent assets. Special deposits are made with fiscal agents or others for the purpose of meeting liabilities (interest payments and repayment of debt principal, for example, and dividend payments in the case of investor-owned water utilities) maturing within a relatively short period of time. The deposits represent a segregation of cash for a specific purpose and are appropriately considered as restricted assets. The NARUC classification of accounts considers special deposits as current assets (see appendix A). Other restricted assets, termed "special funds" by NARUC, are classified as noncurrent assets. On the other hand, in the case of municipally owned water utilities, NCGA recommends that special deposits with fiscal agents be included among the restricted asset accounts as noncurrent assets.

See National Committee on Government Accounting (1968) for further information.

Assets Restricted for Bond Debt Service

In the case of term bonds issued by water utilities, the bond indenture frequently calls for the accumulation of restricted assets (commonly called a "sinking fund") during the life of the bonds to provide for redemption of the bonds at maturity. The restricted assets may be administered by a trustee to whom the utility periodically transfers cash generated from operations for investment by the trustee, or may be administered by the utility itself. If the restricted assets are administered by a trustee, the income from investments, less trustee's fees, is retained by the trustee for reinvestment, and the amount is reported periodically to the water utility for inclusion in net income.

The amount of the periodic contribution to asset accounts restricted for the retirement of term bonds may be calculated by compound interest methods. The procedure for determining periodic contributions are similar to those discussed in chapter 9 in connection with the compound interest method and sinking fund method of determining depreciation charges. Figure 12-7 presents an example of a schedule of periodic contributions to a restricted asset account (or sinking fund) to provide for the retirement of a term bond issue, assuming that the restricted cash can be invested to earn a net return of 4 percent per year. In the schedule in Figure 12-7, at the end of the 20th year, the restricted assets represented by securities are converted into cash that is used to pay off the bondholders. Any deficiency must be made up from other sources, whereas any excess in the restricted asset account over $100,000 would be handled as prescribed by law or at the discretion of management. If the average return actually realized for several years is substantially different from original estimates on which periodic contributions are calculated, it would be advisable to recompute periodic contributions.

Sometimes the trustee or other administrator of restricted cash has the power to buy the utility's own bonds as restricted assets. In such cases, the following two alternative treatments are possible: (1) the bonds are canceled, or (2) the bonds are held "alive" as restricted assets.

Figure 12-7 ⊠ Accumulation of restricted assets (sinking fund) to provide for the retirement of 20-year term bond issue

Year	(1) Restricted Asset Account Balance Beginning of Year	(2) Income Earned on Restricted Assets Each Year	(3) Annual Contribution at End of Each Year*	(4) Restricted Asset Account Balance End of Year (1) + (2) + (3)
1	$ 0	$ 0	$ 3,358.18	$ 3,358.18
2	3,358.18	134.33	3,358.18	6,850.69
3	6,850.69	274.03	3,358.18	10,482.90
4	10,482.90	419.32	3,358.18	14,260.40
5	14,260.40	570.42	3,358.18	18,189.00
6	18,189.00	727.56	3,358.18	22,274.74
7	22,274.74	890.99	3,358.18	26,523.91
8	26,523.91	1,060.96	3,358.18	30,943.05
9	30,943.05	1,237.72	3,358.18	35,538.95
10	35,538.95	1,421.56	3,358.18	40,318.69
11	40,318.69	1,612.75	3,358.18	45,289.62
12	45,289.62	1,811.58	3,358.18	50,459.38
13	50,459.38	2,018.38	3,358.18	55,835.94
14	55,835.94	2,233.44	3,358.18	61,427.56
15	61,427.56	2,457.10	3,358.18	67,242.84
16	67,242.84	2,689.71	3,358.18	73,290.73
17	73,290.73	2,931.63	3,358.18	79,580.54
18	79,580.54	3,183.22	3,358.18	86,121.94
19	86,121.94	3,444.88	3,358.18	92,925.00
20	92,925.00	3,717.00	3,358.00†	100,000.00
Totals		$32,836.22	$67,163.78	

*Amount of an annuity of 1 at 4 percent for 20 years equals 29.778 (arrived at using annuity tables which employ the formula $\frac{(1 + i)^n - 1}{i}$ where n represents the number of years and i the rate of interest). $100,000 (amount of bonds to be retired) ÷ 29.778 (amount of an annuity of 1) equal $3,358.18, which is the amount that must be contributed annually to the restricted asset account (sinking fund) for a period of 20 years in order to accumulate an amount equal to $100,000.

†An adjustment of $0.18, due to rounding errors, required to bring restricted assets to $100,000.

If the bonds are canceled, then the carrying value of the bonds is eliminated from the books. However, due to the dependence on interest income accumulation to make up part of the cash necessary to redeem bonds at maturity, the use of restricted cash to purchase and cancel a portion of the bond issue before maturity may impair the ability of the restricted cash to redeem the remaining bonds at maturity. Therefore, contributions to the restricted asset account may be increased to cover the loss of interest income accruing to the restricted asset account. There is no net loss to the utility because of the offsetting saving of interest expense on the canceled bonds.

If the bonds are held "alive" among restricted assets, then they are accounted for in the same manner as any other investment and the utility pays the regular interest to the trustee or other administrator. However, this investment does create a balance-sheet and income statement problem since the repurchased bonds are shown both as assets and liabilities, and interest expense and interest income earned by restricted assets are overstated. This situation should be disclosed in a note to the financial statements.

In the case of serial bonds (or in the case of term bonds that are callable and that are to be regulatory redeemed), restricted asset accounts also may be employed. Indenture agreements associated with serial bonds (or callable term bonds that are to be regularly redeemed) issued by investor-owned water utilities may provide for periodic contributions to restricted asset accounts sufficient to meet the periodic payments for serial bonds as they mature or to meet the periodic payments for term bonds to be called. In the case of callable bonds, the indenture agreement typically provides that the utility may deliver either cash or redeemed bonds to the trustee. If cash is delivered, then the cash must be used by the trustee to redeem the bonds that are callable. It is apparent that the balance in a restricted asset account associated with serial bonds or term bonds that are to be regularly retired will be relatively small at any given time.

In the case of revenue bonds issued by municipally owned water utilities, the bond indenture typically provides for several restricted asset accounts to be created to protect bondholders against late or inadequate payment of interest and repayment of debt principal as the serial bonds mature. Three typical restricted asset accounts associated with a revenue bond issue are "assets restricted for bond debt service," "assets restricted for reserve use," and "assets restricted for contingencies." These three accounts, together with amounts transferred from the three accounts to fiscal agents for the purpose of making periodic interest and principal payments, are known as the "asset group of accounts restricted for bond debt service."

With regard to the "assets restricted for bond debt service" account (usually called an "interest and sinking fund"), a typical provision is that there be contributed to this account a monthly amount equal to one-sixth of the next maturing semiannual interest payment plus one-twelfth of the next annual repayment of debt principal. Amounts are then transferred from this account to fiscal agents as required to make debt service payments.

The purpose of the "assets restricted for reserve use" account is to provide for the payment of matured bonds and interest in the event of a deficiency in the "assets restricted for debt service" account. The balance in this account is usually accumulated over the first 60 months following the issuance of a series of revenue bonds. The amount to be accumulated is specified (an amount equal to the average or maximum annual debt service, for example) by the bond indenture. Under normal circumstances, the cash accumulated in this account is invested in interest-bearing securities and will not be used until the final retirement of the bond issue.

The purpose of the "assets restricted for contingencies" account is to provide cash for meeting unforeseen operating expenditures of an emergency nature or replacement of plant assets. The balance to be accumulated in this account over a prescribed number of months following a bond issue is specified in the bond indenture. Figure 12-8 presents an example of a

Figure 12-8 ⊠ Statement of changes in the group of assets restricted for revenue bond debt service

The Municipal Water Utility
Statement of Changes in the Group of Assets Restricted For Revenue Bond Debt Service
For the Year Ended Dec. 31, 19CY

	Cash With Fiscal Agents	Assets Restricted for Debt Service	Assets Restricted for Reserve Use	Assets Restricted for Contingencies	Total Restricted Assets
Total Balance, Cash and Investments, Jan. 1, 19CY	$240,000	$ 6,000	$168,000	$22,500	$436,500
Cash Balance, Jan. 1, 19CY	$240,000	6,000	8,000	2,500	256,500
Cash Receipts					
Transfers from general cash (see Figure 19.2)		230,000	50,000	6,000	286,000
Income from restricted investments			5,600	700	6,300
Intergroup transfer of cash restricted for revenue bond debt service	226,500				
Total Cash Available	$466,500	$236,000	$ 63,600	$ 9,200	$775,300
Cash Disbursements					
Principal payments	$108,000				$108,000
Interest payments	216,000				216,000
Fiscal agents' fees	500				500
Purchase of investments			$ 59,000	$ 9,000	68,000
Intergroup transfer of cash restricted for revenue bond debt service		$226,500			226,500
Total Disbursements	$324,500	$226,500	$ 59,000	$ 9,000	$619,000
Cash Balance, Dec. 31, 19CY	$142,000	$ 9,500	$ 4,600	$ 200	$156,300
Investment Balance, Jan. 31, 19CY					
Additions			$160,000	$20,000	$180,000
Deductions			59,000	9,000	68,000
Investment Balance, Dec. 31, 19CY			$219,000	$29,000	$248,000
Total Balance, Cash and Investments, Dec. 31, 19CY	$142,000	$ 9,500	$223,600	$29,200	$404,300

statement that summarizes the annual changes that take place in an asset group of accounts restricted for revenue bond debt service.

As in the case of temporary investments, municipally owned water utilities generally are limited by statute or charter as to the types of securities in which cash restricted for debt service can be invested. Such investments include certificates of deposit, and federal, state, and municipal securities. Investor-owned water utilities are subject to no such legal restrictions regarding the investment of restricted cash. However, the trustee administering the restricted assets must exercise reasonable care in investing restricted cash. In some instances, the board of directors may specify the types of securities which can be purchased. Within the limits set by law, or directives of policy-making groups, an attempt should be made to invest restricted cash in securities that will bring the greatest return consistent with the maintenance of a reasonably low degree of risk of loss of principal. In general, securities should be selected so that they will mature as required to meet disbursements that must be made from restricted assets. In this way, realization of loss of principal due to the sale of securities before maturity is eliminated.

Particularly in the case of municipally owned water utilities, there may be several restricted asset accounts or groups. For the purposes of investment, it may be desirable for the utility to pool cash belonging to the various accounts. In this case, earnings on investments must be prorated among each of the accounts on the basis of the amount of cash contributed by each.

Capital Expenditures

In the case of municipally owned water utilities, the proceeds of both general obligation bonds and revenue bonds issued for or by the water utility usually are segregated in a restricted asset account. This segregation is made to ensure that the cash proceeds are spent only on authorized capital expenditure projects and are not commingled with general utility cash. Cash is disbursed from the restricted asset account as required to meet liabilities incurred with regard to authorized capital expenditure projects. Eventually, the balance in the restricted asset account is depleted to zero or to an amount near zero, as all authorized expenditures from the bond proceeds are completed. If the proceeds exceed the total of all authorized expenditures, then the balance is returned to general utility cash or is disposed of in accordance with the terms of the bond indenture or other applicable statutory provisions. The restricted cash should be invested in interest-bearing securities until needed to meet authorized expenditures. Generally, investments should be made in highly marketable securities that can be liquidated as needed without loss of principal.

Investor-owned water utilities may also desire to segregate proceeds from security issues in restricted asset accounts. In addition, water utilities may desire to restrict a portion of cash generated from operations in order to provide for future replacement of plant assets. Typically, the cash so restricted is invested in securities until needed for replacement of plant assets.

Other Purposes

In the case of municipally owned water utilities, proceeds from customers' deposits typically are placed in a restricted asset account. The restricted proceeds may be invested in authorized securities with the income from such investments being used to pay required interest to customers on their deposits or to increase general utility cash. Disbursements are made from the restricted asset account as required to reimburse customers for their deposits. Investor-owned water utilities ordinarily do not place proceeds from customers' deposits in a restricted asset account; rather, the proceeds are placed in general utility cash, and repayment of deposits is made from general cash.

Assets (cash and investments) may be restricted for many other purposes. Included among other types of restricted assets are (1) those established for the redemption of preferred stock (in the case of investor-owned water utilities) as a result of contractual agreement or management policy, (2) those established for self-insurance, and (3) those established for employees' pensions. Although assets restricted for employees' pensions (that is, pension funds) may be established, many utilities enter into contracts with insurance companies to provide for employee's pensions. This procedure eliminates any beneficial interest in amounts of cash paid to the insurance companies and no restricted asset account is called for. Similarly, amounts deposited with a trustee under the terms of an irrevocable trust agreement for pensions are not included in a restricted asset account. In the event that the pension plan is revocable by the utility, regardless of whether or not the fund is internally managed or trusteed, amounts contributed under such a plan should be included in a restricted asset account. Disbursements for pensions likewise are made from restricted assets.

Some municipally owned water utilities maintain their own retirement systems and establish a separate fund (as used in the governmental accounting sense) to account for the transactions associated with the retirement systems. Payments made by the utility to the retirement fund are classified as pensions expense to the utility and no related restricted asset accounts are required to be maintained within the water utility fund.

Relationship to Various Liability Accounts

The restricted asset accounts discussed in this section are often associated with appropriations of retained earnings or with liabilities to be paid from restricted assets. See chapter 13 for additional discussion.

⊠ Deferred Charges

Deferred charges are debit entries that cannot be classified as a current asset, long-term investment, property plant and equipment, or an intangible asset. Typically these assets are restricted to assets that cannot be classified otherwise.

Deferred charges are prepaid expenses that will not be amortized during the current period. Examples include receivables that cannot be classified as current due to the payment terms associated with the receivable, or premiums on bonds issued that will be amortized over the life of the bonds to increase the effective interest rate. Some accountants classify intangible assets as a deferred charge. Utilities that have their rates prescribed by a rate-making bond may be allowed to capitalize items, as a deferred charge, which will be recovered in rates over subsequent periods.

Typically, deferred charges will arise due to the utility's prepayment of the deferred charge. The utility may be required to make the prepayment to allow some other occurrence to happen. The classic example is bond premiums that are a reduction in the cash received for the issuance of bonds. The bonds are issued at a face amount with a stated interest rate. To accomplish this requirement, the purchaser will pay a lower amount than the face amount and receive the full amount at the maturity. In effect, the purchaser receives a higher rate of interest than the amount stated on the bond. The seller of the bond will pay a higher rate of interest due to the lower cash received at the sale. Other deferred charges come about in like manners.

Disposition

The utility will dispose of the deferred charge over a period of time that reflects the cause of the charge. If the charge is a long-term receivable, the receivable would be transferred into current assets in the period in which the payment is expected. Most other deferred charges are amortized into the utility's expense during the periods that the utility has received some benefit from the charge.

Rate-making Treatment

Not all deferred charges of a utility arise from transactions that are a result of normal activities. Utilities whose rates are set by a rate-making body are allowed to defer charges into periods in which they will have revenue resulting from the charge.

Financial Accounting Standards Board Statement Number 71 (SFAS 71) allows regulated enterprises to defer and amortize costs that are likely to be recovered in rates in a future period. For a utility to apply SFAS 71, the utility must meet the following criteria:

- the utilities rates must be regulated by an independent third party or a governing board authorized by law

- the approved rates are designed to cover explicit costs of the utility

- the rates are likely to be collected by the utility

To defer the explicit cost, the utility must demonstrate that the intent of the regulatory body is to provide recovery of the cost through rates that will produce sufficient revenue to cover the cost deferred. The utility will then amortize the deferral in the years the regulatory body has provided rates to cover the deferred cost.

⊠ References

Bierman, H. Jr. 1963. *Topics in Cost Accounting and Decisions.* New York: McGraw-Hill Book Company, Inc.

Horngren, C.T. 1977. *Cost Accounting—A Managerial Emphasis.* Englewood Clifts, N.J.: Prentice-Hall, Inc.

Killough, L.N. and W.E. Leininger. 1977. *Cost Accounting for Managerial Decision Making.* Encino, Calif.: Dickenson Publishing Company.

Matz, A. and M.F. Usry. 1977. *Cost Accounting: Planning and Control.* Cincinnati, Ohio: South-Western Publishing Company.

Mason, P. 1961. *Cash Flow Analysis and the Funds Statement.* Accounting Research Study No. 2. New York: American Institute of Certified Public Accountants.

National Association of Accountants. 1961. *Cash Flow Analysis for Managerial Control.* Research Report No. 38. New York: National Association of Accountants.

———. 1964. *Techniques in Inventory Management*. Research Report No. 40. New York: National Association of Accountants.

National Committee on Government Accounting. 1968. *Governmental Accounting, Auditing, and Financial Reporting*. Chicago, Ill.: Municipal Finance Officers Association.

Neuner, J.J.W. and E.B. Deakin III. 1977. *Cost Accounting: Principals and Practices*. Homewood, Fla.: Richard D. Irwin Inc.

CHAPTER THIRTEEN

Liabilities and Other Credits

The "liabilities and other credits" side of the balance sheet presents the sources from which the assets of the water utility are financed. These sources reflect both external financing (liabilities, contributions, and, in the case of investor-owned utilities, common and preferred stock) and internal financing (through the retention of earnings). This chapter is devoted to a discussion of the following major categories of liabilities and other credits:

- current and accrued liabilities
- long-term liabilities
- capital paid in by stockholders (applicable in investor-owned water utilities)
- retained earnings
- customer advances for construction and contributions

⊠ Differences Between Publicly Owned and Government-Owned Utilities

Utilities may have recorded three types of credits that do not relate to owner's equity. These credits are current liabilities, long-term liabilities, and deferred credits.

Generally, both government-owned and publicly owned utilities have similar current liabilities. Both types of organizations will have accounts payable, payroll payable, notes payable, and similar type obligations to others. Dividends payable will only be seen on the balance sheet of the publicly owned utility.

Long-term liabilities will also appear the same on the balance sheet of the government-owned and publicly owned utility. Long-term notes payable and bonds payable will be the liabilities typically seen in the long-term liabilities.

Accounts identified as deferred credits are those accounts that represent a balance carried into a future period to amortize against income in that period. Examples of deferred credits are deferred income, deferred income taxes, and unamortized premiums on bonds. Deferred income taxes will only be found in a publicly owned utility, a government-owned utility will be exempt from income taxes.

⊠ Current and Long-Term Differences

As in the case of assets, the historical cost standard should be employed to record liabilities. In general, current liabilities represent liabilities that are definite in amount and that are due either as of the date of the balance sheet, within a year from the date of the balance sheet, or on demand by creditors. Accrued current liabilities are those not yet payable but that will mature within one year and that are being provided for or accumulated over the period to date of maturity. The National Association of Regulatory Utility Commissioners (NARUC), however, makes some exceptions to these definitions, as indicated by the following description of current and accrued liabilities:

> current and accrued liabilities are those obligations which have either matured or which become due within one year from the date thereof; except, however, bonds, receivers' certificates and similar obligations which shall be classified as long-term debt until date of maturity; accrued taxes, such as income taxes, which shall be classified as accrued liabilities even though payable more than one year from date; compensation awards, which shall be classified as accrued liabilities regardless of date due; and minor amounts payable in installments which may be classified as current liabilities. If a liability is due more than one year from date of issuance or assumption by the utility, it shall be credited to a long-term debt account appropriate to the transaction, except, however, the current liabilities previously mentioned.

In this definition, NARUC recommends that bonds payable be classified as current liabilities only if the bonds have matured and have not yet been retired. On the other hand, the National Council on Governmental Accounting (NCGA) recommends that debt obligations be classified as current liabilities if matured or if due within a year from the date of the balance sheet. The latter view is consistent with generally accepted accounting principles.

⊠ Definitions of Key Liabilities

Liabilities come in many varieties. They can be classified as current or long term. Following are liabilities and their definitions, which may be reported on the utility's balance sheet.

Accounts Payable

Accounts payable are those liabilities that are recurring trade obligations of the utility. The liability is incurred at the point of time that the title to the goods passes. Specific attention should be paid to goods that are in transit at the end of a period. In most instances, the liability will be recorded when the goods or services have been received.

Notes Payable

Notes payable are liabilities that identify obligations of the utility that contain a definite payment schedule. Obligations identified by notes payable are usually trade notes, short-term loan notes, or current-year maturities of long-term debt. The note payable may contain obligations that are current liabilities and long-term liabilities. Occasionally, notes payable may be secured with specific assets. When assets are secured, the note should be reported consistent with the collateral that is pledged to the note. The reporting can be accomplished in a footnote or as a pledged asset.

Short-term Obligations

Short-term obligations expected to be refinanced may be classified as a long-term obligation. To be classified as such, the utility must show that it intends to refinance the obligation and demonstrate that it has the ability to consummate the refinancing.

Declared Dividends Payable

Declared dividends payable are liabilities. If the intent is to pay the liability within the current period, the dividend payable is classified as a current liability. Dividends that have not been declared or preferred stock dividends in arrears are not to be recorded as a liability. Dividends payable will only be found on the balance sheet of an investor-owned utility.

Advances and Returnable Deposits

Advances and returnable deposits representing the obligation of the utility to provide service in the future are a liability to the utility. The utility may require that a customer make a deposit for future services when the customer's credit history is unknown. The deposit agreement must be reviewed to determine if the deposit is to be classified as current or long-term liability. The time period between the date of the deposit and the end of the relationship requiring the deposit determines the classification.

Water Service Billed

Water service billed in advance will be a liability of the utility. Revenue will be recorded and the liability reduced as the period of time of the advance billing expires. Typically, water service billed in advance is used when customers do not have meters.

Taxes Payable

The utility collects taxes from employees and customers for third party governments. Sales taxes are collected on the sale or transfer of personal property by the utility to the customer. Various governmental bodies will collect a percentage of the value of the item transferred. Governmental bodies require the collection of taxes from employees' wages.

Accrued Liabilities

Utilities will have liabilities that have not been recorded at the end of an accounting period. These liabilities will be recorded as accrued liabilities. Accrued liabilities may be found in all the liabilities discussed in this chapter.

Salary and Wages Payable

Payroll-related liabilities consist of all amounts owed to the utility's employees. The liabilities will include the wages and salaries owed at the end of an accounting period. Liabilities will also be recognized for rights that an employee may have earned but are not currently payable to the employee. To be recognized as a liability these rights must meet four conditions

- the employee's obligation relating to the employee's rights to receive compensation for future absences is attributable to the services the employee has already rendered
- the obligation relates to a right that vests or accumulates
- the payment of the compensation is probable
- the amount can reasonably be estimated

Income Taxes Payable

Income taxes payable will be recognized by utilities that are not municipally owned. Utilities that recognize a liability for income taxes will record a liability proportional to the net income of the utility. The income to which tax rates are applied may differ from the income reported on the income statement. The tax laws may allow the recognition of expenses in a different manner than is allowed under generally accepted accounting principles.

Bonds Payable

Bonds payable represent the promise to pay that the utility has made under a contract known as an indenture. The bond describes the utility's promise to pay a sum of money on the maturity date and the promise to pay interest at a specified rate on face value of the bond. Various types of bonds may be found in practice, including secured, unsecured, term, serial, convertible, commodity backed, zero interest, registered, and bearer bonds. Bonds have numerous types of features that can be included in the issue. The issuance of bonds allows the utility to borrow money for a long term in an amount that a single lender may not be able to provide.

Leases Payable

Leases payable are the obligations a utility has incurred while obtaining the right to use a property owned by another. The lease document will specify the term of the lease and the periodic payments that are due. Leases come in two varieties, operating or capital. To be classified as a capital lease, the lease at inception must meet one of the following four criteria:

- the lease transfers ownership of the property to the lessee by the end of the lease term
- the lease contains a bargain purchase option
- the term of the lease at inception is at least 75 percent of the estimated economic life of the property being leased
- the present value of the minimum lease payments at the beginning of the lease term equals or exceeds 90 percent of the fair value of the leased property at the inception of the lease

If the lease does not meet any of these criteria, then the lease is an operating lease. Property acquired under a capital lease is identified separately, as is the obligation on the balance sheet.

⊠ Definitions of Other Credits

Deferred Credits

Deferred credits are credit balances normally carried forward into future periods to be matched against the income in that period. Other credits may represent other obligations into which the utility has entered. These obligations represent items the utility currently has an obligation for, but may not in the future when an action has occurred. Examples of these credits are customer advances for construction and obligation for deferred compensation.

Customer Advances for Construction

Deposits that customers have made to facilitate the construction of assets that will serve the customer in the future are deferred credits. The credit (if not refundable) will be converted into contributions when the construction of the asset has been completed. The utility may have an obligation to refund the advance if the construction is not completed.

Obligation for Deferred Compensation

Municipal utilities may choose to allow their employees to participate in a deferred compensation plan under section 457 of the Internal Revenue Code. Section 457 allows the utility's employees to defer a portion of their wages. Section 457 requires the deferral to remain property of the municipality and not the employee. The employee retains all rights to determine the investment of the deferral and rights to receive the money under specified conditions. As the Internal Revenue Code requires the property ownership to remain within the municipality, the utility continues to have an obligation to the employee. Employees making deferrals have rights to the funds deferred and earnings equal to that of a general creditor of the utility. In addition to being shown as a liability, the deferred compensation plan under section 457 should be footnoted in the financial statements.

Bond Premiums

When bonds are sold at a premium, the utility receives more cash than the face value of the bonds. The additional amount is the premium on the bond or a prepaid interest. The premium will be amortized over the life of the bond as a reduction of interest expense. The amortization can be done in either of two methods, straight-line or present value. Theoretically, the use of the present value method is preferred.

⊠ Chart of Accounts

NARUC's 1984 edition of the *Uniform System of Accounts for Class A Water Utilities* defines that accounts 221 through 224 (see appendix A) be used for long-term debt. Accounts 231 through 241 are to be used for current and accrued liabilities. Deferred credits are found in accounts 251 through 265. Accounts 271 and 272 identify contributions in aid of construction. Accumulated deferred income taxes, for nongovernmental utilities, will use accounts 281 through 283.

Specifications of suggested long-term debt accounts are as follows:

- Bonds (221). With a separate subaccount for each class and series of bonds, the face value of the bonds issued and not matured will be recorded.

- Reacquired Bonds (222). Bonds issued and reacquired by the utility.

- Advances from Associated Companies (223). The face value of notes payable to associated companies.

- Other Long-Term Debt (224). All long-term debt not classified as bonds or advances from associated companies.

Specifications of suggested current and accrued liability accounts are as follows:

- Accounts Payable (231). All utility amounts payable within one year.

- Notes Payable (232). The face value of all indebtedness payable within a year of the financial statement date.

- Accounts Payable to Associated Companies (233). The face value of amounts payable to associated companies within one year of the financial statement date.

- Notes Payable to Associated Companies (234). The face value of notes payable to associated companies due within one year of the financial statement date.

- Customer Deposits (235). The amounts deposited by the customers as security for the payment of bills.

- Accrued Taxes (236). The estimated taxes due based on amounts due reduced by any credits available.

- Accrued Interest (237). The interest accrued on all debt but not paid will be recorded in this account. Each issue of debt should have a subaccount.

- Accrued Dividends (238). Dividends declared before payment will be recorded as a liability in this account. Each type of capital and preferred stock will have a subaccount.

- Matured Long-Term Debt (239). Matured long-term debt that has not been paid will be recorded in this account. Each debt issue will be recorded in a subaccount.

- Matured Interest (240). The amount of matured interest on obligations at the date of the financial statements. If the matured interest is added to the principal of the obligation, then the interest will not be recorded in this account.

- Miscellaneous Current and Accrued Liabilities (241). Any current liability that cannot be recorded in a previously identified account will be recorded in this account.

Specifications of suggested deferred credit accounts are as follows:

- Unamortized Premium on Debt (251). With a subaccount for each debt issue, the premium received on the debt issue. This amount will be amortized over the life of the bond issue.

- Advances for Construction (252). Advances made by customers for construction of assets to serve the customers. Depending on utility or commission policy, the advance may be refunded in part or in its entirety. Remaining balances will be transferred to the contributions in aid of construction.

- Other Deferred Credits (252). This account will contain all deferrals not provided elsewhere. Once the credit is identified it can be cleared or disposed.

- Accumulated Deferred Investment Tax Credits (255). Investment tax credits that have not been realized will be recorded in this account and amortized as the credit is realized.

⊠ Controlling and Monitoring Current and Accrued Liabilities

Satisfactory management control of current and accrued liabilities requires that all proposed commitments associated with incurring a liability be reviewed before they are approved and become actual liabilities. Proposed commitments should not exceed the limits established by the operating budget, capital expenditure budget, or the materials and supplies budget, unless additional authorization to commit funds is obtained through the approval of top management or policy-making groups. Procedures associated with the purchase of materials and supplies are discussed in chapter 12. In the case of the purchase of personnel services, procedures also must be adopted to ensure proper control over commitments associated with the payment of wages and salaries. Typically, control over the hiring and firing of employees is centralized in a personnel department, which is responsible for ensuring that personnel requirements, as reflected by the operating budget and capital expenditure budget, are met. The selection of new employees, the discharge of employees, the transfer of employees between positions in the utility organization, and the setting of wage rates and salary levels should be subject to review and approval by top management. This review and approval helps ensure that proposed commitments associated with wages and salaries are properly considered before they become actual liabilities and that personnel requirements are being met adequately and efficiently.

Satisfactory management control of current and accrued liabilities requires that all obligations be properly recorded, that procedures for cash disbursement be followed, and that all due dates for the payment of obligations be met. A sound routine for the recording of liabilities is basic to a sound disbursements procedure. Procedures related to the recording and discharge of obligations arising from the purchase of materials and supplies have been described previously. Similar procedures are also required with regard to the purchase of labor services.

Detailed records pertaining to other current obligations, such as those related to bank borrowings, taxes, customer meter deposits, interest, construction contracts, dividends, and matured or maturing long-term debt also must be maintained. The detailed or supporting records permit the identification of a water utility's current obligations with specific individuals or other entities. Identification of liabilities is necessary to properly discharge obligations through payments to the proper individuals or other entities in the correct amounts. All disbursements associated with current obligations should be vouchered and properly authorized for payment.

To ensure that payment of obligations are made on the due dates, schedules of due dates that identify payment of taxes, interest, and other contractual obligations should be maintained. This will permit the scheduling of disbursements and will help ensure that legal penalties and other costs associated with late payment are avoided. In the case of accounts payable, files of vendors' invoices should be maintained by purchase discount dates to facilitate payment within the discount period.

Accountants and financial analysts not concerned with governmental entities often use the term "funds" to mean working capital. Accordingly, a "statement of sources and uses of working capital" may be called a "statement of sources and uses of funds." The term "working capital" is preferred to distinguish this definition of funds from other definitions, such as cash.

⊠ Statement of Changes in Financial Position

The definition of current assets is closely related to that of current liabilities. The difference between these two balance-sheet subtotals is often called "working capital" and, sometimes, "net working capital." In comparison with most industrial firms, the working capital requirements of a utility are generally much lower and somewhat less important. This is reflected in the balance sheet of a utility where the investment in the utility plant and the capitalization of the utility are generally listed before current assets and current liabilities.

⊠ Types of Financial Reports

Corporations will report the changes in the capital stock accounts with each balance sheet. The report will identify the beginning balance of the capital stock account and all additions, reacquisitions, and restructuring of the account.

Corporations, proprietorships, partnerships, and governmental utilities will report the changes in the appropriated and unappropriated retained earnings each year. The report of changes will include the beginning balances, additions from net income, transfers to and from appropriated retained earnings, depreciation of utility plant acquired through contributions in aid of construction, and prior period changes that relate to accounting policies.

The footnotes of the utility's balance sheet will contain a paragraph detailing any capital leases. All capital leases, of a material nature, will be detailed in the footnote. The lease payments for the next five years and the remainder of the lease will be itemized.

Long-term debt will also be detailed in the footnotes. The type of long-term debt will be noted with the range of interest rates and the average interest rate. The maturities in the current year and the next four years will be stated. Maturities greater than five years will be summarized into five-year blocks.

See appendixes B and C for example presentations of current and noncurrent liabilities in financial reports.

CHAPTER FOURTEEN

Equity, Capital, and Financial Ratios

This chapter discusses the following major categories of equity in the utility: (1) capital paid in by stockholders (applicable to investor-owned water utilities), (2) retained earnings, and (3) customer advances for construction and contributions.

⊠ Publicly Owned Utilities

The publicly owned utility is one in which the owners are the citizens, those who elect the body that controls the utility. As the organization is owned by the citizens (a governmental body), the equity representation differs from that of a corporation.

The utility may be a subdivision of another governmental body. As a subdivision, the utility will be a fund account of the principal governmental body's component financial statements. The equity consists of the retained earnings reinvested in the utility.

Governmental utilities may require contributions from those seeking to acquire service from the utility. The contributions may be in the form of cash, which enables the utility to acquire the assets required to service the customer, or specific assets. The contributions are recorded as equity in the organization, but do not indicate an ownership interest of those making the contribution.

⊠ Investor-Owned Utilities

An investor-owned utility may be organized as a corporation, partnership, or sole proprietorship. The utility organized as a partnership or sole proprietorship is unusual and will not be discussed.

The corporate equity will be recognized by the owner's equity, legal or stated capital, and retained earnings. The legal or stated capital represents the issued capital stock at the par value of the stock. Owner's equity describes the amount the owners of the corporation have contributed reduced by the legal capital. Retained earnings recount the net income of the corporation reduced by the dividends paid to the owners of the corporation.

Public utility commissions may require contributions be made to the utility from those seeking to acquire service from the utility. The contributions may be in the form of cash, which enables the utility to acquire the assets required to service the customer, or specific assets. The contributions are recorded as capital invested in the organization, but do not indicate an ownership position to those who have made the contributions.

⊠ Retained Earnings

The retained earnings of a water utility can be characterized as the portion of the ownership interest in the utility's assets that is not represented by paid-in or contributed capital. Retained earnings represent the ownership interest by the net incremental assets resulting from water utility operations. Common items that affect the retained earnings balance are

- income or loss from the normal and incidental operating activities of the water utility
- extraordinary gains and losses of the utility
- prior-period adjustments, such as corrections of errors of prior periods concerning the first two items
- recapitalizations (in the case of investor-owned water utilities)
- distributions of retained earnings through asset transfers to other municipal funds (in the case of municipally owned water utilities) or through the payment of dividends to stockholders (in the case of investor-owned water utilities)

If retained earnings exist, then in order to distribute them by the transfer of assets to other municipal funds or through the payment of dividends to shareholders, it is necessary that a utility have cash or assets in a form readily convertible into cash, which can be distributed. However, the utility may still be unable to distribute retained earnings because such earnings have been appropriated or restricted and are unavailable for distribution to the municipality or to shareholders.

Appropriated Retained Earnings

When operating reserve accounts arise from charges to operating expense (decreasing retained earnings), appropriations of retained earnings are created by direct charges to unappropriated retained earnings. The general theory underlying the restriction or appropriation of retained earnings is as follows: If transfers to the general fund or other municipal funds (in the case of municipally-owned water utilities) or dividend payments (in the case of investor-owned water utilities) are restricted by an appropriation of retained earnings, then assets that might otherwise be paid out for other purposes will be retained to discharge such appropriated obligations.

The appropriation of retained earnings may be required by law or contract, or may be an expression of utility policy. In some states, for example, the law requires that retained earnings of an investor-owned water utility may be restricted in an amount equal to the legal capital (par or stated value, or amounts paid in on no par stock) associated with reacquired capital stock (treasury stock). This requirement, in effect, substitutes retained earnings for legal capital of the reacquired stock. Bond indentures may require that an annual appropriation of retained earnings be made so that the sum of the appropriations will, over the life of the bonds, equal the bond indebtedness at the time the bonds mature. Creditors supplying relatively short-term funds may require that no distribution of retained earnings be made during the time the short-term debt is outstanding. This implies a restriction of the entire retained earnings balance. Restrictions of retained earnings may also be an expression of a utility policy that requires appropriations to provide working capital.

The appropriation of retained earnings for specific purposes does not ensure that assets of the utility will be available in a form that can be used by the utility for specific purposes giving rise to the appropriations. To ensure the availability of assets for a specific purpose, assets (cash and investments) must be either segregated or restricted for the specific purpose.

As noted earlier in this chapter for municipally owned water utilities, retained earnings typically are restricted in amounts that, together with the amount of current and accrued liabilities earmarked to be paid from restricted assets, are sufficient to balance or offset the restricted assets. In some cases, no appropriated retained earnings are necessary to offset a particular restricted asset account because current and accrued liabilities to be paid from restricted assets are equal to the balance in the restricted asset account. Such is the case for assets restricted for repayment of customer meter deposits. In other cases, such as for restricted asset accounts associated with a bond issue, current and accrued liabilities to be paid from restricted liabilities may be less than the balance in the restricted asset account; therefore, an appropriation of retained earnings is required to offset the restricted asset account.

Statement of Changes in Retained Earnings

A statement of changes in retained earnings customarily is prepared at the end of each accounting period. This statement presents an analysis of the changes that have taken place during the accounting period in both appropriated and unappropriated retained earnings balance.

⊗ Contributed Assets

As previously mentioned, the Governmental Accounting Standards Board's (GASB's) 1993 discussion memorandum "Reporting Contributions, Subsidies, Tap Fees, and Similar Inflows to Enterprise and Internal Service Funds and to Entities Using Proprietary Fund Accounting" may affect the following discussion. The user of this book may want to determine the final disposition of this issue.

Sources

Customer advances for construction and contributions arise from several sources. Municipally owned water authorities may be established by capital contributions from the governmental unit of which the utility is a part and/or from persons and organizations outside the governmental unit. The amount of cash or value of services and property so contributed should be credited to an appropriately labeled contributions equity account (see accounts 272–275 in appendix A). To the extent that the establishment of municipally owned water utilities is financed by the issuance of bonds or by advances from the municipality, the amounts so obtained should be included in the appropriate liability accounts. The establishment of investor-owned water utilities usually is financed by bond and stock issues.

Once a water utility is established, a portion of the financing of plant expansion frequently is provided by advances and/or contributions from customers, subdividers or developers, and governmental agencies. Contributions from governmental units may also be provided for plant replacement, particularly in cases where utility plant assets must be relocated due to highway construction or urban renewal projects.

The NARUC classification of accounts provides deferred credit account 252, "customer advances for construction," to which is credited amounts advanced by or on behalf of customers for construction and that is to be refunded either entirely or in part. On completion of the project, if a person is refunded the entire amount to which he or she is entitled according to the agreement or rule under which the advance was made, then any amounts originally advanced but no longer refundable because of the expiration of the agreement normally are transferred to an appropriately labeled contribution account. As shown in appendix A, the NARUC classification of accounts provides account 271, "contributions in aid of construction," for investor-owned or municipally owned water utilities to use for this purpose. With regard to account 271, NARUC states that the balance in this account includes credits for donations or contributions in cash, services, or property from states, municipalities, or other governmental agencies, individuals, and others for construction purposes. NARUC classifies contributions in aid of construction as a major and distinct category in the balance sheet. Typically, for rate-determination purposes, the balance in the account is deducted from the cost of the utility plant or the related asset is otherwise treated as a zero cost rate base element.

NCGA also provides specific recommendations concerning accounting and reporting for governmental grant, entitlement, and shared revenue resources, as defined by the National Council. Such resources received for operations and/or for either operations or capital acquisitions or construction are to be reported as nonoperating revenues. Governmental grant, entitlement, or shared revenue resources specifically restricted for the acquisition or construction of capital assets are to be reported as contributed capital within the equity capital (fund equity) section of the balance sheet of the municipally owned water utility. It also should be noted that NCGA permits (but does not require) the depreciation expense associated with fixed assets acquired or constructed through the use of these externally restricted resources to be treated as a reduction of contributed equity, as opposed to retained earnings. As shown in appendix A, four accounts — "contributions from municipality" (account 272), "contributions from customers" (account 273), "contributions from developers" (account 274), and "other contributions" (account 275) — are provided for municipally owned water utilities to record contributions in aid of construction.

Extension Policies

A large portion of advances or contributions made by or on behalf of customers for construction frequently arises in connection with the extension of distribution facilities to provide water service to new customers. The reasons for requiring customer advances or contributions for this purpose are (1) to protect existing customers served by the system by ensuring that the existing customers do not bear, in a discriminating manner, the specific costs of extending service to new customers; and (2) to ensure that an adequate return will be realized on the incremental plant investment required to service prospective customers.

The cost of providing service to new customers varies depending on the distance the proposed customers are located from existing distribution mains and on requirements for any special construction to provide the quality and quantity of water service needed by the customers. In addition, with rising construction costs, the construction expenditures required to add new customers frequently exceed the expenditures that were made with respect to existing customers. As a result, customer advances or contributions may be required in order to equalize investment per customer in relation to revenue per customer. Further, customer advances or contributions must be sufficient to permit the water utility to earn an adequate return on its investment in the new facilities. To this end, customer advances and contributions may be considered as sharing the cost of plant construction. In lieu of requiring advances or contributions, some utilities recover the cost of construction by means of special rate agreements. (Municipally owned water utilities frequently charge customers located beyond city limits higher rates for water service than those inside city limits in order to compensate for the added cost of serving outside-of-city customers.)

The water main extension policies employed by water utilities vary widely. For water utilities subject to public service commission jurisdiction, extension policies generally are a result of commission rule or are subject to the approval of the commission. Customarily, amounts paid by or on behalf of customers for construction are in the form of advances, with a provision for refunds against the advances. Refund provisions typically reflect a desire to return that portion of the advance that is in excess of the contribution necessary to permit the utility to make an adequate return on the incremental plant investment that is financed by the utility. It is extremely difficult to devise extension policies that result in a water utility retaining only that portion of an advance, as a contribution, that is necessary for the realization of an adequate return on investment and that avoids all discrimination among customers.

In some cases, an advance of the entire estimated construction cost is required by the utility. In other cases, the excess of estimated construction cost above a fixed limit is required to be advanced. The fixed limit typically is based on the construction costs associated with a minimum size and length of main. Advances made by customers, groups of customers, subdividers, or developers typically are not interest-bearing. Frequently, different policies regarding the portion of cost to be advanced are applicable to customers and subdividers.

Methods of making refunds of customer advances for main extensions also vary widely among utilities. Any excess of the advance over actual construction cost is refunded in a lump sum. Additional refunds frequently are based on established schedules that permit refunds according to the number of customers using the extension or the amount of revenue derived from customers using the extension.

It is imperative that detailed records be maintained concerning advances and contributions from customers, subdividers, and other persons. Such records include information concerning the names and addresses of those providing advances and contributions, the amounts advanced or contributed by each, and the terms of the extension agreements. These detailed records serve not only as supporting documents for the "customer advances for construction" account and for the contributions accounts but also as evidence supporting refunds of advances or portions of advances. When a person is refunded the entire amount to which he or she is entitled, as evidenced by the detailed records, any remaining balance of advances is transferred to the appropriate contributions account.

Frequently, the customer is charged for the cost of the service line, either from the meter to the curb or from the meter to the distribution main. The cost of the meter, in some instances, also is paid by the customer. Amounts paid by customers for service and meter installations should be considered as contributions for construction.

Customer advances and contributions for main extensions, service and meter installations, and other plant construction should not be considered as a reduction of the cost of plant construction (unless a utility is required to do so by a public service commission). The construction should be recorded in the plant accounts at its full cost, with the advances or contributions for construction included on the liability side of the balance sheet.

Accounting Alternatives

NCGA's Statement Number 2 allows the depreciation of contributions. The depreciation of contributions allows the utility to match the depreciation on the contributed asset with amortization of the contribution.

Without amortizing the contributions, the utility's contributions will continue to increase while the assets that have been contributed will be depreciated and retired. The amortization of the contribution is through a transfer from the contribution account to the retained earnings account. The transfer will approach the depreciation of the contributed asset.

The transfer is reported on the statement of changes in retained earnings.

⊠ Policy and Legal Requirements From Governing Authorities

Credit ratings for publicly owned utilities are reviewed and updated periodically. The reviews are made for those utilities with outstanding general obligation bond issues to aid the investor in the bond issue. The utility develops a plan that includes the credit agency review requirements. Plans should cover the bond covenants that currently exist and other considerations.

Bond covenants are designed to protect the bondholder's interest. The rating agency is concerned with the degree to which the utility is complying with the covenants.

The utility may issue revenue bonds or certain general obligation bonds that are backed with an assurance of the utility's revenues. The covenants may specify the security of the bonds, the priority of revenues, and coverage of the debt service with financial planning. The bond resolution cites the pledge of specific revenues to meet operation and maintenance expenses, debt service, and capital expenditures.

Equity accounts will be found in the accounts 201 through 218 (appendix A), depending on the type of organization of the utility. A corporate utility will use accounts 210 through 213 to identify common and preferred stock. Proprietorships and partnerships identify the proprietary capital in account 218. Corporations, proprietorships, partnerships, and governmental utilities use accounts 214 and 215 to identify appropriated and unappropriated retained earnings.

Specifications of suggested equity accounts are as follows:

- Common Stock Issued (201). The par or stated value of the capital stock actually issued by the utility.

- Common Stock Subscribed (202). The legally enforceable subscriptions to capital stock of the utility.

- Common Stock Liability for Conversion (203). The par or stated value of the capital stock the utility has agreed to exchange for securities of other companies.

- Preferred Stock Issued (204). The par or stated value of the preferred stock actually issued by the utility.

- Preferred Stock Subscribed (205). The legally enforceable subscriptions to preferred stock of the utility.

- Preferred Stock Liability for Conversion (206). The par or stated value of the preferred stock the utility has agreed to exchange for securities of other companies.

- Premium on Capital Stock (207). The excess of the actual value received over the par or stated value for capital stock issued. The account will be subdivided for all issues of capital stock.

- Reduction in Par or Stated Value of Capital Stock (209). Credits resulting from the reduction of the par or stated value of the capital stock.

- Gain on Resale or Cancellation of Reacquired Capital Stock (210). The credits resulting from the resale or cancellation of reacquired capital stock.

- Other Paid-In Capital (211). The balance for credits of paid-in capital for items not properly includable in other accounts.

- Discount on Capital Stock (212). With a separate subdivision for each class of capital stock, all discounts related to the original issue and sale of the capital stock will be recorded.

- Capital Stock Expense (213). With a separate subdivision for each class and series of capital stock, all expenses incurred in the issuance of the stock.

- Appropriate Retained Earnings (214). Retained earnings that have been set aside for specific purposes. Subaccounts will be required for each appropriation.

- Unappropriated Retained Earnings (215). The balance of net income less any transfer to or from retained earnings.

- Reacquired Capital Stock (216). In a subaccount for each class and services of capital stock, the cost of capital stock reacquired.

- Proprietary Capital (218). For proprietorships and partnerships, the investment of the proprietor or partners in an unincorporated utility. Each year, income or loss will be entered into this account. Separate subaccounts will be in a partnership for each partner.

⊠ Generally Accepted Measures for Financially Stable and Secure Utilities

Utilities may be in various states of financial condition. Financial analysts and credit agencies use a variety of financial ratios to determine the utility's financial condition. The analysts will not only determine the various ratios but also will track the trend of the ratio over several years. The change in the ratio allows the determination of the utility's progress, improvement or deterioration.

Financial statements are presented with comparative statements for the current year presented and at least one prior year. The comparative statement allows the reader to determine the variation in the accounts from one year to the next. A percentage analysis allows the determination of how each item is a percentage of a base item. The percentage analysis can also be used with the comparative statement; this will allow the reader to determine changes in the composition of the accounts over the period presented.

Management reporting uses a variety of comparative statements in which the actual experience is compared to the budgeted amounts. This provides management the ability to determine factors that have changed since the budget was developed. Unusual nonrecurring items should be reported separately to avoid distortion.

⊠ Ratio Analysis

Ratio analysis is the selection of two amounts from the financial statements and dividing one into the other. The analysis allows the reader to determine additional factors than can be obtained from individual amounts. The ratios typically used involve the following three types:

- those that indicate the current position
- those that indicate the equity position
- those that indicate the income or operating position

Ratios used in analyzing the current position refer to the relationship of the current asset to current liabilities. These ratios indicate the overall solvency of the utility or the movement of the utility's current assets. Examples of the ratios used to determine the overall solvency of the utility are current ratio, net current assets divided by the current liabilities, quick ratio, net quick assets divided by the current liabilities, and working capital to total assets. Ratios relating to the movement of current assets can be in the receivable, inventory, or working capital asset types.

Equity ratios are used to determine the financial condition of the utility. The equity ratio can be seen from different viewpoints. From a creditor's view, a high proportion of equity to debt is preferred. The equity holder will prefer a high proportion of debt to equity. The types of equity ratios that an analyst may use are

- owner's equity to total assets
- creditor's equity to total assets
- owner's equity to total liabilities
- net income to owner's equity
- sales to owner's equity

- fixed assets to fixed liabilities
- fixed assets to owner's equity
- sales to total equity
- sales to fixed assets
- book value per share of common stock

Investors may find the ratios relating to income or operation of more interest than the equity or current position ratios. Income ratios will give an indication of the utility's profitability. Creditors may not grant loans to a utility that does not indicate a profitable position even though adequate collateral is available. Management will also be concerned with the utility's income ratios, as they may indicate the trend that income is following. Examples of income or operation ratios are

- net income to net sales
- net income to owner's equity
- investment turnover
- net income per share of common stock
- earnings rate on market value per share
- price–earnings ratio
- return on investment

PART FOUR

⊠ Accounting
Reports

CHAPTER FIFTEEN

Financial Statement Reports

The purpose of financial reporting is to convey information about the water utility. The information presented in financial reports serves as an important foundation on which decisions by regulatory authorities, taxing authorities, owners, creditors, customers, employees, management, and other groups interested in the affairs of a water utility are based. The information needs of each group are discussed in chapter 6.

The end products of the accounting system used by the water utility are the financial reports presented to interested groups in an effort to satisfy the information requirements of each. Although the data accumulated by the accounting system are not the only sources of information available to those interested in the affairs of the water utility, they do represent a significant portion of such information. Therefore, it is important that the financial reports generated by the accounting system present information relevant to the specific needs and problems of the interested groups in a form readily understood by the intended readers.

⊠ Guidelines For Reporting — Financial Statement Standards

Many factors may need to be addressed within financial reporting. These include

- presentation in accordance with generally accepted accounting principles (GAAP)

- compliance with the reporting requirements of the Securities and Exchange Commission (SEC)

- information needs of regulatory commissions

- disclosures required or of interest to creditors

- demonstration of compliance with legal requirements

Each factor has its own unique characteristics. Financial reporting must consider each element, but more importantly must be developed to meet the needs of each unique user. This may require various forms of reporting designed to satisfy these needs.

The format and content of certain reports to public service commissions, to the Securities and Exchange Commission, and to taxing authorities are usually designed by these particular groups. When this is the case, the water utility merely furnishes information in the manner prescribed. In preparing reports for which the format and content are not specified by law, the utility is free to apply general principles of report preparation. Briefly, these principles may be stated as follows:

- the requirements of the readers for whom the report is intended should dictate the nature of the data presented and the manner of presentation

- the data reported should be arranged in a logical and readily understandable manner

- the wording of the report should convey to the reader the precise meaning intended

- the information should be reported at the time it is needed

- the time and effort expended in obtaining the information reported should be commensurate with the worth of the information

The first of these principles is the most important. Reports are compiled in order to convey a message. For the message to be read and understood, preparers of the report must understand the uses that the intended readers may be expected to make of it. The second and third principles amplify the first: like items should be grouped; as much or as little detail should be shown as the intended readers are expected to need; and the significance and relative importance of the various groups of data should be brought out through the use of subtotals, totals, various typographic styles, and other devices. The third principle suggests that language familiar to the intended readers should be employed, that is, technical terminology should be used in a report only if the intended readers have a technical background.

The fourth of the general principles of report preparation is concerned with timeliness. In order to report information by the time it is needed or required, the information demands of the intended users must be foreseen and a system designed to provide the needed information routinely. The design of the information system should also facilitate the presentation of data needed occasionally but not routinely. Accuracy is often of less importance than timeliness; estimates are adequate for many purposes.

The fifth principle is a corollary of the fourth. Some of the information desired by water utility managers, or by individuals or groups outside the management team, would cost more to obtain than the information would be worth. The fifth principle also places a lid of reasonableness on the other four; however, it should not be used as an excuse for failure to be diligent and creative in attempting to meet the needs of those who have a valid claim for information about the water utility and its activities.

The preparation of reports involves the accumulation, sorting, and summarization of detailed financial and statistical data generated by the accounting system. Report preparation is costly, and procedures that minimize its expense must be employed. The procedures instituted are, to a certain extent, dictated by the size of the water utility organization. In some cases, manual preparation may be the most economical. For large systems, the use of electronic data processing equipment will be feasible. In other cases, a combination of these data processing systems may be the most efficient and economical. The application of various combinations should be studied before a decision is reached concerning the most appropriate method for report preparation.

⊠ Reports of Investor-Owned Water Utilities

Reports to External Users

External users of investor-owned utility financial reports are varied. This section is primarily devoted to reporting to stockholders. Subsequent sections of this chapter will discuss other forms of external reporting.

Stockholders or prospective stockholders of an investor-owned water utility usually are not involved in the day-to-day operations of the entity and thus do not have a complete knowledge of the utility's activities. To a considerable extent, stockholders depend on reports rendered by the water utility as their principal source of information. In examining the reports of an investor-owned water utility, a stockholder is most interested in the earnings and dividend record, financial position, and growth (in revenues, profits, and assets) during recent years. Information concerning these aspects and other information of interest permit the stockholder to estimate the future financial success of a utility and to estimate the risk and return associated with ownership of this stock.

In preparing reports to stockholders of investor-owned water utilities, there generally are some restraints, either legal or conventional, within which water utility management must operate. For example, the form and content of a report (prospectus) including financial information to potential stockholders concerning a new securities issue is dictated by SEC under the Securities Act of 1933 if the investor-owned water utility issuing the securities falls within SEC jurisdiction. After securities have been issued, SEC under the Securities Exchange Act of 1934 specifies the frequency, form, and content of reports filed directly with SEC by publicly held corporations, including the annual (10-K) and interim (10-Q) reports. Although adherence to SEC reporting regulations is not generally required in reports not filed with SEC, SEC has had a substantial influence on the content of external financial reports issued to stockholders.

Annual financial reports to stockholders are subject to audit by an independent certified public accountant, who is charged with rendering an opinion concerning whether or not the financial statements and accompanying footnotes present fairly, in conformity with GAAP, the operating results, financial position, and cash flows of the water utility. The three principal accounting and financial reporting standards underlying corporate financial reporting have been the Committee on Accounting Procedure (CAP) of the American Institute of Certified Public Accountants (AICPA) from 1939–1959, the Accounting Principles Board (APB) of AICPA from 1959–1973, and presently the Financial Accounting Standards Board (FASB). Unless superseded by a more recent standard, pronouncements of all three accounting organizations remain in effect today. Although the pronouncements of these authoritative accounting organizations are not legally binding, as SEC reporting requirements are, members of AICPA are required to disclose all material departures from authoritative accounting pronouncements in the companies' published financial statements to stockholders.

GAAP for Investor-Owned Water Utilities

Uniform systems of accounts prescribed by state public service commissions to control the accounting practices of water utilities customarily serve as the foundation for rendering financial reports to SEC and to stockholders, as well as to the state public service commissions. The uniform system of accounts basically follows GAAP promulgated by organizations such as APB and FASB. Nevertheless, there commonly exist certain differences between accounting requirements of state public service commissions and GAAP applicable to nonregulated enterprises. The differences, which can have a significant effect on financial statement measurements, result mainly from the regulatory emphasis on achieving rate-making objectives.

The influence of rate regulation on accounting practices of investor-owned utilities has been recognized by accounting rulemaking organizations. In 1982, FASB issued its Statement of Financial Accounting Standards (SFAS) Number 71 — *Accounting for the Effects of Certain Types of Regulation*. This statement recognized that

- Regulation of an enterprise's prices (hereinafter referred to as "rates") is sometimes based on the enterprise's costs. Regulators use a variety of mechanisms to estimate a regulated enterprise's allowable costs, and they allow the enterprise to charge rates that are intended to produce revenue approximately equal to those allowable costs. Specific costs that are allowable for rate-making purposes result in revenue approximately equal to the costs.

- In most cases, allowable costs are used as a means of estimating costs of the period during which the rates will be in effect, and there is no intent to permit recovery of specific prior costs. The process is a way of setting prices — the results of the process are reported in general-purpose financial statements in accordance with the same accounting principles that are used by unregulated enterprises.

- Regulators sometimes include costs in allowable costs in a period other than the period in which the costs would be charged to expense by an unregulated enterprise. That procedure can create assets (future cash inflows that will result from the rate-making process), reduce assets (reductions of future cash inflows that will result from the rate-making process), or create liabilities (future cash outflows that will result from the rate-making process) for the regulated enterprise. For general-purpose financial reporting, an incurred cost for which a regulator permits recovery in a future period is accounted for like an incurred cost that is reimbursable under a cost-reimbursement-type contract.

- Accounting requirements that are not directly related to the economic effects of rate actions may be imposed on regulated businesses by orders of regulatory authorities and occasionally by court decisions or statutes. This does not necessarily mean that those accounting requirements conform with generally accepted accounting principles. For example, a regulatory authority may order an enterprise to capitalize and amortize a cost that would be charged to income currently by an unregulated enterprise. Unless capitalization of that cost is appropriate under this Statement, generally accepted accounting principles require the regulated enterprise to charge the cost to income currently.

Under SFAS 71, an enterprise may capitalize all or part of an incurred cost that would otherwise be charged to expense if both of the following criteria are met:

- It is probable that future revenue in an amount at least equal to the capitalized cost will result from inclusion of that cost in allowable costs for rate-making purposes.

- Based on available evidence, the future revenue will be provided to permit recovery of the previously incurred cost rather than to provide for expected levels of similar future costs. If the revenue will be provided through an automatic rate-adjustment clause, this criterion requires that the regulator's intent clearly be to permit recovery of the previously incurred cost.

Rate actions of a regulator can also reduce or eliminate the value of an asset. If a regulator excludes all or part of a cost from allowable costs, and it is not probable that the cost will be included as an allowable cost in a future period, the cost cannot be expected to result in future revenue through the rate-making process. Accordingly, the carrying amount of any related asset shall be reduced to the extent that the asset has been impaired. Whether or not the asset has been impaired shall be judged the same as for enterprises in general.

Rate actions of a regulator can also impose a liability on a regulated enterprise. Such liabilities are usually obligations to the enterprise's customers. The following are the usual ways in which liabilities can be imposed and the resulting accounting:

- A regulator may require refunds to customers. Refunds are recognized as liabilities and as reductions of revenue or as expenses of the regulated enterprise.

- A regulator can provide current rates intended to recover costs that are expected to be incurred in the future with the understanding that if those costs are not incurred, future rates will be reduced by corresponding amounts. If current rates are intended to recover such costs, and the regulator requires the enterprise to remain accountable for any amounts charged pursuant to such rates, those amounts are recognized as liabilities and taken to income only when the associated costs are incurred.

- A regulator can require that a gain or other reduction of net allowable costs be given to customers over future periods. That would be accomplished, for rate-making purposes, by amortizing the gain or other reduction of net allowable costs over those future periods and reducing rates to reduce revenues in approximately the amount of the amortization.

At present, important areas of conflict between water utility regulatory accounting and accounting for nonregulated enterprises under the provisions of SFAS 71 include accounting for extraordinary gains and losses through early extinguishment of debt, accounting for income tax expense, accounting for leases, accounting for pension and other postemployment retirement expenses, and accounting for the cost of funds used during construction. These issues, and others, are discussed later in this book.

Annual Reporting

An annual financial report is one of the principal sources of information to stockholders concerning the operations of an investor-owned water utility. An annual report is primarily an account of management's stewardship. The primary financial statements included in an annual report are the balance sheet, income statement, statement of retained earnings, statement of cash flows, and five-year summary of operations accompanied by management's discussion and analysis. A portion of the report is also devoted to explaining the activities of the water utility and to highlighting future plans and prospects. Appendix B contains an excerpt from a sample investor-owned utility's annual report.

Content. As previously noted, the form and content of this annual reporting is dictated by the standards of SEC. This reporting may be satisfied in one annual filing (Form 10-K) or in two fillings (an annual report to stockholders and a Form 10-K that incorporates information contained in the annual report to stockholders). The structure and content of annual financial reports to stockholders typically include the following:

Highlights of the financial and operating results of the year. The summary of current financial results may be compared with that of the previous year.

A letter to stockholders by the president or board chairman, or both. The letter generally includes a brief statement concerning the year's activities and the plans and prospects of the utility.

A detailed narrative review of the activities of the water utility. This review may include brief discussions concerning revenues, operating expenses, pumpage and production, new construction, new franchise areas, subsidiary operations, water rates and service, stockholder relations, employee relations, customer and public relations, marketing programs, relations with public utility commissions, new financing, and plans for the following year and beyond. The discussions may be supplemented by graphs, charts, maps, and pictorial representations where applicable.

The informal explanation and review of operations is prepared at the discretion of management. Additional information to be included is specified by SEC in its Regulation S-K, which requires public companies to include in both the 10-K annual report to SEC and in the annual report to stockholders (1) a summary of operations for the last five years and (2) management discussion and analysis of financial condition and results of operations, including unusual variations, for the most recent three years. Although the exact content and format of management's narrative explanation of changes in operating results will vary somewhat among companies, the essential purpose of the year-by-year narrative explanation is to analyze major reasons for changes in the company's liquidity, capital resources, and operating results over the most recent three-year period.

A brief description of the business and properties, as well as legal proceedings, security ownership, and management remuneration, are disclosures required by SEC in the Form 10-K filing.

Financial statements. Financial statements in comparative form, supplemented by explanatory notes and supporting schedules and accompanied by the report of an independent public accountant, provide the basic data concerning the financial position and results of operations of the water utility.

Balance sheet. The balance sheet shows (1) the assets of the water utility and (2) the creditor and stockholder interests in the assets on a specified date.

Income statement. The income statement shows the operating revenue and expenses of the water utility along with other revenue and expense items. Computations for earnings per share for common stockholders are also shown.

Retained earnings statement. The statement of retained earnings shows the beginning balance in retained earnings, the transfer of income, deductions for dividend declarations, other adjustments, and the ending retained earnings balance. In some cases, the income statement and the retained earnings statements may be combined into a single statement. In other cases, it may include changes in other equity components.

Statement of cash flows. The statement of cash flows shows the cash flows for the year from operating, investing, or financing activities. Two formats may be used in the preparation of this statement for the operating activities. The formats include reporting actual cash receipts and payments (the direct method) or a reconciliation of net income to these cash flows using changes in other working capital components (an indirect method).

Explanatory notes. The amount and type of information required both by SEC and GAAP have expanded significantly since the early 1970s. In order to better understand the nature and content of this material, the following comments highlight selected notes found in water utility reporting:

Accounting policies. In 1972, the Accounting Principles Board (APB) issued Opinion Number 22, *Disclosure of Accounting Policies*, which recommends that companies disclose in the annual report the identification and description of all significant accounting principles and methods that involve selection from among alternatives and/or those that are common to a given industry. This information is generally shown in the first note to the financial statements.

Assets subject to lien. Assets mortgaged, pledged, or otherwise subject to lien, and the approximate amounts thereof, are to be designated and the obligations collateralized briefly identified in accordance with SEC Regulation S-X.

Restrictions that limit the payment of dividends by the company. Regulation S-X requires disclosure of the most significant restrictions on the payment of dividends by the company, indicating dividends' sources, dividends' pertinent provisions, and the amount of retained earnings or net income restricted or free of restrictions.

Significant changes in bonds, mortgages, and similar debt. Any significant change in the authorized or issued amounts of bonds, mortgages, and similar debt since the date of the latest balance sheet are disclosed in the notes. Debt disclosures include annual maturity and sinking fund requirements, letter-of-credit arrangements, and a summary of short-term debt activity.

Income tax expense. APB Opinion Number 11, SFAS 96, and Regulation S-X include note disclosure requirements for income tax expense. This includes:

- the components of income (loss) before income tax expense (benefit) as either domestic or foreign

- the components of income tax expense, including (1) taxes currently payable and (2) the net tax effects, as applicable, of timing differences (indicate separately the amount of the estimated tax effect of each of the various types of timing differences, such as depreciation)

- a reconciliation between the amount of reported total income tax expense (benefit) and the amount computed by multiplying the income (loss) before tax by the applicable statutory federal income tax rate, showing the estimated dollar amount of each of the underlying causes for the difference. This reconciliation may be presented in percentages rather than in dollar amounts.

Leased assets and lease commitments. SFAS 13 and Regulation S-X both call for lease disclosures. Among other items, lessees must disclose total rental expense associated with leased assets, minimum rental commitments for future periods, and the rate-making treatment of the leases.

Pension and postretirement benefits. SFAS 87 and 106 include disclosure requirements related to these benefits. These disclosures include the components of benefit cost, funded status of the plan, and significant actuarial assumptions used in the determination of the funded status.

Segment information. SFAS 14 requires industry and geographic segment reporting. This includes summarized income statement and balance-sheet information.

Commitments and contingencies. SFAS 5 requires note disclosure of significant commitments and contingencies affecting the company. This may include construction commitments as well as legal and regulatory proceedings.

Report of independent public accountant. Independent auditors attest to the fairness of the financial statement presentation in conformity with generally accepted accounting principles. Note that the financial statements remain the responsibility of management and not of the independent auditor.

Interim Reports

Another primary financial report issued to stockholders that attempts to disclose the stewardship function of corporate management is the interim report. Unlike annual reports, which are audited by independent public accountants, interim reports are generally unaudited, and the type and amount of data presented in them have, for the most part, been left to the discretion of management. As a result, a wide variety of interim reporting formats have existed, and the information presented has ranged from a minimum of publication of quarterly sales and earning figures as required by most stock exchanges to comprehensive reports containing a complete set of comparative financial statements and explanatory notes.

In May 1973, APB issued Opinion Number 28 on interim financial reporting. The opinion (1) attempts to clarify the application of generally accepted accounting principles as they apply to interim periods and (2) sets forth the minimum disclosure requirements for interim reports of publicly owned companies. In addition to disclosing summarized revenues and net earnings, companies are encouraged to publish balance-sheet and cash flow data on an interim basis.

SEC has also influenced the type and amount of information disclosed in quarterly reports to shareholders. This includes quarterly filings on Form 10-Q of summarized financial information, along with updates to the annual reporting for known or anticipated changes.

⊠ Reports of Government-Owned Water Utilities

Reports to External Users

The primary users of financial reports for government-owned water utilities are the citizens within the utility's service territory. The form and content of reports to citizens are not dictated by law or regulation to the same extent as reports to stockholders of investor-owned water utilities. Generally, in the case of reports to citizens, there are no specific legal requirements for reporting. The information to be included in the reports, the form of the reports, and the frequency of the reports are largely dictated by conventional reporting practices. However, this does not mean that citizens are any less entitled to a full disclosure of the operating results and activities of a government-owned water utility than are stockholders of investor-owned utilities. The Government Accounting Standards Board (GASB) has stated

> Timely and properly presented financial reports are essential to managers, legislative officials, creditors, financial analysts, the general public and others having need for government financial information.

The extent of reporting to citizens is primarily at the discretion of water utility management. Distribution of detailed and comprehensive reports to citizens is not deemed necessary by the managers of some government-owned utilities. Other managers believe that communication of selected information is useful for maintaining and promoting the goodwill of the general public and for keeping citizens adequately informed of the operations of the water utility. Increased public interest in and concern for the activities and operating results of governmental entities in recent years has caused local governments to disclose more information to citizens.

To create good relations and provide useful information, many water utilities publish pamphlets or booklets to acquaint the citizens of the municipality with facts concerning utility operations. The publications often stress the history of the utility, the relationship of the utility to the community, research activities, the quality and cost of water service, and future plans and outlooks for the utility. In addition to background information, reports to citizens may include other financial data, such as taxes and contributions paid by the water utility to finance publicly supported activities (for example, municipal government operations). In the case of government-owned water utilities, the citizens may require reports concerning the efficiency of the utility's operations (in terms of meeting budgeted costs), the degree to which the utility is self-supporting, and the extent, if any, that the taxpayer is supporting the operations and capital construction activities of the water utility. Media for distributing information to the general public include direct mail and notices or advertisements in the financial or other sections of the public press.

In 1992, GASB issued a Preliminary Views statement on "Service Efforts and Accomplishments Reporting." The final position on this issue may affect the preceding discussion.

GAAP for Government-Owned Utilities

Financial reporting and accounting standards for government-owned utilities are similar to investor-owned utilities. Established in 1985, GASB is the recognized authoritative standard-setting body for governmental units. Prior to GASB, the National Council on Governmental Accounting (NCGA) set standards for government.

When formed, GASB dealt with the issue of which accounting principles government-owned utilities should use. Since the activities of government-owned utilities were similar to those of investor-owned utilities, it only made sense that the reporting standards be similar. The structural agreement establishing GASB recognizes that separately issued financial statements of utilities in the public sector, prepared in accordance with GAAP, should be guided by the standards of FASB unless GASB has issued a pronouncement applicable to utilities. As previously mentioned, GASB Statement Number 20 also provides interim guidance.

Conflicts can arise between the two standard-setting bodies. Government in structure is unique and often requires different standards to meet its users' needs. Specific conflicts will be discussed later in this section.

Nature of Fund Accounting and Reporting

Because a government-owned water utility endeavors to be a self-supporting activity of a governmental unit, financed primarily by charges to consumers, the water utility should be accounted for as a separate enterprise fund. The significant attribute of an enterprise activity is that the accounting for it must make it possible to determine if the unit operated at a profit or loss. In this regard, a government-owned water utility is comparable to an investor-owned water utility.

Generally, the government-owned water utility should use the same system of accounts as an investor-owned water utility. Minor variations in the NARUC *Uniform System of Accounts for Class A Water Utilities* to accommodate the particular needs of a government-owned unit, such as interfund transactions and restricted assets, are included in the modified system of NARUC accounts.

The reports rendered by a government-owned water utility to citizens may include annual financial statements audited by an independent public accountant and interim financial statements. An annual financial report to citizens may include a balance sheet, an income statement, a statement of revenue and expense compared to budget, a statement of changes in retained earnings, and a statement of cash flows.

Annual Reports

Annual financial reports to citizens of government-owned water utilities are generally subject to some variation, both in content and format. In a majority of areas, a close parallel can be drawn between the content of the annual reports of government-owned water utilities and the content of the annual report of an investor-owned water utility. Appendix C contains excerpts from the annual report of a government-owned utility.

The GASB standards state that "every government should prepare and publish, as a matter of public record, a comprehensive annual financial report (CAFR)." If the government is a component of a larger government (i.e., a city-owned water utility), this report would be a component unit financial report (CUFR).

The CAFR and CUFR generally contain three distinct sections — introductory, financial, and statistical. These sections may be supplemented by certain specialized sections as the need arises.

The introductory section is the first section of a CAFR or CUFR. It is intended to familiarize the reader with the organizational structure of the utility, the nature and scope of the services it provides, and a summary of the utility's financial activities and the factors that influence these activities. Some of the introductory material is subjective in nature, in contrast to the relatively objective information reported in the financial and statistical sections. The introductory section also includes future-oriented information, such as economic forecasts and discussions of future initiatives. Because of the subjective and predictive nature of the introductory section, it is ordinarily excluded from the scope of the independent auditor's examination.

The financial section includes the utility's financial statements. As in the case of an investor-owned water utility, financial statements in comparative form, supported by notes and schedules and accompanied by the report of an independent public accountant, provide basic information concerning the financial position and operating results of the government-owned water utility. Differences in financial presentations between investor-owned and government-owned water utilities primarily result from (1) particular governmental or fund accounting requirements for government-owned water utilities and (2) the greater dependency on creditor financing by government-owned water utilities. The second difference may be reflected by the inclusion of special tables or schedules in the annual report to provide information concerning long-term debt, including amounts outstanding, annual debt service requirements, and annual debt service coverage.

Balance sheet. The balance sheet for a government-owned water utility shows assets, liabilities, and equity. They may be listed in order from current to fixed items, consistent with that recommended by GASB, or presented on a basis more in keeping with that generally used by investor-owned water utilities.

Statement of revenue and expense. A comparative statement of revenues and expense, or a variation thereof, will typically be included in the annual report to citizens. Changes in revenue invested in the water system (analogous to a retained earnings statement) are also included as part of this presentation.

Statement of cash flows. This statement is similar to the cash flow statement used by investor-owned utilities to classify cash flows by operating, investing, or financial activities. GASB, in its Statement Number 9, chose to divide the financing component into two activities — capital and noncapital. This was done because government is somewhat different from investor-owned utilities in that it may borrow for operating purposes.

Summary of debt service requirements and coverage. Special tables or schedules that provide information concerning long-term debt balances outstanding, annual debt service requirements, and annual debt service coverage may also be included in annual reports of government-owned water utilities. This information serves to provide additional data on debt service and is supplemental to the financial statements.

Explanatory notes. Explanatory notes for government-owned water utilities contain much the same types of disclosure as the investor-owned utility notes previously discussed. Because of its governmental nature, government-owned water utilities also disclose the legal aspects of their structure and compliance with legal provisions. This includes disclosures on the legally adopted annual operating budget and the utility's compliance or noncompliance with the provisions of the budget.

Report of the independent public accounting. This reporting by the auditor is no different than with investor-owned water utilities.

The third section of the CAFR or CUFR contains comprehensive statistical data for the utility. It is intended to provide CAFR or CUFR users with a broader understanding of the utility and the trends in its financial affairs than is possible from the financial statements and supporting schedules included in the financial section alone. Most of the data included in the statistical section cover a period up to ten years. Another distinguishing feature is that some of the data — physical, economic, and social in nature — are derived from sources outside the formal accounting maintained by the utility. In contrast to financial-section information, statistical-section data usually are not susceptible to independent audit. Again, refer to GASB's 1992 Preliminary Views on "Service Efforts and Accomplishments Reporting" and research possible recent updates on the issue.

Interim Reports

Formalized interim reporting by government-owned water utilities is not required. As a result, these reports are not frequently prepared. When prepared, their format is similar to the annual reporting format, only at a summarized level. This could include (1) a letter from the general manager disclosing highlights and a comparison of operating results of the previous year, (2) a comparative balance sheet showing assets and equities as of the end of the quarter and at the end of the previous fiscal year, (3) a comparative statement of revenues and expenses for the quarter and for the same quarter of the prior year, and (4) various other statistics that might prove of interest to external users.

⊠ Other Financial Statement Reporting

Creditors, customers, employees, and other groups interested in the activities and operating results of a water utility seek information relative to their special interests. Such information may be obtained from general-purpose reports, such as the annual reports to stockholders and citizens discussed earlier, or in special-purpose reports prepared for specific purposes or specific interested groups or persons.

Reporting to Creditors — General

Present and prospective creditors are interested in a water utility's financial condition, the results of its operations, and other information that can be used to evaluate the risk involved in lending funds to the utility. Loans obtained from commercial banks, although varying in length of maturity, are in the broad category of short-term credit. Bonds generally are in the category of long-term credit. Therefore, information included in reports from commercial bankers is relevant to other short-term credit grantors, and information included in reports for bondholders or their representatives is relevant to other long-term creditors.

Reports to Commercial Bankers

Reports to bankers must answer such questions as "Why does the utility need money? How much is required? Will the loan be repaid? How?" The particular reporting requirements (specific financial statements and extent of detail) accompanying the extension of credit to a water utility by a bank typically depends on the size and term of the loan. Other factors, such as the size of the water utility and the quality of management, also affect reporting requirements. The request for a small loan usually does not require as much information as a request for a large loan, since bankers assume less risk in accepting a small loan. In granting short-term loans, bankers are primarily interested in reports that emphasize the manner in which the proposed loan is to be repaid. If it is to be repaid from cash generated from operations, a projection of earnings, together with a cash flow forecast showing estimated sources and uses of cash and the estimated future cash balance available for repaying the loan, should be made available to the bank. If the loan is to be repaid by issuing long-term debt, bankers generally will be interested in the effect of the added burden of noncurrent indebtedness on the capital structure of the utility and in the ability of the utility to market proposed long-term issues successfully. Bankers also are interested in the income statement as an indication of the earning power or potential of the utility.

In addition to financial statements, the report accompanying a request for a short-term loan or a line of credit typically includes supplementary information related to other aspects of the water utility, including the following:

- contingent liabilities
- assets pledged as collateral
- insurance carried
- names and addresses of officers and directors
- statement by board of directors or other policy-making group indicating that the proposed loan is authorized or approved by them

As the size or term of the requested loan increases, commercial bankers desire additional, more detailed financial statements. In such cases, audited financial statements and supporting schedules similar to those found in the published annual report ordinarily serve the needs of commercial bankers. The financial statements and supporting schedules that accompany a request for an extended-term loan customarily include the following:

- balance sheet
- statement of income
- statement of changes in retained earnings
- statement of cash flows
- notes to financial statements
- independent public accountant's report

The preceding discussion has been limited primarily to historical financial statements. However, it should be emphasized that because commercial bankers are concerned with whether or not the water utility will be able to repay the loan at maturity, the future is of great interest. Therefore, requests by water utilities for bank loans should be supported by projections expressed in terms of forecasts and budgets. Specifically, such requests for loans should be accompanied by the following:

- a statement of estimated revenue and expense for the forecast period
- a statement of estimated cash flow for the forecast period indicating source and application of cash
- a statement of financial position at the end of the forecast period

Once a loan is obtained or a line of credit is established, a utility will be required to render to the bank periodic financial reports, reports regarding the fulfillment of protective covenants, and reports concerning any material changes affecting the water utility. The sophistication of a utility's financial reporting system, and the size and term of the loan are some factors that may influence a bank's request for additional information during the period when loans are outstanding.

Protective covenants contained in loan agreements impose restrictions on the financial activities of the water utility. Protective covenant clauses in loan agreements may include provisions that (1) limit the issuance of additional debt instruments until the loan is repaid, (2) limit payment of dividends (in the case of investor-owned water utilities), or (3) limit payments to the general fund (in the case of government-owned water utilities). Water utility management must understand the provisions contained in the loan agreement so that the utility will adhere to the restrictions and obligations imposed on it.

Reports to Bondholders

Another major class of creditors to whom reports must be rendered is comprised of present and prospective bondholders or their representatives. The prospectus or bond-offering document is the major report rendered by the water utility to prospective bondholders. In the case of bonds already issued, periodic reports by water utilities are usually required by bondholders or trustees acting as agents for bondholders.

In the case of an investor-owned water utility under the jurisdiction of SEC, a public bond offering and the prospectus relating to the sale of the bonds must comply with requirements of that regulatory agency. Bonds of an investor-owned water utility generally are issued under an indenture that defines the rights and privileges of the bondholders and the duties and obligations of the utility. Among other items, the indenture will specify the principal and interest payments to be made by the issuing utility to the bondholders, identify pledged assets, state call provisions, provide details as to the levels of working capital that the issuing utility must maintain, and specify the annual and interim reports that must be rendered to bondholders or their trustees. Restrictions or protective covenants contained in the indenture, such as liquidity requirements and maximum cash dividend distributions, are included to indicate the protection afforded the bondholders.

A bond issue of an investor-owned water utility generally is covered by an indenture; however, some government-owned water utility bonds, such as general obligation bonds, are usually not issued under the terms of a trust indenture. In cases where bonds issued by a government-owned water utility are not covered by an indenture, the rights and obligations of the government-owned water utility typically are defined by statutes and ordinances. In addition to providing details as to various terms and restrictions, such ordinances generally specify the audited financial reports that periodically must be made available to bondholders.

Content of bond offering. The contents of a prospectus or official statement relating to the sale of water utility bonds typically include the following information:

- history and nature of the water utility's operations

- purpose of the bond issue and expected use of the proceeds

- description of the bond issue, including details concerning interest rates, interest payment dates, maturity schedule, redemption provisions, security, and priority

- authority for the issuance of the bonds (in the case of government-owned water utilities) and provisions of the bond ordinance or indenture

- description of the management and operating personnel of the utility, including names, addresses, background, and experience of members of the board of trustees or board of directors of the utility, executive officers, and key operating personnel

- important terms of franchises under which the utility operates

- details of bonded debt, other long-term debt, short-term debt, and capital stock (in the case of investor-owned water utilities)

- details of the utility plant and other property, including cost, accumulated depreciation, age, and location of major units of property

- audited financial statements, including comparative balance sheets, income statements, retained earnings statements, statements of cash flows, and a complete set of explanatory notes

- projected debt service requirements for interest and principal

- other forecasted and historical financial and statistical data reflecting operations of the water utility for a number of comparative years

Regardless of whether bonds are issued by a government-owned or an investor-owned water utility, prospective bondholders will be greatly concerned with the total amount of bond indebtedness, the annual fixed requirements for interest and principal payments on bonds, and the relationship between earnings of the utility and fixed interest charges. Therefore, some of the most important information in a notice of bond sale or a prospectus will be shown in tables of interest coverage and bond indebtedness.

Periodic reports to bondholders. As indicated earlier in this chapter, once bonds are issued, periodic reports to bondholders or their representatives may be required under the terms of the bond ordinance or indenture. The reports rendered by a water utility to bondholders or their trustees include both annual financial statements, audited by an independent public accountant, and interim financial statements. In general, the periodic reports provided to bondholders or their trustees for investor-owned and government-owned water utilities will parallel the annual and interim reports issued to stockholders and citizens, which were discussed earlier in this chapter.

Information other than financial statements is generally included in reports to holders of debt instruments issued by water utilities. In each case, the trust indenture or other agreement between the water utility and the security holder must be considered in determining what information, at a minimum, must be included in creditor reports. The information may include detailed financial and statistical data concerning the utility plant and other property, operating revenues and expenses, and other aspects of the water utility's activities. In addition, information relating to the fulfillment of protective covenants may also be required.

In the case of loan agreements, protective covenants included in a trust indenture or ordinance are quite detailed and complex, imposing restrictions on the financial activities of the water utility as well as providing increased security to the creditors. Protective covenants contained in a trust indenture or other agreement between the water utility and the security holders may include provisions that (1) limit the issuance of additional debt instruments, (2) limit the payment of dividends (in the case of investor-owned water utilities) or payments to the general fund (in the case of government-owned water utilities), (3) limit the sale of mortgaged plant assets and stipulate that money received from sale of such property be substituted as security, (4) require that specified amounts be expended annually for maintenance, replacement, and improvement of mortgaged property (this requirement frequently may be met, in part, by certifying that plant additions shall not serve as the basis for issuing additional bonds) and (5) require the segregation of assets for the purpose of retiring bonds. It is important that water utility management understand the provisions contained in trust indentures or other agreements between the water utility and security holders to ensure that the restrictions and obligations imposed on the utility are respected. Thorough understanding of the provisions will enable management to certify in reports to bondholders or their representatives that the provisions of indentures or other agreements are being fulfilled.

Reporting to Customers and Employees

The extent of reporting to customers and employees is primarily at the discretion of the water utility. Investor-owned and government-owned water utilities may wish to design a single annual report to be published and distributed to stockholders (in the case of investor-owned water utilities), citizens, creditors, customers, and employees. A single comprehensive report to all interested groups may be adequate in situations where stockholders, citizens, creditors, customers, and employees form a homogeneous group whose information needs and interests are similar. In cases where the needs and interests are divergent, specialized reports directed to particular groups may be most effective. As a practical alternative, a published annual report may be issued to all interested groups, supplemented by specialized reports to meet the particular needs of customers and employees.

Reports to customers. Information for customers (such as operating income as a percentage of operating revenue, comparison of current income with that of other periods, cost of water service, reasons for rate increases, and facts relating to the quality of water) may be included in reports accompanying customer water bills. Additionally, some utilities supply each customer with a rate schedule and a set of rules and regulations governing the relationship between customer and water utility.

The general public, which is the source of present and potential customers, is interested in much of the same information as are customers. In addition to information supplied to customers, reports to the general public may include some financial data, such as taxes and contributions paid by the water utility to finance publicly supported activities (for example, municipal government operations). In the case of government-owned water utilities, the general public may require reports concerning the efficiency of the utility's operations (in terms of meeting budgeted costs), the degree to which the utility is self-supporting, and the extent, if any, to which the taxpayer is supporting the operations and capital construction activities of the water utility. Media for distributing information to the general public include direct mail and notices or advertisements in the financial and other sections of the public press.

Reports to customers and the general public must be presented in an understandable manner. Generally, detailed financial information should be omitted and pertinent information should be expressed in terms of basic relationships and trends, using graphs and charts as aids. Such reports should use wording that is familiar and understandable to customers and the general public.

Reports to employees. Employee earning reports, such as federal wage and tax statements (Form W-2), must be furnished to employees in accordance with applicable regulations. Specified information concerning pension plans must be furnished to employees in accordance with provisions of the *Employee Retirement Income Security Act of 1974* (ERISA). Beyond required earnings and pension information, the nature of reports submitted to employees is determined primarily by water utility management. As in the case of reports to customers, reports to employees should present this message in a clear and understandable manner.

In addition to general information, employee reports often emphasize information pertaining to wages, pension plans, fringe benefits, and other data of particular concern to employees. For example, labor costs (wages, pension plan costs, and other fringe benefits) may be expressed as a percentage of revenues of operating expenses. Labor costs and other employee benefits also may be compared with similar elements in other water utilities or in other industries. Employee reports also may emphasize employee productivity and efficiency. For example, operating costs per unit of processed water and the extent of customer complaints may be compared for a number of years. Information expressed in terms of investment, profit, taxes, and labor costs per employee, also may be included in employee reports.

Where possible, information expressed in terms of pie charts, bar graphs, and other graphic representations should be used to emphasize various relationships and trends to employees. The financial and statistical data furnished to employees should be supplemented with a narrative report that further explains the data, indicates future plans and outlook for the utility, outlines job opportunities, and explains any changes in wage, pension, welfare, and other employee benefits and policies.

CHAPTER SIXTEEN

Rate and Regulatory Reports

Government-owned water utilities in the United States are seldom subject to the types of rate and regulatory reporting of their investor-owned counterparts. As a result, rate and regulatory reporting for government-owned utilities is widely variable both as to its extent and content. Therefore, this chapter presents rate regulation essentially from the viewpoint of an investor-owned utility.

State agencies generally establish the rate and regulatory reporting requirements for investor-owned utilities subject to their jurisdiction. The intent of this approach is to provide government-owned utilities with some alternatives for developing their own rate and regulatory evaluation processes from those established by investor-owned utilities over many years.

The rate-making process represents an important aspect of the operations of a public utility. It is the process that determines the utility's ability to charge customers for services rendered and to earn a fair return on assets invested for utility operations. The ultimate outcome of the rate-making process is the tariff sheet, which indicates the rates that can be charged to a customer based on the type of customer and volume of service provided.

Rate-making can be a long, political process. The utility designs a "rate case" that presents its proposed rate structure based on historical or projected financial and operational results. The case is presented to the appropriate regulatory body for their review, consideration, and approval. The case is reviewed by the regulator and its staff, plus interested third parties, such as large customers or consumer interest groups (commonly referred to as interveners). Hearings are held on the merits of the utility requests and an order is issued by the regulator. This chapter expands on this process and discusses the theories behind the determination of the utility rate design.

⊠ Goals

The rate-making process is generally designed to accomplish three goals. The first is to protect the consumer. Because a water utility is usually a monopoly in a given service territory, there is limited, if any, competition to control prices. The regulator acts as this control and designs rates that are as low as possible considering the next two goals and still ensures reliable service to the utility's customers. The rate-making process includes a review of expenditures to ensure prudent management operating decisions and efficient operations. It provides a forum for customers to review management decisions and plans and it challenges the utility to provide reliable service at the lowest cost possible.

The second goal is to protect the financial integrity of the utility. The rate-making process ensures that the utility is reimbursed for prudent expenditures related to providing services to its customers so that rates achieve equity among customer classes. This includes recovery of period costs, plus depreciation and amortization of long-lived assets. Although a regulator's goal is to keep prices low, it must ensure that the utility has sufficient resources available to provide the necessary services.

The third goal of the rate-making process is to provide the opportunity for shareholders of the utility to earn a fair rate of return on their investment. The process results in the computation of a rate of return to be earned on assets invested in utility operations. This return is designed to recover debt and equity costs, including a return on common equity. It should be noted that the rate-making process only provides the opportunity to earn a fair return. It does not guarantee that return. The utility must operate in an efficient and effective manner in order to achieve its desired return.

⌗ Rate Process

The rates that the utility may charge for its services are generally established through a formal proceeding. The amount of revenues that the utility ultimately earns is a product of its rates multiplied by the volume sold. The rates are designed to recover the utility's cost of service (operation and maintenance expense, depreciation, taxes, and other general utility costs) for each customer class, plus a fair return on the invested assets. When volumes sold and actual expenses incurred vary significantly from expectations, the utility's return will be adversely or positively effected. When the variance is material, the utility will enter into new proceedings by filing a rate case with its regulators. The rate case process can take up to 18 months or more and includes planning, preparation, testimony, hearings, rebuttal, and, ultimately, an order. It involves an accumulation of data from all sources within the utility and many external sources.

The rate case is designed to determine the revenue requirements necessary to permit the utility to recover its reasonable expenses of operation, plus earn a fair return on assets devoted to providing utility service. The rate increase required is measured by the difference between the utility's anticipated revenue requirements and the projected revenue that would be produced by the utility's current rate tariffs. The regulator will usually suspend the utility's request for an increase to conduct an investigation of the data supporting the utility's request. The investigation is usually conducted in a public hearing format, where all qualified persons have an opportunity to present evidence or cross-examine utility witnesses about details of the utility's request.

⌗ Test Period

For purposes of determining a utility's reasonable cost of operation, a regulatory body usually requires the utility to present details of its actual experience during a 12-month "test period." This test period can be historical in nature and represents the results of actual experience during the period presented. Alternatively, it can be prospective in nature and represent a period in the future based on the utility's forecasts and projections. Although revenues and expenses for the test period will initially be historical by nature, the utility will propose certain adjustments, known as pro-forma adjustments, to "normalize" conditions in the test period and to provide for certain "known and measurable changes" that have occurred and need to be reflected in rates of future periods. Normalizing represents adjustments to the test period to reflect the effects of changes that the utility knows will occur if those changes had taken place at the beginning of the test period. For example, if a utility negotiated a new agreement with its union for an increase in pay that will take place in the middle of the test year, the utility will make adjustments to payroll expense to reflect this agreement as if it takes place for the entire year. Thus rates will be set to recover all costs of this new agreement in future periods.

Selection of an appropriate test year is important because the utility must ensure that the test period is representative of its costs of doing business. If all costs are not properly included, rates may be set lower than needed, resulting in possible liquidity concerns.

There are advantages and disadvantages of both historical and prospective test years. The advantage of the historical approach is that the regulator can review known costs that the utility has incurred and evaluate them as to whether or not they were prudently incurred. The historical costs can then be adjusted to reflect known changes. These known changes can be evaluated by the regulator and interveners to determine whether or not they are reasonable and prudent. Under the prospective filing, the regulator must assess the utility's ability to budget and forecast — a subjective process. However, under the prospective reporting methodology, a better recovery of current costs is provided for the utility.

⊠ Rate Case

The rate-making process generally involves the utility filing a rate case. The regulatory body accepts the filing and, in certain instances, appoints an administrative law judge or hearing examiner to hear the case. In other jurisdictions, the commissioners themselves hear the case. Prehearing conferences are held and schedules are set for the case, including dates for interveners and other people to become involved. Effected parties intervene and request information from the utility. This is called the "discovery stage." An analysis of the case is prepared by the regulatory agency's appointed staff. Direct testimony of the interveners and witnesses are filed and rebuttal testimony of all witnesses is filed. Hearings are held and witnesses are cross-examined by attorneys. Attorneys prepare briefs of issues and suggested findings and reply briefs. If an administrative law judge is involved in the case, he or she issues an order or report. Attorneys then file exceptions to the report. The attorneys present oral arguments before the commission and finally the commission issues its order. The utility can petition for reconsideration on issuance of the order and the petition is then ruled on by the commission. A legal appeal process can follow if the utility or interveners do not agree with the commission's final order.

⊠ Rate Base, Cost of Service, and Cost of Capital

There are three basic components decided in a rate case. These components are rate base, cost of capital, and cost of service. Each of these will be discussed in more detail in the following paragraphs. Again, these rate elements are those generally associated with investor-owned utilities. Readers should consult AWWA Manual M1, *Water Rates*, for revenue requirement issues usually associated with government-owned utilities.

Rate Base

Rate base represents the amount of capital invested by the utility in order to provide utility services. It is often referred to as the amount of investment "used and useful" in serving the public. A typical determination of rate base includes utility plant in service, less accumulated provision for depreciation, less accumulated deferred income taxes, less contributions in aid of construction, plus a working capital allowance. Net utility plant in service is frequently included in the rate base on an "average basis." This average basis could be a 13-month average balance, a 12-month average balance, or another method used by the regulator. One alternate method permits end-of-test-period balances.

In certain instances, in order to protect the financial integrity of the utility, construction work in progress is included in the rate base. Contributions in aid of construction are deducted from the rate base because they represent assets that have been contributed to the utility but which the utility did not have to fund with utility resources. Therefore, the utility should not earn a return on those assets.

Working capital can be determined in many different ways, based on the jurisdiction in which the utility operates. Working capital can be a simple balance-sheet method, which would include current assets less current liabilities. Some jurisdictions use a one-eighth of cash operating expenses methodology or 13-month averages to determine working capital. Others use lead lag studies, which represent an analysis of the amount of time incurred and cost of generating current assets and current liabilities.

The determination of the rate base is an essential part of the rate case because it represents the assets on which the utility will be allowed to earn a return.

Cost of service. The second aspect of a rate case is the determination of the cost of service. The cost of service represents reimbursement of utility costs, such as operations and maintenance, depreciation, taxes, and other general utility costs. These costs are determined using historical information. They are adjusted for any known and measurable changes. There is a significant amount of judgment involved in determining these changes. There can also be many questions as to whether costs are properly classified as utility costs and whether they should be above or below the line and therefore included in the cost of service. Cost of service includes depreciation, which is the recovery of assets invested in providing utility services.

Cost of capital. The final component of the revenue requirement calculation is the determination of the cost of capital and rate of return. This is frequently the most debated item in a utility's rate case. It involves a considerable amount of subjectivity in its calculation. Return is what the utility shareholders receive for the use of their money. Return is designed to provide the recovery of interest and equity costs, including preferred and common dividends. The appropriate overall rate of return is based on the weighted cost of the various sources of capital reflected in the utility's capital structure. An example of the development of an overall rate of return would include long-term debt, and preferred and common stock of the company. The amount of each one of these sources of capital is multiplied by its percentage of the total amount of its capital and then multiplied by the cost of the capital. Refer to Figure 16-1 for an example.

The costs of long-term debt and preferred stock are often easily attainable because most debt and preferred stock has a stated rate. The most debated issue in the cost of capital is the cost of common equity. There are no stated rates for the cost of common equity and this area involves the most judgment. The concept of the cost of capital as an opportunity cost is consistent with the standards of fair rate of return that were formulated in *Bluefield Water Works and Improvement Company v. Public Service Commission of West Virginia* (262 U.S. 679,692). In that case, the court ruled

> A public utility is entitled to such rates as will permit it to earn a return on the value of the property which it employs for the convenience of the public equal to that generally being made at the time and in the same general part of the country on investments in other business undertakings which are attended by corresponding risks and uncertainties ...

Additionally, in 1944, in *Federal Power Commission v. Hope Natural Gas Company* (320 U.S. 591), the court found that the standards of a fair rate of return require that the return be (1) commensurate with the return to enterprises of corresponding risks, (2) sufficient to maintain the credit and financial integrity of the regulated company, and (3) adequate to allow the company to attract capital.

Generally, there are two common methods used to determine return on equity — comparable earnings and discounted cash flow. Comparable earnings consists of developing (1) historical earnings by various comparison groups, with consideration given for relative risks and uncertainties; and (2) the level of earnings needed to attract capital, including data regarding interest coverages and bond ratings. The principle problem in applying the comparable earnings test is in selecting an acceptable sample of comparable companies.

The discounted cash flow technique for determining return on common equity is a formula approach based on the fact that the price of the common share is equal to the present value of the investor's expectation of all future income to be received from such share. The number of assumptions required to solve for the required discounted return, such as projecting what investors

Figure 16-1 ⊠ Cost of capital example

	Amount	Percent of total	Cost, *percent*	Composite Cost, *percent*
Long-term debt	$100,000	50	9	4.5
Preferred stock	20,000	10	6	.6
Common equity	80,000	40	13	5.2
	$200,000	100		10.3

expect when they purchase the stock, does not make this method any more reliable than the comparable earnings approach.

Some regulators will include other items in determining the cost of capital, such as accumulated deferred income taxes, accumulated deferred investment tax credits, customer deposits, and short-term debt.

The overall rate of return is multiplied against the rate base to determine the return requirement. Return requirement is added to the utility's cost of service to arrive at an overall revenue requirement. The revenue requirement is compared to the revenues generated from the current rate structure to determine the revenue increase or decrease that will result from the rate proceeding.

Once the total revenue requirements have been established, an equitable distribution of the cost of service to the various customer classes must be devised. The cost of serving each customer class is different, depending on the type of facility being served and the usage pattern of each class. Generally, these are broken up into residential, commercial, and large industrial users. There also may be separate classifications for municipal or federal usage.

The final step in the rate-making process is to set rates that reflect the results of the allocation cost study and collect the authorized revenue requirement. This process is called rate design. The rate design process applies information obtained from the cost study to the class billing data to develop the rate charge for each service offered.

The cost-of-service studies are usually based on one or two methodologies — imbedded or marginal. An imbedded cost-of-service study represents the total historical or forecasted cost of serving each consumer group. A marginal cost study looks at the cost of providing each consumer group with an additional increment of service.

⊠ Reporting

Regulators may impose various reporting requirements on the utility. Many regulators require annual financial reports to be filed. These reports generally include year-end financial statements and detailed supporting financial and operating statistics. The purpose of the reports is to enable the regulator to monitor the financial and operating performance of the utility. If a utility is operating at levels significantly above or below results expected from its last rate hearing, the regulator may require the utility to file a rate case in order to adjust rates appropriately. Annual reports are completed based on a prescribed format so that regulators can compare utilities and easily identify required data.

In addition to annual reports, a regulator may require special reports related to monitoring specific data, such as cost conservation efforts, construction, or compliance with agreements. Reports may also result from rate hearings in order to provide additional or continued information on subjects of interest to the regulator.

CHAPTER SEVENTEEN

Management and Other Reports

Effective decisions by water utility management are critical for the successful operation of a utility. In order to make effective decisions, managers must be provided with appropriate, timely information. The following general principles of financial report preparation (presented in chapters 6 and 15) are particularly relevant to management reports:

- the requirements of the readers for whom the report is intended should dictate the nature of the data presented and the manner of presentation

- the data reported should be arranged in a logical and readily understandable manner

- the wording of the report should convey to the reader the precise meaning intended

- the information should be reported at the time it is needed

- no more time or effort should be expended in obtaining the information reported than the information is expected to be worth

The purpose of this chapter is to illustrate the application of these general principles to reports for water utility management.

⊠ The Nature of Accounting Reports for Management

Accounting reports provide water utility management with information required for the fulfillment of its basic tasks — the formulation of plans to achieve the objectives of the enterprise, and the control of operations to accomplish planned results. Financial reports to external groups provide summarized financial and other information about the water utility. Conventional financial statements and other information published for external groups are reported and recognized internally as well. These reports include a balance sheet providing information concerning asset, liability, and equity balances as of the end of the accounting period; an income statement furnishing information about revenues earned and expenses incurred during a given accounting period; and a statement of cash flow providing information about changes in cash position during a given accounting period. This historical information provided by conventional financial statements furnishes an overall means for evaluating prior decisions and serves as a basis for planning the future operations, financial needs, and conditions of the enterprise.

An important distinction exists between financial reporting to external groups and internal reporting to management. External financial reporting traditionally has been oriented toward providing historical stewardship information. Internal reporting, on the other hand, emphasizes information for management planning and control, and thus is oriented toward providing forecasted as well as historical information. Since management alone is responsible for planning and controlling day-to-day operations of a water utility, and is principally responsible for formulating and implementing overall policies and long-range plans, the accounting information needs of management typically are more extensive than those of external groups. Hence, the number and frequency of management reports, and often the detail presented therein, are greater. The formulation by water utility management of overall policies and long-rang plans is often subject to influence or approval by external groups such as state public service commissions.

⊠ The General Structure of the Management Reporting System

The degree of detail presented in a report to management depends on the level of management for which the report is intended. The generally accepted reporting rule is that the higher the echelon of management to which a report is directed, the more summarized and broadened in scope the report should be.

Each manager should receive action reports concerning those activities for which he is responsible. Typically, managers at the lower levels in the organization have direct responsibility for detailed operation of their segment of the organization. At succeeding higher levels the responsibility becomes more general in nature. Consequently, action reports to managers with direct operating responsibility for a relatively small segment of the utility should furnish detailed information as to that segment. However, reports to managers at successively higher levels should furnish less and less detail about larger and larger segments. Summarized reports may be accompanied by supporting schedules of detailed information if managers at higher echelons desire.

The concept of reporting discussed above is sometimes called "responsibility reporting." In applying the responsibility concept to report preparation, and to the underlying information collection system, historical costs must be accumulated and reported by "responsibility unit" to provide managers with a basis for budgeting future operations. Thus, the management information flow is designed to coincide with lines of responsibility and authority within the water utility's organizational structure. Individual managers and supervisors receive reports that emphasize the costs that they can control and for which they are held responsible.

For control purposes, exception reporting may be employed. In applying the exception concept within the framework of the responsibility reporting system, material or significant deviations from plans are emphasized. Water utility managers, particularly those managers holding high-level positions within the water utility's organizational structure, do not have time to continually oversee every aspect of the operations for which they are responsible. Therefore, reports to managers should highlight the trouble spots that require the attention of management, rather than emphasizing those aspects of the water utility's activities that are proceeding satisfactorily and are conforming to plans.

Each water utility's management reporting system should be tailored to the existing organizational structure. A management reporting system encompasses the concept of different reports for different levels of management and the concept of responsibility reporting.

⊠ Types of Management Reports

Although reports to water utility management can be classified in several different ways, a convenient grouping consists of planning reports (forecasts and budgets), control (performance) reports, and informational reports. Each of these categories of reports has a different purpose and requires different report design, content, and timing.

Planning reports are concerned with proposed programs for a water utility's operating activities, capital investment, and financial condition. The purpose of control reports is to assist in controlling operations, capital investment, and financial condition, by emphasizing areas in need of corrective action. Informational reports are intended to furnish water utility management with pertinent information for use in formulating long-range plans, in coordinating activities of the various segments of the organization, and for determining policy.

Many planning, control, and informational reports are prepared routinely for management. However, routine reports are not always suited to meet particular problems faced by water utility management. Special reports may be needed to furnish information relevant to particular decisions. The accounting and reporting system must be capable of producing information appropriate to these special needs. Examples of nonroutine situations requiring special reports or studies are proposed rate changes and the issuance of new securities. Although each special study is unique, certain steps are common to all. These steps include (1) defining the problem, (2) estimating costs, revenues, and investment affected by alternative proposals, (3) comparing costs, revenues, and investment associated with alternatives, and (4) choosing among alternatives.

The scope and content of planning, control, and informational reports vary depending on the particular level of management to which the reports are directed. Following is a discussion of the application of specific planning, control, and informational reports to each level of management. The discussion is limited to a description of the information included in reports to water utility management.

⊠ Planning Reports

Planning reports may be very broad in scope, encompassing a major portion of the activities of a business. Planning reports may also be specialized, focusing on a specific aspect of the activities of a water utility. Planning reports are a formal expression of a utility's objectives and the means to be used in achieving those objectives. Budgets, forecasts, proposals, or estimates are names given to reports in this category.

Routine Planning Reports for Policy-Making Groups

The policy-making group for a water utility establishes the objectives of the utility. This group is responsible for authorizing plans and overseeing the activities of the water utility. It is generally not involved with the day-to-day operations of the utility. In the case of a government-owned water utility, the policy-making groups may include the city council (or water commission, city water board, or water authority board) and the mayor or city manager. In the case of an investor-owned water utility, the board of directors serves as the policy-making group.

Planning reports for the policy-making group include both utility-wide planning reports and specialized planning reports. Major, routine, utility-wide planning reports may include

- an operating budget
- a capital expenditures budget
- a financing plan
- forecasted financial statements

Each of these reports should be presented in summarized form accompanied by detailed supporting statements. A summary statement of estimated revenue and expense (or operating budget summary statement), for example, should be submitted to the policy-making group to aid it in its review of the detailed budget. Approval by that group is a necessary legal step for a municipal utility, and a customary step for an investor-owned utility. The proposed budget figures in this statement for the budget year may be compared with the adopted budget figures and the actual figures for the current year. The comparison permits the reader of the statement to observe significant changes in revenues and expenses occurring from one year to the next.

The detailed operating budget should be developed along the lines of authority and responsibility. Budgets should be developed for each operating department of the utility, for each section of each department, and for any further subdivisions within the utility organization.

In addition to a report concerning the operating budget, the policy-making group generally receives reports concerning the capital expenditures budget. These reports frequently are prepared for a five-year period, although some water utilities prepare capital expenditures budgets to cover more extended periods. Usually the five-year budget is revised annually, with the current year being dropped and the plan extended for an additional year, so that it remains a five-year plan. As in the case of reports concerning the operating budget, reports to the policy-making group concerning proposed capital expenditures are typically composed of a summary statement supported by detailed information concerning individual capital expenditure projects. The budget shows the estimated cost of additions and the credits to the utility plant accounts that reflect retirements. The budget may also show estimated amounts expended as of the beginning of the budget period for capital investment projects in progress.

The summary of budgeted capital expenditures is supported by individual project budgets. Typically, each individual project budget includes a project number, a description of the project, the purpose and necessity of the project, the scheduled starting and completion dates for the project, the estimated cost of the project, the estimated incremental operating revenues and expenses associated with the project, and the estimated return on the investment. Individual project budgets are prepared for uncompleted major projects (carry-over projects from the current year) as well as for new projects.

A summary of proposed capital expenditures, together with individual project reports, are submitted to the city council or board of directors for review and approval. Capital expenditures budgets and supporting documents are further discussed in chapter 4.

Based on the operating budget and capital expenditures budget, a proposed financing plan should be developed to present the proposed means of financing operating activities and capital expenditure activities for a given period of time (typically for one year or more). Frequently, the financing plan takes the form of a cash flow forecast, by months or quarters, that includes not only estimated cash receipts and disbursements resulting from operating activities and capital expenditure activities, but also proposed sources of cash to meet cash shortages.

Using a one-year forecast of cash receipts and disbursements by quarters, with the earliest quarter forecast by month, one can forecast the need for short-term and long-term borrowing in order to meet any cash shortages and to maintain a minimum cash balance. Cash flow estimates typically require periodic revisions so that estimates serve as useful financial planning guides. Cash flow forecasts are discussed in detail in chapter 4.

Reports of forecasted financial position at the end of a given period of time (that is, at the end of the next year or quarter) also may be rendered to the city council or board of directors. A statement that summarizes the estimated financial position may take the form of a traditional balance sheet for a water utility, with estimated figures as of the end of the planning period substituted for actual amounts. A statement of estimated financial condition reflects contemplated changes in utility plant, current assets, long-term debt, current liabilities, and equity accounts. The summary statement should be accompanied by detailed schedules and, where appropriate, other information in support of the principal balance-sheet accounts. A report of the forecasted financial position typically represents the final routine report prepared for a particular planning period. The preparation of this report depends to a large extent on information generated by other planning reports, such as the operating budget, the capital expenditures budget, and the financing plan.

Special Planning Reports for Policy-Making Groups

In addition to routine planning reports prepared for policy-making groups, special planning reports also may be required from time to time. The preparation of special planning reports usually involves analysis of a particular aspect of the water utility's activities.

Probably the most important of all special planning reports is the report which deals with proposed rate changes. Rate case preparation and presentation is extremely complex. In the case of investor-owned and municipally owned water utilities subject to rate regulation by state public service commissions, revenue requirements generally are determined by applying the traditional public utility approach, that is, establishing rates sufficient to permit a given return on a defined rate base. Within the context of the general approach, however, there is much variation among the many different regulatory jurisdictions as to the exact procedures for establishing rate structures to meet the anticipated revenue requirements. In the case of government-owned utilities not subject to rate regulation by regulatory commissions, revenue requirements may not be founded on any rate base or rate of return, but rather on the cash needs of the water utility. There is a wide variation among government-owned water utilities as to the kinds of cash outlays that are to be covered by revenues. In addition, no complete conformity among government-owned water utilities regarding the techniques for establishing a rate structure that will meet the anticipated revenue requirements has been attained. The subject of water rates and rate structures is discussed further in chapter 16. This section is limited to a general discussion of the types of information and financial statements found in a report concerning proposed rate changes.

The purpose of a rate study is to establish the need for a rate change and to propose and justify a rate structure that meets a utility's revenue requirements. Rates should be at a level that permits a water utility to receive total revenues in an amount sufficient "to provide adequate water service and assure the maintenance, development, and perpetuation of the system." In the case of investor-owned and government-owned water utilities subject to control by state regulatory commissions, a rate study in accordance with the traditional public utility approach, typically will determine the amount of total revenues needed to cover operating expenses (operation and maintenance expenses, depreciation and amortization charges, and taxes) and to permit a reasonable rate of return on an established rate base.

The report concerning proposed rate changes typically includes both historical and pro forma schedules of operation and maintenance expenses, depreciation and amortization charges, and taxes, all supported by detailed analyses. The report also includes information concerning rate base elements (valued at original cost, reproduction cost, or other bases specified by the applicable regulatory agency) on which the allowed return is computed.

In the case of municipally owned water utilities not subject to rate regulation by state commissions, a rate study in accordance with the "cash needs" approach, typically will determine the amount of total revenue needed to cover operation and maintenance expenses, debt service requirements, plant replacements, and normal plant extensions and improvements. In some cases, total revenues also may be required to cover other cash outlays, such as appropriations for major improvements, contributions to other municipal funds, and payments in lieu of taxes. The report concerning proposed rate changes should include pro forma statements of cash outlays that are required to be covered by revenues. The pro forma statements should be accompanied by supporting schedules.

In addition to establishing the amount of total revenue required, the report will present a proposed schedule of rates and charges for attaining the needed revenue. The process of developing this proposed schedule requires extensive analyses of plant investment costs and the various costs of service. Ultimately, the annual revenue requirements (or costs of service) must be distributed among the various customer classes in order to develop and design the proposed schedule of rates and charges. Ordinarily, once the revenue requirements have been established, the development of the proposed rate schedule involves three major steps, which may be briefly summarized as follows:

Step 1 — Allocation of the costs of service to cost functions. This allocation is most commonly founded on either the "base-extra capacity" method or the "commodity-demand" method. The first method results in assignment of costs of service to the following three cost functions or categories: base costs, extra capacity costs, and customer costs. The commodity-demand method also results in assignment of costs of service to the following three cost functions or categories: commodity costs, demand costs, and customer costs. Fire protection costs may be an additional basic cost function employed under either method of allocation. Applied properly, the two methods provide quite similar final results.

Under each method, utility plant and other rate base elements are also allocated to the cost functions. The allocation of rate-base elements serves as a useful basis for the allocation of certain cost-of-service elements to the cost functions. For example, under the public utility approach, depreciation, taxes, and the return on the rate base may be allocated to the cost functions in proportion to the allocation of rate-base elements. Similarly, under the "cash needs" approach, annual debt service requirements, outlays for plant replacements, and outlays for normal plant extensions and improvements may be so allocated.

Step 2 — Allocation of functional costs to customer classes. Costs of service, having been classified into the functional groups, are subsequently allocated to customer classes. To the extent practical, each group of functional costs should be allocated among customer classes in proportion to the relative responsibility that each class bears for cost incurrence. Typically, there are three principal customer classes, including residential, commercial, and industrial. Fire protection, both public and private, may be considered to be a separate class. Additionally, special customers (such as large institutions and other water utilities) and special uses (such as air conditioning and irrigation) may be given separate consideration in the allocation.

Step 3 — Development of rate schedules. Once costs have been distributed to customer classes, the last step is to develop a schedule of rates and charges. The objective is to establish a schedule of rates and charges for water service that will, insofar as possible, result in the recovery of costs of serving different classes of customers, while maintaining reasonable equity within and between customer classes. A proposed rate schedule for normal uses (domestic, commercial, and industrial) typically is composed of a series of rate blocks combined with a periodic service charge or minimum charge. Charges for fire protection typically take the form of a charge per hydrant or per connection.

The three-step analysis outlined above is commonly referred to as a cost-of-service study. It represents a critical component in the total report of, or application for, proposed changes in water rates. A cost-of-service study, which is prepared by water utility staff and/or outside consultants, typically results in a voluminous and detailed document. Successful completion of such a study requires the expertise of accountants, statisticians, engineers, and others experienced in rate matters.

There are procedures other than the one outlined above that may be used for determining rate change proposals. Rate determination is influenced by many factors, including past practices, legal requirements, local conditions, form of ownership, and nature of control (state regulatory commission or local). Depending on these and other facts, the form and content of the final document submitted to a policy-making group concerning proposed rate changes will vary among water utilities. However, every report of proposed rate changes should include all pertinent details of the analysis used in developing the proposal.

There are many other circumstances that require the submission of special planning reports to top management. These reports typically involve an evaluation of alternative solutions to particular problems. For example, special reports concerning long-term financing alternatives may be required by a policy-making group. Special reports also may be needed to evaluate alternative capital investment projects. As an example, a special report may be needed to show the evaluation of alternatives for increasing the capacity of the water system, perhaps comparing additional pumping facilities with additional distribution reservoirs or standpipes.

Planning Reports at the General Manager Level

As in the case of a policy-making group, the interests of a general manager or other executives with comparable management responsibilities encompass the entire operation of a water utility. However, a general manager is concerned with more detailed aspects of operations and day-to-day activities of a water utility than is the policy-making group. A general manager directs and conducts the operations of a water utility in accordance with objectives and policies established by the policy-making group. The general manager is responsible for keeping the policy-making group informed and recommending changes in objectives and policies.

The major routine planning reports at the general manager level include the operating budget, the capital investment program, and the financing plan. Whereas a policy-making group may be interested primarily in the summaries of routine planning reports, a general manager is also concerned with the information underlying the summaries.

In the case of operating budgets, a general manager's attention typically would be focused on the higher levels of budget responsibility. The first level is of particular interest to the general manager, because at this level operating expenses are budgeted for activities over which he or she has direct control. The general manager is also concerned with the next level, since he or she will use the planned expenses developed for this level as guidelines for evaluating the performance and efficiency of division managers who are under his or her direct supervision.

The capital expenditures budget also is of interest to a general manager, assuming that the capital expenditure activities of the utility are his or her responsibility. The general manager is responsible for preparing the capital expenditures budget to be submitted to the policy-making group for approval. A proposed capital expenditures budget, which typically covers a five-year period, is revised annually based on individual proposed capital expenditure projects submitted to a general manager by subordinates. Individual capital expenditure projects are then summarized and included in the new proposed five-year capital investment program. A capital expenditures budget, once approved by the policy-making group, provides authorization for conducting specific extension and improvement projects, replacement projects, and relocation projects. Each capital expenditures budget is supported by individual project budgets that summarize the important aspects of particular capital investment projects. A general manager is responsible for execution of the approved capital expenditures budget.

Ordinarily, a general manager also is responsible for the preparation and execution of a financing plan. In some municipalities this responsibility is given by law to the chief financial officer. Actual preparation would usually be delegated by the finance officer. An approved financing plan indicates to a general manager the availability of cash for financing the activities of a water utility and the sources from which the cash may be obtained. A financing plan also permits a general manager to plan a financing schedule. For example, a monthly statement of estimated cash receipts and disbursements resulting from current operations may indicate a deficiency of cash from time to time during the year. Based on this statement, a general manager or chief financial officer can plan a short-term borrowing schedule, if legally permitted, to finance current operations during these times of cash shortages. Likewise, monthly statements of cash receipts and disbursements expected to result from current operations allow a general manager to plan a schedule for repaying short-term debts. A financing plan also indicates cash requirements and approved sources of cash for financing a capital expenditures program. Hence, a general manager can plan a time schedule for obtaining long-term sources of cash.

There also are special planning reports prepared for a general manager. For example, he or she is interested in reports concerning rate changes because rate changes affect the activities of a water utility, particularly the commercial division, which, in the figures given, is responsible for billing, collecting, and customer contact. In addition, a general manager is concerned with the evaluation of alternative sources for obtaining borrowed funds, and special planning reports that deal with the activities of the operating divisions of the water utility.

Planning Reports for Division Managers and Supervisors

The duties and responsibilities of division managers and supervisors are more restricted than those of a general manager, and relate to particular divisions (in the case of division managers) and to particular sections and subsections of divisions (in the case of supervisors).

Each division manager should be particularly concerned with the operating budget as it relates to his division. A division manager is interested in the division-level budget because this portion of the budget concerns planned division operating costs that he must strive to meet. A division manager is also concerned with the section level of the budget since he or she uses budgeted operating expenses at this level to evaluate the performance of section supervisors.

Section supervisors are concerned with a budget as it relates to their performance and the performance of those persons directly responsible to them. Supervisors of subsections are concerned with the budget level that relates to their responsibilities and duties.

Each division manager should be interested in those projects included in a capital expenditures budget that relate to his or her division because these projects affect the divisional operations and because he or she is responsible for supervising construction work if it is performed by division personnel instead of by a contractor.

Other planning reports should be of interest to division managers and subordinated supervisors. For example, the commercial division's management personnel should be particularly interested in reports concerning estimated operating and nonoperating revenue budgets, rate studies (especially the parts of the study that outline estimated revenue requirements and proposed rate schedules), and other planning reports concerning meter reading, billing, and collection functions.

⬦ Control Reports

As in the case of planning reports, control reports are prepared for all management levels and for the policy-making group. The purpose of control reports is to indicate performance over a period of time, to point out weaknesses, and to permit appropriate corrective action to be taken.

Control Reports for Policy-Making Groups

A policy-making group is responsible for the performance of an entire utility. The group delegates authority to a general manager for operations, but it cannot delegate responsibility. In order to discharge its responsibility, the policy-making group must evaluate the effectiveness with which the general manager performs his duties. The general manager's effectiveness is indicated by trends of earnings, changes in the utility's financial plan, and other financial and operating statistics.

Policy-making groups should receive a monthly summary of operating results in terms of revenue and expense. Statements of revenue and expense should show both actual results for the month and budget figures for the same month. Actual results also may be compared with actual results for the corresponding period during the previous year. Variations between actual results and budgeted results (or actual results for the current period and actual results for the corresponding preceding period) may be pointed out with an explanation of the causes of any significant variations. In addition to presenting a comparison of monthly figures, the monthly statement of revenue and expenses also may show comparative actual figures for the current fiscal year-to-date and actual figures for the corresponding period of the preceding fiscal year.

A policy-making group requires the monthly statements of revenue and expense for the entire utility in order to be aware of overall trends. The group also needs to receive comparative statements of actual operating expenses and budgeted operating expenses, by major responsibility areas, so that specific problem areas are brought to its attention. The group needs to be aware of problem areas so that it can guide and evaluate the general manager's handling of the problems.

In addition to monthly operating reports, control reports concerning the amount of capital expenditures and the status of capital expenditure projects also should be prepared for policy-making bodies as frequently as needed, typically at monthly or quarterly intervals. Capital expenditure control reports are usually composed of a listing of major individual capital expenditure projects; minor projects may be grouped. The report indicates for each project the amount authorized for expenditure, the amount of actual expenditures to date, the amount committed or encumbered (purchase orders, contracts, or salary commitments not yet paid or recorded as a liability), the balance of authorized funds available to complete the project, and the percentage of completion.

For projects that show an insufficient balance of authorized funds to complete the projects, status reports should include an explanation of the reason for the deficiencies. If total costs to complete a given project are expected to exceed budget authorization by a substantial amount, then authorization to make additional expenditures should be required. In the case of municipally owned water utilities subject to a legally binding capital expenditures budget, it may be necessary for utility management to obtain a supplemental appropriation in order to issue commitment documents and make expenditures beyond original authorizations.

Control reports concerning financial condition also should be submitted to individuals at the policy-making level. Balance sheets ordinarily are rendered on a monthly or quarterly basis and should present comparative data for at least two comparable periods. Particular balance-sheet accounts, such as cash, receivables, materials and supplies, utility plant, and retained earnings, may be supported by detailed schedules if the policy-making group desires the information. Supporting schedules may indicate the detailed composition of accounts or may analyze changes in particular balance-sheet accounts from the end of a preceding period to the end of the current period.

Control Reports at the General Manager Level

As in the case of control reports at the policy-making level, major control reports at the general manager level also include reports concerning operating results, capital expenditures, and financial position. Whereas reports at the policy-making level are stated in summary form, reports for the general manager include as much detailed information as is necessary for effective control of operations of a utility and its operating divisions.

The primary report for controlling operations is the report that compares actual operating results with budget estimates or other standards of performance. For control purposes, reports of operating results should classify expenses by responsibility areas. A general manager is interested primarily in reports of operating results generated for levels reporting directly to him or her. The general manager is also interested in the next level because control reports at this level are used by him or her to guide and evaluate the performance of division managers. Responsibility reports should be prepared and submitted to a general manager on a monthly basis, or more frequently if needed for adequate control of operations.

A general manager also is concerned with the status of capital expenditure projects. Periodic project status reports submitted to the general manager, preferably on a monthly basis, should include information similar to that included in capital expenditure control reports submitted at the policy-making level. For each project, information concerning actual labor costs, material costs, and overhead costs should be included in the status report and compared with original estimates. If actual labor costs, material costs, or other costs vary (or are expected to vary) from original estimates, then the reasons for each variation should be explained in the status report.

The financial condition of a water utility is also of concern to its general manager. Therefore, reports concerning the financial position, and particularly the working capital position, are required by him or her. To keep abreast of the working capital position, frequent reports may be developed for the general manager concerning current assets and current liabilities. For example, daily or weekly reports of cash receipts, disbursements, and balances reflect the cash position of a water utility. Other monthly status reports concerning current assets and current liabilities include aged listings of accounts receivable, listings of investment in and usage of materials and supplies, and statements of bank borrowings and loan repayments.

Control Reports for Division Managers and Supervisors

The primary control reports at the division manager and supervisor levels concern operating results. Responsibility reports concerning operating expenses should be prepared on a monthly basis. Division managers are primarily interested in reports that reflect their performance and that reflect the performance of supervisors directly accountable to the division managers. Supervisors are interested in control reports that relate to their particular duties.

Division managers and supervisors also are concerned with progress reports covering capital expenditure projects that relate to their particular areas of responsibility. Since division managers and supervisors may be directly involved in construction activity and may be directly responsible for control of labor and material costs incurred in particular capital expenditure projects, they should be furnished with periodic status reports.

There are control reports other than those dealing with operating expenses and capital expenditure projects that may be required by division managers and supervisors. For example, in the case of a commercial division manager and the supervisors within his division, monthly reports that compare actual and budgeted (or estimated) revenue by customer classification, monthly aged listings of accounts receivable, and monthly tabulations of customer complaints, may prove helpful for pointing out deficiencies and improving future operations. For all division managers and supervisors, weekly labor cost reports that indicate both labor costs for regular operations and overtime costs incurred due to special work conditions or emergencies, can be helpful in controlling operations.

⊠ Informational Reports

There are other reports to various levels of water utility management that cannot be classified as planning reports or control reports — they may be called informational reports. The purpose of informational reports is to supply information to water utility management for use in future planning, coordinating activities of the various segments of the organization, and policy determination. Informational reports may be broad in scope or may focus on specific aspects of the activities of the water utility.

Informational reports should not be confused with planning reports. Planning reports involve proposed programs concerning a water utility's operating activities, capital investment, and financial condition; they relate to the means for achieving predetermined objectives. Information reports, on the other hand, provide data to be used by management to evaluate alternatives to proposed programs and to establish future plans and objectives.

Informational reports also may be used to familiarize divisional management and supervisors with all aspects of a utility's activities. Divisional managers and supervisors should be furnished with information about segments of the organization other than their own in order to promote coordination among all segments of the utility. Information indicating to the manager the contribution made by his responsibility area to the overall effort of a water utility can aid in keeping morale at a high level.

Long-Range Study

A long-range study concerned with various aspects of a water utility's future, including estimates of the future demand for water and future sources available for water supply, is one type of major information report. Long-range studies, frequently conducted by outside research organizations, may serve as the basis for developing future capital expenditure programs.

Trend Report

Another type of informational report is the trend report, which is concerned with changes over a period of time in various aspects of a utility's activities or in conditions affecting a utility's activities. Important types of information pertaining to various aspects of utility activities found in trend reports are as follows:

Relationships between various balance-sheet accounts. These are ordinarily expressed as ratios or percentages, such as a debt-to-equity ratio.

Relationships between revenues and various expense accounts. These are ordinarily expressed as ratios or percentages. Examples include maintenance expense as a percentage of operating revenue, taxes as a percentage of revenues, and taxes as a percentage of net income.

Relationships between particular balance-sheet accounts and particular expense or revenue accounts. These are ordinarily expressed as ratios. Examples include accounts receivable turnover and materials and supplies turnover.

Sources of revenue. Examples include the number of customers within various classifications and the number of fire hydrants.

Operating revenues and operating costs on a per unit basis. Examples include average revenue per customer per unit of time, revenue per million gallons (or litres) metered, and operating cost per million gallons (or litres) metered.

Water pumpage and usage. Examples include millions of gallons (or litres) pumped per unit of time, average daily pumpage, maximum daily pumpage, and average metered water usage per day.

Information pertaining to external conditions affecting a water utility's activities should also be presented in trend reports. Important categories are as follows:

Rainfall. Examples include actual inches (or centimetres) of rainfall per unit of time, normal rainfall in inches (or centimetres) for a particular period of time, and the number of days of rain during a period of time.

Temperature. Examples include actual temperature over a period of time and normal temperature for a particular period of time.

Population in franchised areas. Examples include industrial firms, residential homes, and people.

Analytical Report

Another type of information report that may be used is an analytical report. Analytical reports are concerned with many facets of the activities of a water utility. Examples of analytical reports include analyses of operating revenues by customer or territory, changes in net operating revenues, and changes in retained earnings. Also, refer to the Governmental Accounting Standard Board's (GASB's) Preliminary Views on "Service Efforts and Accomplishments Reporting" for proposed performance measures reporting.

⊠ Summary

This chapter outlines a basic structure for a water utility management reporting system and presents some basic guidelines for the development of management reports. The management reporting principles outlined in chapter 6 serve as useful guidelines for preparing management reports. The management reporting principles may be restated as follows:

1. A report to a member of a water utility management team should present information concerning the particular area over which the manager has responsibility.
2. A report to a member of a water utility management team should emphasize the information needed by the manager to discharge his planning and control responsibilities efficiently and effectively.
3. The amount of detail presented in a management report should be inversely related to the breadth of responsibilities exercised by the manager for whom the report is intended.
4. All important information relevant to a decision should be provided at the time needed.
5. The terminology used in a report and the manner of presentation of the information should be understandable by the individual for whom the report is intended.
6. The expenditure of time and effort to provide information must be no greater than the expected value of the information.

The first and third principles are achieved primarily through a system of responsibility reporting, the structure of which, as discussed in this chapter, should coincide with organizational lines of authority and responsibility. The second management reporting principle is achieved primarily through the use of exception reporting. Interpretative remarks should be included in management reports to explain significant deviations from plans and to indicate what corrective actions have been taken.

The fourth principle concerns the timeliness of reports. The purpose of reports determines their required frequency and promptness. To be useful, reports, particularly control reports, must be prompt; forfeiture of a certain amount of accuracy may be called for to ensure against tardy reports. Care in report preparation should be commensurate with use. All water utility reports should be accurate to the degree consistent with timeliness; however, the more important a report, the greater should be the care extended in its preparation.

The fifth principle concerns the format of management reports and the terminology used in management reports. The format of a report should be suited to the individual using the report. Formal accounting statements, statistical tabulations, pictorial presentations (graphs, charts, and diagrams), or a combination of these may be used to present information. The forms used depend on the desires and sophistication of the reader. When possible, the format of reports should be consistent from one period to another. People become accustomed to certain formats and frequent changes may cause confusion. Where desirable changes can be made, however, a standard format should not serve as a barrier to improvement. Reports also should be concise, simple, and clear so that the reader may secure essential facts with a minimum of time and effort. The language and terms employed in the report should be familiar to management. The use of accounting language and terms should be commensurate with the sophistication of the reader.

Finally, the sixth principle concerns the cost of report preparation. The cost of any report (in terms of time, effort, and money) should be no greater than the benefits derived from having the report (or the loss incurred from not having the report). The cost of report preparation is substantial and water utility management should ensure that the information that it requests can be supplied at a reasonable cost.

PART FIVE

⬦ Financial Management Functions

CHAPTER EIGHTEEN

Financing

The accounting policies, systems, and procedures of the water utility must be integrated with its overall financial goals and objectives. In turn, the financial goals and objectives should support the overall mission of the water utility. The mission of the utility and the goals and objectives associated with the financial management function (and other functions as well) should be documented to both establish a direction for, and to provide a measure of, financial management performance. This chapter focuses on the financing of water utility operations and how the accounting system helps support the funding process.

⊠ Financing Water Utility Operations

There are three primary funding sources for government-owned-and-operated water utilities

- revenues from rates and other fees and charges

- proceeds from issuance of debt

- receipts from contributions in aid of construction

Occasionally, ad valorem taxes are also used by local governments for repayment of general obligation debt used to finance water facilities, although this source is becoming rarer. The use of proceeds from the sale of common or preferred stock (a source widely used by investor-owned utilities) is unavailable to government-owned utilities.

A more comprehensive discussion of these financing sources is contained in the Manual of Water Supply Practices series published by the American Water Works Association. Among them include the following:

- Manual M1, *Water Rates*, discusses the development of rates, including the development of revenue requirements, cost allocation, and rate design.

- Manual M26, *Water Rates and Related Charges*, discusses other rates and charges, such as those for fire-protection services, capital contributions, and dedicated capacity.

- Manual M29, *Water Utility Capital Financing*, discusses the various means to finance plant investment and the numerous financial instruments involved.

- Manual M34, *Alternative Rates*, discusses such topics as lifeline rates, inverted-block rates, and uniform volume rates.

- Manual M35, *Revenue Requirements*, details the determination of revenues required from rates.

These manuals should be consulted for detailed presentations on financing sources. The focus here will be on how the accounting system supports the various financing mediums. The following discussion on accounting requirements is not intended to encompass all circumstances but rather to indicate how accounting requirements may differ as financial policy and local economic conditions vary.

⊠ Accounting Requirements

Rate Financing

Rates, fees, and other charges usually are the major sources of funding for operation and maintenance expenses, and the repayment of principal and interest costs of debt issues. In addition, some portion of plant investment is usually financed through rates. Accounting system requirements for rates and other fees are highly dependent on financial policy.

For example, if a financial policy of a water utility is to provide water service at cost, then the accounting function must produce the necessary information to permit the cost of service to be calculated. The more expansive the services provided (e.g., raw water, wholesale, retail, taps, plat review, etc.), the more detailed and extensive the accounting systems should be in order to provide for a determination of the cost of each service. Expanding the accounting system to provide particular cost information should, however, be weighed in relation to the benefits of that cost information. If, for instance, the cost to provide adequate information for a particular service is quite costly, the service provided is limited to a few customers, and it produces limited revenues, then expansion of the accounting system to produce that information may be inappropriate. Instead, one could rely on cost estimates or special studies to provide the needed cost data.

Another financial policy that can have an impact on accounting-system requirements is the method used to determine revenue requirements. Almost all local government utilities use either the cash or the utility method of calculating revenue requirements. Most governments use the cash basis method, which consists of determining the annual operating and maintenance expenses, debt service repayments, and capital outlay funded from revenues. The cash method is highly adaptable to the standard accounting and budgeting functions of most local governments that focus on the annual cash resources needed to provide service during the year.

The utility method, however, requires substantially different accounting information not customarily maintained in many local government accounting organizations. The different revenue requirement components include

- development of a rate base — generally original cost of plant investment less accumulated depreciation

- calculation of depreciation and amortization expense on plant investment

- determination of the cost of capital to apply as a rate of return on capital invested in plant

These different revenue requirement components call for much more emphasis on accounting for plant investment and depreciation, and how the plant was financed. Guidance for the added accounting needs can be obtained from investor-owned utility regulatory bodies that exclusively prescribe the utility method. Their long-standing, record-keeping practices can be very useful in developing the appropriate accounting practices for using the utility method in a governmental environment. While each state establishes its own accounting practices, the National Association of Regulatory Utility Commissioners (NARUC) has created a standard chart of accounts and other accounting guidelines that are widely adopted by the various state utility regulatory authorities. Even these guidelines, however, must be modified to meet the utility's goals, the local economic conditions in each community, and the governmental environment.

When a government utility offers both retail service to its citizens and wholesale service outside its corporate boundaries, record-keeping practices are likely to be affected. Those utilities that also provide wholesale service, for example, are more likely to use the utility method of determining revenue requirements at least for determining the cost of service to its wholesale customers. Thus, more emphasis should be given to such activities as plant accounting, depreciation studies, and the financing of plant facilities. Further, the utility's distribution system will probably be constructed in such a manner that one portion of it is used only by the retail customers, another portion is used in common by both wholesale and retail customers, and another portion may be used only by the wholesale customers. Under these circumstances, continuing property records need to be kept in sufficient detail to provide the information needed for allocation of distribution system costs to water service functions and customer classes. Such an allocation is frequently performed using the diameter of mains as an allocation basis. If the diameter of mains is used as the allocation basis, then the continuing property records should provide cost by main size as well as the related data on plant financing.

Many government water utilities also offer wastewater service, which adds considerable complexity to the accounting process. Ordinarily, there is an initial need to keep the costs of water service separate from those of wastewater. This separation of service costs frequently is derived from a policy to have each of the services be self-supporting. How the separation of costs is accomplished varies considerably and can have significant impacts on the cost and complexity of the accounting process. The two major bases are

- budget and account for all costs separately (e.g., 100 percent of all distribution system costs would be recorded as water costs; general management costs may be split one half to water and one half to wastewater or on some other defined basis)

- budget and account for all costs together and when cost-of-service studies are necessary, a separate cost allocation study is performed to separate water costs from wastewater costs

Many utilities use a combination of the two accounting bases to maintain a balance between service-cost separation and the cost to account for an increased level of detailed data.

Debt Issuance

There are two primary types of accounting data requirements related to the issuance of debt, especially revenue-supported bond issues. The most standard accounting system need for outstanding debt issues is the preparation of annual financial statements attested to by independent accountants. Almost all debt issues have a covenant requiring the preparation of annual financial statements within a stated time frame after the end of the utility's fiscal year. Chapter 15 contains considerable detail on how these annual financial reports are prepared.

The second type of accounting requirement is also related to the bond covenants, but the individual covenants may vary considerably from utility to utility. Typical covenant requirements include

- maintenance of cash reserves at specified levels for principal and interest, major repairs, or other purposes
- maintenance of revenue bond coverage at prescribed level(s) for various stated purposes
- definition of how net revenues available for coverage are to be calculated
- prescription of insurance coverage requirements
- use of proceeds from disposition of major assets used to provide service
- other matters that may be particular to any specific utility

Management should also be alert to any accounting definitions in long-term contracts, which from a legal standpoint, may be different for coverage calculation purposes than for financial statement presentation purposes. For example, recent contracts with the US Army Corps of Engineers for water supply storage have defined the payments for debt service on the cost to construct the reservoir as "operation and maintenance expenses." Therefore, for calculating revenue bond coverage, such payments should be treated as operation and maintenance expenses in arriving at net revenue available for debt service. For financial statement purposes, the outstanding debt and annual payments thereon would be classified as debt and payments thereon.

Besides historical accounting requirements for debt already issued, accounting records can also be used to help forecast the need for debt issues and other financing. Continued property records, for instance, should contain data on the date of asset acquisition and the asset's useful life so that replacement of these assets can be anticipated. If a particular type of asset (e.g., a distribution main), usually needs replacement in 50 years, then all distribution mains with acquisition dates about 50 years ago may need replacement. While it is recognized that few assets follow a precise useful-life pattern, the availability of historical asset data is very useful in forecasting an order of magnitude of financing needs for replacing assets. If the continuing property records also have the ability to use indices to indicate replacement cost, then the calculation of potential financing needs can be more easily performed.

Contributed Capital

Accounting for contributed capital is needed for rate-making, financial statement, and financial planning purposes. The financial statement and financial planning requirements can be met at a fairly high level of detail. For financial statement purposes, there is a need to classify contributed capital as a separate source of funding on the statement of cash flows and on the balance sheet. Additional detail, such as the source of the contribution (e.g., federal grant, or customer or developer contribution), can also be disclosed.

Financial planning requirements for contributed capital information relates primarily to the need to finance the replacement of those assets originally funded through contributions. Thus, the timely recording of all contributed assets in much the same detail as those funded from other sources is important.

For rate-making purposes, accounting for contributed assets must get quite detailed. The level of detail should be the same as that used to categorize plant investment (e.g., water supply, treatment, etc.). Probably the best way to accomplish this level of detail is to indicate the funding source(s) on the fixed-asset records at the time the asset is completed and put in plant-in-service. Information on the funding source(s) of assets by plant category, especially as to contributed assets, will permit the calculation of plant investment funded by debt and revenues for use in cost allocation under the cash basis method and the calculation of net plant investment for rate base determination under the utility method. Further, the amount of depreciation expense on contributed assets can also be determined for rate purposes and for financial statement purposes when depreciation expenses on contributed assets is charged to contributed capital accounts instead of retained earnings.

Also, refer to the Governmental Accounting Standards Board's (GASB's) 1993 Discussion Memorandum on "Reporting Contributions, Subsidies, Tap Fees, and Similar Inflows to Enterprise and Internal Service Funds and to Entities Using Proprietary Fund Accounting" for further information. The issues may have been resolved since publication of this manual.

CHAPTER NINETEEN

Audits

Audits are a fundamental element of corporate accountability. Audits provide objective, relevant information for decision making to the end users of that information, whether it be utility management, a regulatory agency, or the public.

Audits of water utilities consist of two general types, financial and performance, conducted by three different groups, independent or external auditors, internal auditors, and contracted consultants, and are typically monitored by the audit committee of the board of directors.

⊠ Financial Audits

Role of the Independent Auditor

Financial audits are primarily concerned with attesting that a utility's annual financial statements comply with generally accepted accounting principles (GAAP). Financial audits are conducted by independent auditors (certified public accountants) for use by third parties, particularly stockholders and bondholders, rating companies, and regulatory agencies. In order to attest to the fairness and dependability of the annual financial statements, the independent auditor examines not only the financial statements but also the underlying accounting records of the company and its systems of internal controls. In addition to the annual financial audit, the independent auditors may also perform special-purpose audits, such as those that may be required for special financing arrangements or grant audits required by granting agencies or organizations.

Internal Auditor's Role

The internal auditor shares with the independent auditor the same general concerns about corporate accountability, although the scope of responsibilities is generally larger. The internal auditor often assists the independent auditor with the financial audit of the company's financial statements and may even perform other financial-related audits for internal use by management, including those related to management performance.

The modern internal auditor's primary goal should be to provide management with independent and objective reviews of operational performance and assessments of the degree to which performance meets expectations. The internal auditor is in the unique position of being able to evaluate efficiency, effectiveness, and legitimacy of objectives, as well as to evaluate and improve internal controls and to perform other traditional auditing duties. Management and performance audits are further discussed later in this chapter.

The most difficult job for the internal auditor is remaining independent while being a "part" of management. To ensure independence, the internal auditor should adhere to the Institute of Internal Auditor's *Standards for the Professional Practice of Internal Auditing* and, if the utility is part of a governmental agency or unit, the internal auditor should also adhere to the General Accounting Office's (GAO's) *Standards for Audit of Governmental Organizations, Programs, Activities, and Functions.*

An important factor in maintaining independence is the internal auditor's organizational structure and lines of reporting responsibilities. These should be such that the auditor is free to examine any records, procedures, or processes deemed necessary under the circumstances. However, to further enhance independence, the internal auditor must have free access to the audit committee of the board of directors and the chief executive officer (CEO). This will also strengthen the auditor's image in the corporate structure. As a practical matter, however, neither the audit committee nor the CEO may be able to give the internal auditor adequate day-to-day attention. Therefore, the internal auditor usually has a "dotted-line" relationship with the audit committee and the CEO, while reporting directly to a senior officer, normally the chief financial officer, on a day-to-day basis. It is important that this organizational structure and associated reporting lines be clearly defined and communicated to the organization.

Cooperation between the internal auditor and the independent auditor is important to provide adequate audit coverage without duplicating efforts, and to control audit costs. The two groups are similar in that they employ comparable procedures and are both concerned about corporate accountability and the system of internal controls. Both examine accounting records and procedures and prepare working papers. Often the work of the internal auditor will reduce the amount of substantive testing the independent auditor will perform on the system of internal controls, a critical element supporting the fairness of the financial statements, thus reducing the independent auditor's time and cost. Because both groups are similar, their work plans should be coordinated and closely monitored by the audit committee of the board of directors to ensure adequate audit coverage while controlling audit costs.

The scope of the internal auditor's work is broad. As discussed, the internal auditor may assist the independent auditor with the annual financial audit, perform other financial audits for internal management, and perform performance audits of operations. In addition, many internal audit departments conduct special investigations of fraud, waste, and abuse. They may also conduct postcompletion reviews of capital projects. Often the internal auditor is requested to provide technical assistance in such areas as internal controls or performance measures. However, to protect his or her independence, the internal auditor must be careful *not* to make the decisions of management, but rather provide management the information necessary to make informed decisions.

The Role of the Audit Committee

The audit committee performs a critical role within the framework of corporate accountability since the jurisdiction of the committee is to oversee and monitor the activities of the corporation's financial reporting system and the internal and external audit processes (Braiotta 1984). The audit committee also should be concerned about complying with reporting requirements of any governmental regulatory agencies.

Influenced by the Foreign Corrupt Practices Act of 1977, the New York Stock Exchange (NYSE) in 1978 began requiring each listed firm to establish standing audit committees on the firm's board of directors. Although they may not be required for firms not listed on the NYSE, audit committees provide a viable mechanism by which directors can meet their oversight responsibilities.

The audit committee's primary responsibilities regarding the independent auditors are to nominate the independent auditors, discuss their function with them, monitor and evaluate their work, study and evaluate the independent auditor's conclusion about the effectiveness of the internal control systems, and review annual and interim financial statements before they are submitted to the full board. The audit committee is also responsible for monitoring and evaluating the work of the internal auditor.

The size of the audit committee depends on the organization. It should be large enough to involve a reasonable range of viewpoints, yet small enough to work efficiently and to give the members a share of importance. Typically, audit committees have three to five members.

Members of the audit committee should have knowledge of the industry, history of the company, and an understanding of planning and controlling concepts. The majority, if not all, of the members should be from outside the company. They do not necessarily have to be financial professionals, as nonfinancial members provide a different and valuable perspective.

Management and Performance Audits

Management or performance audits are independent, objective reviews of management's performance and the degree to which the performance of the audited entity meets predetermined expectations. The purpose of such audits is to ascertain the degree of correspondence between performance and established criteria and to communicate the results to interested users.

Management and performance audits may be mandated by regulatory agencies or may be conducted voluntarily by the utility to identify opportunities to improve operational efficiencies and reduce costs. Audits mandated by regulatory agencies are called "management audits," but the term "performance" is often interchanged with the term "management" and is perhaps more descriptive of the function. Utilities typically hire independent experts to conduct such audits, and are required to do so with mandated audits. For voluntary performance audits, utilities may use either outside consultants or in-house personnel, such as internal auditors, to reduce costs.

Management and performance auditing is a natural extension of financial auditing that significantly broadens the scope of the auditing activities. Management or performance audits examine the degree to which management and operations are achieving desired results. These results fall into the following three basic categories: efficiency and economy, effectiveness, and compliance.

Efficiency and economy relate to the use of resources. Effectiveness is related to the achievement of objectives. Specifically, efficiency measures the amount of resources (inputs) received to accomplish an output. Economy measures the relative costs involved in acquiring and maintaining the resources. Effectiveness may be defined as the degree of achievement of the legitimate and desirable objectives of the organization. Compliance is the conformance with the constraints and requirements imposed by internal policies, and relevant laws and regulations.

Management and performance audits may include assessments of the organizational structure, the overall planning and control process, financial management, engineering and construction activities, operations and maintenance practices, facilities utilization, personnel management, accounting and data processing systems, the internal control system, material management and inventory controls, employee and customer relations, quality of service, and environmental impact.

Commission-Mandated Management Audits

As water and sewer rates continue to climb and take an ever-larger portion of consumers' income, many consumers and state public service commissions are becoming more interested in the performance and efficiency of water utilities. Many of the state commissions now require that utilities under or within their jurisdiction undergo a management audit to identify poor management practices and suggest organizational and procedural changes for more efficient operations. The approach generally taken is to have commission-selected or approved independent, or outside, consultants conduct the management audit. The cost of the management audit is typically covered by the audited utility and is treated as an allowable, above-the-line (i.e., chargeable to customers), expense for rate-making purposes. Often, such commission-mandated management audits are performed in conjunction with an application for a rate increase, but may be conducted independently of any particular request for a rate change. In some cases, management audits may be required by law to be conducted on a periodic basis, such as once every three to five years.

Although mandated management audits are intended to benefit consumers, utility management, and the commission, they remain controversial. Utility management may view such audits with some hostility and may not be fully cooperative because less-than-satisfactory performance has been implied. In addition, utility management may also find itself in an informal adversarial relationship with the outside consultant because any attempt to either assist or correct factual errors may be construed as uncooperative defensiveness. The procurement and supervision of a management audit can strongly influence the ultimate value of its results. The commission should be wary of being placed in the position of having to support or reject its chosen auditor's position, or to verify, or have them verified. The public, meanwhile, must indirectly pick up the tab for an audit that may not benefit anyone.

Voluntary Management Audits

Because management audits can have a beneficial impact, utility management may voluntarily contract for or conduct its own management or performance audit. By doing so, management will benefit in three ways. First, a voluntary audit indicates to both the commission and consumer management's desire to improve operations and reduce costs without a regulatory mandate. Second, it can help circumvent the stigma attached to a commission-mandated audit. Third, the utility would have an audit report available and a program of corrective action in effect to present to the state regulatory commission in the event of a subsequent commission order for a management audit. Because of the audit's voluntary nature, utility management (rather than the commission) can decide who they want to conduct the audit — in-house staff or outside consultants.

Using in-house staff to perform the audit or assist in its preparation can increase cooperation from utility employees and reduce the costs of the audit. At the same time, it allows more utility management control over the scope of the audit work and the report itself. By controlling the scope of the audit, utility management can ensure that the areas they are concerned about are examined. For this same reason, however, concerned consumers and commission members may not view the in-house staff as completely independent and objective reviewers. Therefore, management may desire to use outside consultants to ensure independence and objectivity. In addition, outside consultants often have more knowledge of how other utilities perform similar functions and can make more effective recommendations with less analysis. Outside consultants may also have more credibility with line management than in-house staff from the "ivory tower."

Also, these issues may be resolved in followup to the GASB's *Service Efforts and Accomplishments Reporting* Preliminary Views issued in 1992.

⊠ Summary

Corporate accountability is demanded by state commissions, consumers, and investors. To be successful, utility management must address the issue of accountability, and the audit committee must ensure it. For maximum effectiveness, it is important that all audits be conducted in an atmosphere of cooperation; this necessitates a complete understanding and appreciation of the importance and usefulness of audits, whether financial or management/performance, by all participants.

Audits of financial and operational performance are a fundamental element of corporate accountability. Audit reports provide needed objective information about whether or not management is performing as expected. While the evaluation process associated with management/performance audits is sometimes more subjective than that of independent financial audits, such audits, whether commission-mandated or voluntary, whether performed by in-house staff or outside consultants, can benefit the utility.

⊠ Reference

Braiotta, L. Jr. 1984. *The Audit Director's Guide*. Malabar, Fla.: Robert E. Krieger Publishing Company.

CHAPTER TWENTY

Automated Information Systems

Increased usage of and reliance on automated information systems is occurring in both large and small water utilities. Computer hardware and software are readily available and are frequently less expensive now than a few years ago. In fact, there seems to be a condition of almost too much choice in the computerized tools available. The rate of innovation in computer technology available to water utilities can be overwhelming. Thus, selecting the appropriate computer hardware and software to resolve your business needs requires deliberate planning and proven approaches. This chapter outlines some considerations for managing the information system's function.

The primary purpose of the information technology (IT) function is to provide information services to all other functions of the water utility. Like the other functions, the IT function has limited resources to operate with and must allocate those resources based on the priorities established by management. No matter how large or how critical the IT function may become, it must be remembered that the utility is in the business of providing water service and all functions must assist in achieving that mission.

The following are generally considered to be two major activities for the IT function: (1) the operation and maintenance of existing information systems, and (2) the development of new systems or the major enhancement of the existing system. To use an analogy from financial management, the operation and maintenance activity is more akin to the day-to-day process of the accounting function while system development activities are more comparable to the budget or financial planning processes. As in financial management, different qualifications and skills are needed for operating personnel and financial planners. Many government-owned water utilities have been successful in acquiring personnel for operating and maintaining the existing information systems. They have had less success, however, in obtaining and retaining personnel for successful development projects. Thus, there has been a great tendency for utilities to use outside vendors and consultants for system development projects.

Historically, the IT function has been a part of the accounting and finance organization largely because the initial automated software applications used were for accounting processes. In more recent times, the employment of computer technology has spread to engineering and operation and mainte-nance activities in water utilities. This expanded usage of computer technology has raised a question in many water utility organizations about where the IT function should be placed. Should it continue to report to the financial management function? Should it report to the operations management function? Should it be decentralized and be a part of all major functions? Should it become a separate function and report directly to the chief executive officer? While each utility organization must decide this placement question based on its own goals and conditions, as long as the purpose of providing all functions with information services in accordance with management's priorities is satisfied, then the placement decision is less critical.

The following section reviews some of the factors to consider in assessing the capability of the utility's IT resources. An outline format will be used to present the factors to be considered. While the outline assumes a relatively large IT function, smaller utilities can select from the list those operating factors which are applicable to them.

⊠ Inventory Process

A utility should inventory existing IT functions. The inventory is used to determine

- compatibility with the future direction of operations
- available system capacity
- system downtime and response-time experiences
- user equipment per employee
- extent of IT support needed

The steps of the inventory process are as follows:
1. Determine IT resources, including
   - available applications, communications, and hardware
   - profiles of staff skills related to
     1. Applications.
     2. Management.
     3. Operations.
     4. Technicians.
     5. Users.
2. Analyze IT expenditures.
   - spending by year
   - spending by performance measure (e.g., number of customers)
   - spending by major program area (e.g., engineering, operations, etc.)
   - spending by activity
3. Review how the IT function is organized, where it is placed in the organization, and what controls management exercises over daily operations.
4. Determine the experience level, involvement, and attitude of users of IT resources.
5. Assess existing software applications.
   - review functionality
   - review technical quality
   - review maintenance backlog
   - determine age of application

⊠ Operation

The second major consideration in evaluating the IT function concentrates on how the IT function is conducted. Issues to be considered and selected details thereof follow.

Is there an IT internal audit capability? If so, consider adequacy of staffing, experience of staff, independence from IT function, and adequacy of audit policy and procedures.

Do audit procedures include the following?

- review of such operational matters as data security, controls over libraries and files, segregation of duties, emergency procedures, etc.
- review of systems and programming functions, such as programming standards, documentation procedures, controls over program changes, etc.
- coverage of operating system activities, such as separation of duties between production files and operating system maintenance
- coverage of acceptance and categorizing of programs
- review of data controls, including evaluation of control points, written procedures, and security policies for on-line terminals
- coverage of user support services
- IT services provided by external vendors
- use of microcomputers

Do computer-room controls cover housekeeping, security, expansion needs, and personnel safety? Are controls established for the following?

- computer operators
- job scheduling
- library activities
- disaster recovery
- system assurance

Do data controls cover the following?

- input, output, and record retention
- sensitive or negotiable items
- balancing

Where microcomputers are used, are there the following?

- policies and standards governing their requisition
- training programs to assist users
- disaster recovery and contingency plans
- similar operating controls when it is used in a local area network or as a link to an existing mainframe computer operation?

Does disaster recovery/contingency planning include

- adequate/current off-premise storage of the following?
    1. Source and object code program.
    2. Master and transaction files.
    3. System and program documentation.
    4. Operating system and utility programs.

- controlled access to off-site premises?

- suitable backup site?

- criteria for use of the backup site?

For system development and programming activities, do the following exist?

- provisions to review service agreements and financial stability of any extended software maintenance vendors

- procedures to guide the use of contract programmers

- written policies, procedures, and standards for program development and documentation

- procedures to evaluate the selection of software vendors

⊠ Development of New Applications

One of the more important factors in developing new system applications is to have an established system development methodology. The methodology should cover both the custom development of programs and the use of acquired software packages.

There are a number of proven development methodologies available, and they each have different emphasis on some of the basic considerations involved in system development. A brief description of the six basic steps for a development methodology follows.

Definition of Requirements

The definition of requirements for a new system generally starts with an analysis of the existing system application (whether automated or manual) to determine what the application now does. At the same time, objectives should be established for what the new system is to do, and any budgetary, timing, or other constraints should be defined. At this point, the features and functionality of the new system can be defined and documented to achieve the objectives established. The careful performance of this first step is critical to the success of the overall development of the new application since the requirements defined form the basis for all remaining development activities. Examples of additional steps could include the following:

- analyze the impact of the new system on the organization structure

- identify major inputs and outputs of the system

- identify any interface requirements with other systems

- describe the data processing environment in which the system will operate

- develop estimated costs associated with system development and operating costs
- quantify benefits of the new system to the extent practical

Conceptual Design of New System Application

This step focuses on developing both a functional and a data processing description of the new system. The description in this phase is from the user's perspective. Selected tasks for the functional portion of the system could include the following:

- describe comprehensively the operational and managerial function for the new system
- document the types of transactions and their sources, and the types of editing needed for system inputs
- document processing methods and techniques
- describe data to be maintained within the system's file structure or database
- document system outputs, including report layouts and displays

Selected tasks for the data processing component could include the following:

- estimate input, output, and storage volumes
- describe system interfaces
- describe hardware and communication techniques
- document any special considerations or constraints
- identify performance objectives to be achieved

Detail System Design

At this stage, the functional and data processing system descriptions from the previous task must be converted into detailed data processing specifications. This is the first task in the development process in which most of the effort is performed by technical data processing personnel. Three types of documents are ordinarily prepared for the detail system design, including

- detail design
- development and implementation planning
- program specifications

The detail design document will include

- functional and data processing overviews of the entire system with narrative description and flowcharts
- discussion of system inputs, including:
  1. Transaction description.
  2. Data element edits, error codes, and messages.
  3. Transaction sources.
- complete description of all processing logic
- complete description of the file structure, database elements, and access methods
- complete description of system outputs

- description of all system interfaces
- description of audit trails, backup and security procedures, and specific security provisions

The planning documentation includes such items as

- implementation plan
- system test plan
- data conversion plan
- training plan

Program specifications may contain varying levels of detail depending on the complexity of the program and whether the programmer is also writing the specifications. In any case, the specifications should be sufficiently detailed to permit an independent review. The programs specifications will usually contain the following information:

- purpose and description of each program
- functional flowchart indicating functions, inputs, and outputs
- record, database, report and/or screen layouts
- detailed description of the program using flowcharts and pseudocodes or decision tables
- processing methods and techniques, including codes and messages, flags and switches, and common routines

Development of System

The development phase focuses on converting the detail specifications into an operational system. The nature of this task is substantially associated with technical data processing activities. Since technical data processing matters are beyond the purview of most accounting organizations, the description of activities in this phase was limited. The major efforts in system development include

- program coding and testing
- system testing
- preparation of program, system, operation, and user documentation
- training for management, users, and data processing personnel
- development and testing of conversion procedures

Implementing the System

This task will consist of a considerable amount of work for technical data processing personnel. The various actions may be to

- install the new system in a production environment
- convert files from the existing system and add any new data requirements
- conduct system cutover, through one of the following processes:
  1. Limited parallel processing of the old and new systems.
  2. Phased implementation of the new system.
  3. Complete parallel operation of the old and new systems.
  4. Complete cutover to the new system.

- commence initial system operations, including the following:
  1. Distribute forms, manuals, and procedures.
  2. Conduct final production and data control review.
  3. Perform cutover.
  4. Have standby plan ready for fallback to old system.
  5. Provide guidance on operating the system.
  6. Provide for error-correction support.
  7. Provide additional training as needed.
  8. Fine-tune the new system.

Postimplementation Review

The final step in developing new applications is usually not performed until the new system has been operational for 6 to 12 months. The purpose of this task is to evaluate the new system after it has been in operation on a continuous basis. The evaluations would cover such matters as

- new system characteristics, including
  1. Benefits and features now being realized.
  2. Benefits and features yet to be realized.
  3. Comparative operating costs of the new and old system.

- new system performance
  1. In relation to performance objectives.
  2. In relation to the predecessor system.

- organizational and procedural practices
  1. System being used effectively.
  2. Organization or procedures issues that are impeding effective or efficient use of the system.
  3. Opportunities for further improvements to the organization or to procedural practices.

- use, accuracy, and adequacy of system, program, user, and operational documentation

APPENDIX A

Suggested System of Accounts for Class A Water Utilities

The development of the uniform system of accounts by the National Association of Regulatory Utility Commissioners (NARUC) serves two purposes: uniformity and consistency. Since regulatory commissions perform reviews of the operations of utilities, it is necessary for the accounting information to be consistent from period to period as well as uniform in treatment. The NARUC Committee on Accounts through their "Interpretations" has also defined accounting procedures in detail for the uniform system of accounts. This accounting guidance allows regulators to distinguish capital expenditures from operating and maintenance expenses and to separate utility activities from nonutility operations. In addition, utility management, shareholders, and creditors find the uniformity and consistency important in their use of the accounting information. Periodically, the uniform system of accounts is formally updated to reflect needed changes.

In applying a uniform system, an individual utility is not prohibited from developing subaccounts, departmental accounts, and other accounting records that are supplemental to those required by the uniform system.

⊠ Balance Sheet Accounts

Assets and Other Debits

1. Utility Plant
   a. Utility Plant:
      101. Utility Plant in Service
      102. Utility Plant Leased to Others
      103. Property Held For Future Use
      104. Utility Plant Purchased or Sold
      105. Construction Work in Progress
      106. Completed Construction Not Classified
   b. Accumulated provision for depreciation and amortization of utility plant.
      108. Accumulated Depreciation
         108.1 Accumulated depreciation of utility plant in service

108.2   Accumulated depreciation of utility plant leased to others

108.3   Accumulated depreciation of property held for future use

109. Accumulated Amortization

109.1   Accumulated amortization of utility plant in service

109.2   Accumulated amortization of utility plant leased to others

c.   Utility Plant Adjustment

114. Utility Plant Acquisition Adjustments

115. Accumulated Amortization of Utility Plant Acquisition Adjustments

116. Other Utility Plant Adjustments

2.   Other Property and Investments

a.   Other Property

121. Nonutility Property

122. Accumulated Depreciation and Amortization of Nonutility Property

b.   Investments

123. Investment In Associated Companies

124. Utility Investments

125. Other Investments

126. Sinking Funds

127. Other Special Funds

3.   Current and Accrued Assets

a.   Cash, Special Deposits, and Temporary Investments

131. Cash

131.1   Cash on hand

131.2   Cash in bank

132. Special Deposits

133. Other Special Deposits

134. Working Funds

135. Temporary Cash Investments

b.   Receivables

141. Customer Accounts Receivable

142. Other Accounts Receivable

143. Accumulated Provision For Uncollectible Accounts

144. Notes Receivables

145. Accounts Receivable From Associated Companies

146. Notes Receivable From Associated Companies

c.   Materials and Supplies

151. Plant Material and Supplies

152. Merchandise

153. Other Material and Supplies

161. Stores Expense

d.   Other Current and Accrued Assets

162. Prepayments

171. Accrued Interest and Dividends Receivable

172. Rents Receivable

173. Accrued Utility Revenues

174. Miscellaneous Current and Accrued Assets

4. Deferred Debits
   181. Unamortized Debt Discount and Expense
   182. Extraordinary Property Losses
   183. Preliminary Survey and Investigation Charges
   184. Clearing Accounts
   185. Temporary Facilities
   186. Miscellaneous Deferred Debits
      186.1 Deferred rate case expense
      186.2 Other deferred debits
   187. Research and Development Expenditures
   190. Accumulated Deferred Income Taxes
      190.1 Accumulated deferred federal income taxes
      190.2 Accumulated deferred state income taxes
      190.3 Accumulated deferred local income taxes

Equity Capital and Liabilities

5. Equity Capital
   a. Common Stock
      201. Common Stock Issues
      202. Common Stock Subscribed
      203. Common Stock Liability for Conversion
   b. Preferred Stock
      204. Preferred Stock Issued
      205. Preferred Stock Subscribed
      206. Preferred Stock Liability for Conversion
   c. Other Stockholder Contributed Capital
      207. Premium on Capital Stock
      209. Reduction in Par or Stated Value of Capital Stock
      210. Gain on Resale or Cancellation of Reacquired Capital Stock
      211. Other Paid-In Capital
      212. Discount on Capital Stock
      213. Capital Stock Expense
   d. Retained Earnings
      214. Appropriated Retained Earnings
      215. Unappropriated Retained Earnings
      216. Reacquired Capital Stock
   e. Treasury Stock
   f. Proprietary Capital
      218. Proprietary Capital (for proprietorships and partnerships only)
6. Long-Term Debt
   a. Bonds
      221. Bonds
      222. Reacquired Bonds
      223. Advances from Associated Companies
      224. Other Long-Term Debt
7. Current and Accrued Liabilities
   231. Accounts Payable
   232. Notes Payable
   233. Accounts Payable to Associated Companies
   234. Notes Payable to Associated Companies

235. Customer Deposits
    236.1   Accrued taxes, utility operating income
          236.11   Accrued taxes, taxes other than income
          236.12   Accrued taxes, income taxes
    236.2   Accrued taxes, other income, and deductions
237. Accrued Interest
238. Accrued Dividends
239. Matured Long-Term Debt
240. Matured Interest
241. Miscellaneous Current and Accrued Liabilities

8.   Deferred Credits
251. Unamortized Premium on Debt
252. Advances for Construction
253. Other Deferred Credits
255. Accumulated Deferred Investment Tax Credits
    255.1   Accumulated deferred investment tax credits, utility operations
    255.2   Accumulated deferred investment tax credits, nonutility operations

9.   Operating Reserves
261. Property Insurance Reserve
262. Injuries and Damages Reserve
263. Pensions and Benefits Reserve
265. Miscellaneous Operating Reserves

10.   Contributions In Aid of Construction
271. Contributions In Aid of Construction
272. Accumulated Amortization of Contributions in Aid of Construction

11.   Accumulated Deferred Income Taxes
281. Accumulated Deferred Income Taxes — Accelerated Amortization
282. Accumulated Deferred Income Taxes — Liberalized Depreciation
283. Accumulated Deferred Income Taxes — Other

Water Utility Plant Accounts

301. Organization
302. Franchises
303. Land and Land Rights
304. Structures and Improvements
305. Collecting and Impounding Reservoirs
306. Lake, River, and Other Intakes
307. Wells and Springs
308. Infiltration Galleries and Tunnels
309. Supply Mains
310. Power Generation Equipment
311. Pumping Equipment
320. Water Treatment Equipment
330. Distribution Reservoirs and Standpipes
331. Transmission and Distribution Mains
333. Services
334. Meters and Meter Installation

335. Hydrants
339. Other Plant and Miscellaneous Equipment
340. Office Furniture and Equipment
341. Transportation Equipment
342. Stores Equipment
343. Tools, Shop, and Garage Equipment
344. Laboratory Equipment
345. Power Operated Equipment
346. Communication Equipment
347. Miscellaneous Equipment
348. Other Tangible Plant

⊠ Income Accounts

1. Utility Operating Income
   400. Operating Revenues
   401. Operating Expenses
   403. Depreciation Expense
   406. Amortization of Utility Plant Acquisition Adjustments
   407. Amortization Expense
      407.1 Amortization of limited-term utility plant
      407.2 Amortization of property losses
      407.3 Amortization of other utility plant
   408. Taxes Other Than Income
      408.10 Utility regulatory assessment fees
      408.12 Property taxes
      408.13 Other taxes and licenses
   409. Income Taxes
      409.10 Federal income taxes, utility operating income
      409.11 State income taxes, utility operating income
      409.12 Local income taxes, utility operating income
   410. Provision for Deferred Income Taxes
      410.10 Deferred federal income taxes
      410.11 Deferred state income taxes
      410.12 Deferred local income taxes
   411. Provision For Deferred Income Taxes — Credit
      411.10 Provision for deferred income taxes — credit, utility operating income
   412. Investment Tax Credits
      412.10 Investment tax credits deferred to future periods, utility operations
      412.11 Investment tax credits restored to operating income, utility operations
   413. Income From Utility Plant Leased to Others
   414. Gains (Losses) From Disposition of Utility Property
2. Other Income and Deductions
   415. Revenues From Merchandising, Jobbing, and Contract Work
   416. Costs and Expenses of Merchandising, Jobbing, and Contract Work
   419. Interest and Dividend Income

420. Allowance for Funds Used During Construction
421. Nonutility Income
426. Miscellaneous Nonutility Expenses
c. Taxes Applicable to Other Income and Deductions
408. Taxes Other Than Income
408.20 Taxes other than income, other income and deductions
409. Income Taxes
409.20 Income taxes, other income and deductions
410. Provision for Deferred Income Taxes
410.20 Provision for deferred income taxes, other income and deductions
411. Provision for Deferred Income Taxes — Credit
411.20 Provision for deferred income taxes — credit, other income and deductions
412. Investment Tax Credits
412.20 Investment tax credits — net, nonutility operations
412.30 Investment tax credits restored to nonoperating income, utility operations
3. Interest
427. Interest Expense
427.1 Interest on debt to associated companies
427.2 Interest on short-term debt
427.3 Interest on long-term debt
427.4 Interest on customer deposits
427.5 Interest — other
428. Amortization of Debt Discount and Expense
429. Amortization of Premium on Debt
4. Extraordinary Items
433. Extraordinary Income
434. Extraordinary Deductions
409. Income Taxes
409.30 Income taxes, extraordinary items

⊠ Retained Earnings Accounts

435. Balance Transferred From Income
436. Appropriations of Retained Earnings
437. Dividends Declared — Preferred Stock
438. Dividends Declared — Common Stock
439. Adjustments to Retained Earnings

⊠ Water Operating Revenue Accounts

1. Water Sales
460. Unmetered Water Revenue
461. Metered Water Revenue
461.1 Metered sales to residential customers
461.2 Metered sales to commercial customers
461.3 Metered sales to industrial customers

461.4   Metered sales to public authorities

461.5   Metered sales to multiple-family dwellings

462.   Fire Protection Revenue

462.1   Public fire protection

462.2   Private fire protection

464.   Other Sales to Public Authorities

465.   Sales to Irrigation Customers

466.   Sales for Resale

467.   Interdepartmental Sales

2.   Other Water Revenues

470.   Forfeited Discounts

471.   Miscellaneous Service Revenues

472.   Rents From Water Property

473.   Interdepartmental Rents

474.   Other Water Revenues

⊠ Operation and Maintenance Expense

1.   Source of Supply Expenses

    a.   Operation

601.1   Salaries and wages — employees

603.1   Salaries and wages — officers, directors, and majority stockholders

604.1   Employee pensions and benefits

610.1   Purchased water

615.1   Purchased power

616.1   Fuel for power production

618.1   Chemicals

620.1   Materials and supplies

631.1   Contractual services — engineering

632.1   Contractual services — accounting

633.1   Contractual services — legal

634.1   Contractual services — management fee

635.1   Contractual services — other

641.1   Rental of building/real property

642.1   Rental of equipment

650.1   Transportation expenses

656.1   Insurance — vehicle

657.1   Insurance — general liability

658.1   Insurance — workman's compensation

659.1   Insurance — other

667.1   Regulatory commission expenses — other

675.1   Miscellaneous expenses

    b.   Maintenance

601.2   Salaries and wages — employees

603.2   Salaries and wages — officers, directors, and majority stockholders

604.2   Employee pensions and benefits

618.2   Chemicals

620.2   Materials and supplies

631.2   Contractual services — engineering

632.2   Contractual services — accounting
633.2   Contractual services — legal
634.2   Contractual services — management fees
635.2   Contractual services — other
641.2   Rental of building/real property
642.2   Rental of equipment
650.2   Transportation expenses
656.2   Insurance — vehicle
657.2   Insurance — general liability
658.2   Insurance — workman's compensation
659.2   Insurance — other
667.2   Regulatory commission expenses — other
675.2   Miscellaneous expenses

2. Water Treatment Expenses
    a. Operations
601.3   Salaries and wages — employees
603.3   Salaries and wages — officers, directors, and majority stockholders
604.3   Employee pensions and benefits
618.3   Chemicals
620.3   Materials and supplies
631.3   Contractual services — engineering
632.3   Contractual services — accounting
633.3   Contractual services — legal
634.3   Contractual services — management fees
635.3   Contractual service — other
641.3   Rental of building/real property
642.3   Rental of equipment
650.3   Transportation expenses
656.3   Insurance — vehicle
657.3   Insurance — general liability
658.3   Insurance — workman's compensation
659.3   Insurance — other
667.3   Regulatory commission expenses — other
675.3   Miscellaneous expenses
    b. Maintenance
601.4   Salaries and wages — employees
603.4   Salaries and wages — officers, directors, and majority stockholders
604.4   Employee pensions and benefits
618.4   Chemicals
620.4   Materials and supplies
631.4   Contractual services — engineering
632.4   Contractual services — legal
633.4   Contractual services — management fees
635.4   Contractual services — other
641.4   Rental of building/real property
642.4   Rental of equipment
650.4   Transportation expenses
656.4   Insurance — vehicle
657.4   Insurance — general liability
658.4   Insurance — workman's compensation

659.4   Insurance — other
667.4   Regulatory commission expenses — other
675.4   Miscellaneous expenses

3.   Transportation and Distribution Expenses
    a.   Operations
601.5   Salaries and wages — employees
603.5   Salaries and wages — officers, directors, and majority stockholders
604.5   Employee pensions and benefits
618.5   Chemicals
620.5   Materials and supplies
631.5   Contractual services — engineering
632.5   Contractual services — accounting
633.5   Contractual services — legal
634.5   Contractual services — management fees
635.5   Contractual service — other
641.5   Rental of building/real property
642.5   Rental of equipment
650.5   Transportation expenses
656.5   Insurance — vehicle
657.5   Insurance — general liability
658.5   Insurance — workman's compensation
659.5   Insurance — other
667.5   Regulatory commission expenses — other
675.5   Miscellaneous expenses

4.   Customer Accounts Expenses
    a.   Operations
601.6   Salaries and wages — employees
603.6   Salaries and wages — officers, directors, and majority stockholders
604.6   Employee pensions and benefits
618.6   Chemicals
620.6   Materials and supplies
631.6   Contractual services — engineering
632.6   Contractual services — accounting
633.6   Contractual services — legal
634.6   Contractual services — management fees
635.6   Contractual service — other
641.6   Rental of building/real property
642.6   Rental of equipment
650.6   Transportation expenses
656.6   Insurance — vehicle
657.6   Insurance — general liability
658.6   Insurance — workman's compensation
659.6   Insurance — other
667.6   Regulatory commission expenses — other
675.6   Miscellaneous expenses

    b.   Maintenance
601.7   Salaries and wages — employees
603.7   Salaries and wages — officers, directors, and majority stockholders
604.7   Employee pensions and benefits

618.7   Chemicals
620.7   Materials and supplies
631.7   Contractual services — engineering
632.7   Contractual services — accounting
633.7   Contractual services — legal
634.7   Contractual services — management fees
635.7   Contractual services — other
641.7   Rental of building/real property
642.7   Rental of equipment
650.7   Transportation expenses
656.7   Insurance — vehicle
657.7   Insurance — general liability
658.7   Insurance — workman's compensation
659.7   Insurance — other
667.7   Regulatory commission expenses — other
675.7   Miscellaneous expenses

5. Administrative and General Expenses

601.8   Salaries and wages — employees
603.8   Salaries and wages — officers, directors, and majority stockholders
604.8   Employee pensions and benefits
618.8   Chemicals
620.8   Materials and supplies
631.8   Contractual services — engineering
632.8   Contractual services — accounting
633.8   Contractual services — legal
634.8   Contractual services — management fees
635.8   Contractual services — other
641.8   Rental of building/real property
642.8   Rental of equipment
650.8   Transportation expenses
656.8   Insurance — vehicle
657.8   Insurance — general liability
658.8   Insurance — workman's compensation
659.8   Insurance — other
667.8   Regulatory commission expenses — other
675.8   Miscellaneous expenses

APPENDIX B

Sample
Investor-Owned Utility
Annual Report

This appendix contains excerpts from a recent California Water Service Company annual report. It is presented as an example financial statement from an investor-owned water utility (as discussed in chapter 15, Financial Statement Reports).

FINANCIAL HIGHLIGHTS

	1993	1992	% Change
Operating revenue	$151,716,000	$139,805,000	8.5%
Net income	15,501,000	12,529,000	23.7
Common share data:			
Earnings	$ 2.70	$ 2.18	23.9%
Cash dividends paid	1.92	1.86	3.2
Book value at year-end	21.80	21.02	3.7
Market price at year-end	40.00	33.00	21.2

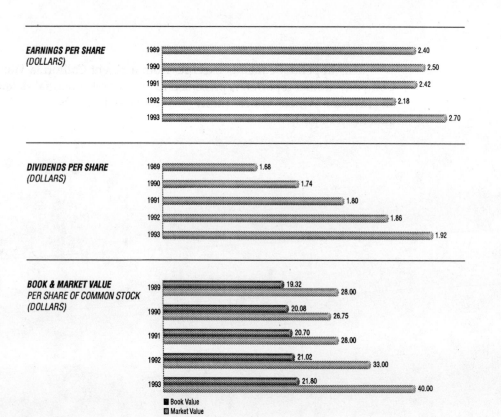

EARNINGS PER SHARE
(DOLLARS)

1989	2.40
1990	2.50
1991	2.42
1992	2.18
1993	2.70

DIVIDENDS PER SHARE
(DOLLARS)

1989	1.68
1990	1.74
1991	1.80
1992	1.86
1993	1.92

BOOK & MARKET VALUE
PER SHARE OF COMMON STOCK
(DOLLARS)

	Book Value	Market Value
1989	19.32	28.00
1990	20.08	26.75
1991	20.70	28.00
1992	21.02	33.00
1993	21.80	40.00

■ Book Value
▨ Market Value

Winter weather conditions during the first quarter of 1993 resulted in heavy rain and snowfall for California, bringing a dramatic end to one of the longest drought periods in recorded state history.

For nearly six years, many customers of the Company along with those of other water utilities throughout the state had been required to reduce water use significantly because of the supply shortage.

The Company ended its first post-drought year with net income up 24% to $15,501,000, primarily the result of rate relief granted by the California Public Utilities Commission. The year brought record earnings of $2.70 per common share, also up 24% from 1992. Operating revenue increased 9% to a record $151,716,000.

Contributing to the $11,900,000 increase in revenue for the year were offset rate adjustments, primarily for purchased water, of $7,300,000, and general and step rate increases granted by the California Public Utilities Commission of $2,700,000. With the ending of the drought, rationing losses declined $1,200,000 from 1992. A more complete review of the Company's Results of Operations for the year is provided in the Management's Discussion on page 14 of this report.

Hearings are scheduled to begin in March 1994 on three general rate case proceedings filed in September 1993 for the Oroville, Chico and Salinas districts. The applications request annual revenue increases of $2,100,000 starting in mid-1994 based upon a requested rate of return on equity of 12%.

Salinas Valley's Arroyo Seco River

Lower interest rates in the bond market during 1993 provided an opportunity for the Company to redeem eight series of bonds outstanding totaling $49,593,000 and bearing interest at rates ranging from 8.6% to 12⅞%. The refinancing, which is described in the Management's Discussion, will result in future interest savings of approximately $1,900,000 annually at new rates ranging from 6.95% to 7.9%.

The Company added 2,200 new services during 1993, bringing total customers to 362,900 at year-end. This included the addition of 150 new customers through acquisition of the Visalia city-owned industrial system. As announced in August, the Company elected not to pursue the purchase of the Del Este Water Company of Modesto after the city initiated condemnation proceedings to acquire the system from the Beard family, the present owner.

Although the drought is officially over, the Company will continue to maintain programs encouraging customer support for water conservation. In the Salinas Valley area, where the Company serves customers in the Salinas and King City districts, customers will be asked this year to reduce water use by 15% to comply with a new local government ordinance which places restrictions on both urban and agricultural water use. The new county law was adopted as part of a Monterey County Water Resources Agency plan to combat salt water intrusion from the ocean which has threatened the underground aquifer in the Salinas Valley. Photography in this year's report highlights the Salinas Valley activities and other statewide water management programs including those in which the Company is an active participant along with local water agencies. These programs provide for the develop-

Monterey County's Nacimiento Reservoir

2

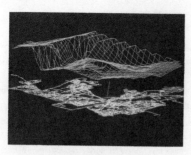

Salinas District Computer Model

ment of long range plans to protect the local water supply and ensure its availability well into the 21st Century.

As noted in our fourth quarter report to shareholders distributed in February 1994, the new year has already brought significant events relating to the Company.

The Northridge earthquake on January 17 fortunately did not impact the Company's Southern California districts to any great degree. Of the more than a quarter of a million population served by Company districts near the earthquake area, less than 100 customers experienced short-term disruption of water service. There was only minor damage to Company facilities.

Also during January, the Board of Directors announced plans to seek listing of the Company's common shares on the New York Stock Exchange. Common shares currently are traded on the NASDAQ National Market. The Board also announced that the Company will issue and sell 600,000 shares of common stock to finance a portion of the Company's $21,600,000 construction program for 1994. The last time the Company sold common stock was during the 1950s.

Finally, during January, the Company received notice it had been awarded the contract by the Central Basin Municipal Water District of Los Angeles for operation and maintenance services relating to the new Rio Hondo Recycled Water System in Los Angeles County. The Rio Hondo program is designed to deliver up to 15,000-acre feet of reclaimed water for irrigation and industrial use. Additional details on the Rio Hondo program are provided on page 8 of this report.

The Company lost a very special friend during 1993 with the passing of Fred L. Dodge, an employee of the Company when it was first formed in 1926. Mr. Dodge was affiliated with the Company for 57 years in various management positions, serving 7½ years as president prior to his retirement. He was a member of the Board of Directors for 28 years.

In September 1993, Robert J. Glaser, M.D. retired as a director of the Company. We are indebted to Dr. Glaser for his 21 years of distinguished and dedicated service as a member of our Board. Elected to fill the Board vacancy was Edward D. Harris, Jr. M.D., Professor and Chairman of the Department of Medicine, Stanford University School of Medicine.

The Board of Directors at its January 1994 meeting, raised the annual dividend on common stock from $1.92 to $1.98 making this the 27th consecutive year the dividend has been increased. The year's first quarterly dividend payment in February 1994, marks the 197th consecutive quarter in which the Company dividend has been paid.

C. H. Stump
Chairman of the Board

Donald L. Houck
President and Chief Executive Officer

February 18, 1994

3

CALIFORNIA WATER SERVICE COMPANY   TEN YEAR FINANCIAL REVIEW

(dollars in thousands except per share and per customer amounts)

	1993	1992	1991
SUMMARY OF OPERATIONS			
Operating revenue			
Residential	$111,526	$101,842	$87,560
Business	25,247	23,670	20,759
Industrial	5,123	4,925	4,490
Public authorities	7,396	6,892	5,734
Other	2,424	2,476	8,633
Total operating revenue	151,716	139,805	127,176
Operating expenses	123,861	116,031	102,855
Interest expense, other income and expenses, net	12,354	11,245	10,393
Net income	$15,501	$12,529	$13,928
COMMON SHARE DATA			
Earnings per share	$2.70	$2.18	$2.42
Dividend paid	1.92	1.86	1.80
Dividend payout ratio	71%	85%	74%
Book value at year-end	$21.80	$21.02	$20.70
Market price at year-end	40.00	33.00	28.00
Common shares outstanding at year-end (in thousands)	5,689	5,689	5,689
Return on common shareholders' equity	12.4%	10.4%	11.7%
Bond interest coverage	3.2	2.9	3.2
BALANCE SHEET DATA			
Net utility plant	$391,703	$374,613	$349,937
Utility plant expenditures	28,829	35,188	34,459
Advances for construction	90,812	89,127	84,424
Capitalization:			
First mortgage bonds	129,608	122,069	103,505
Preferred stock	3,475	3,475	3,475
Common shareholders' equity	123,999	119,574	117,779
Total capitalization	257,082	245,118	224,759
Capitalization ratios:			
First mortgage bonds	50.4%	49.8%	46.1%
Preferred stock	1.4%	1.4%	1.5%
Common shareholders' equity	48.2%	48.8%	52.4%
OTHER DATA			
Water production (million gallons)			
Wells	47,205	52,000	48,930
Purchased	48,089	40,426	36,686
Total water production	95,294	92,426	85,616
Customers at year-end	362,900	360,700	357,600
New customers added	2,200	3,100	4,300
Revenue per customer	$418	$388	$356
Utility plant per customer	$1,469	$1,406	$1,327
Employees at year-end	614	610	593

*Net income excludes $2,196 for a change in accounting for unbilled revenue; $.39 is excluded from earnings per share. Common share data is adjusted to reflect the 2-for-1 stock splits effective October 1987 and May 1984.

1990	1989	1988	1987	1986	1985	1984
$90,178	$84,295	$81,404	$82,254	$79,131	$75,508	$73,204
20,910	19,870	19,480	19,986	19,095	17,847	16,639
5,146	5,166	4,754	4,361	4,539	4,636	4,689
6,412	6,225	6,232	6,491	6,285	6,118	6,117
1,741	1,932	1,885	693	1,385	1,382	1,256
124,387	117,488	113,755	113,785	110,435	105,491	101,905
101,017	95,150	91,265	90,587	87,788	83,722	80,729
9,004	8,566	8,416	8,026	8,808	9,115	9,396
$14,366	$13,772	$14,074	$15,172 *	$13,839	$12,654	$11,780
$2.50	$2.40	$2.45	$2.63 *	$2.40	$2.21	$2.06
1.74	1.68	1.60	1.48	1.40	1.30	1.20
70%	70%	65%	49%	58%	59%	58%
$20.08	$19.32	$18.59	$17.72	$16.11	$15.03	$14.07
26.75	28.00	25.50	30.00	26.625	22.625	15.25
5,689	5,689	5,672	5,636	5,607	5,576	5,528
12.4%	12.4%	13.2%	14.8%	14.9%	14.7%	14.6%
3.6	3.4	3.8	4.3	3.9	3.5	3.3
$325,409	$307,802	$289,363	$273,619	$262,216	$246,467	$236,881
26,861	27,277	23,994	19,511	22,710	16,469	17,177
77,202	69,016	59,145	54,887	50,907	45,790	43,869
104,905	86,012	86,959	73,930	77,056	84,009	86,478
3,475	3,475	3,475	5,783	5,909	6,031	6,178
114,244	109,929	105,435	99,897	90,336	83,818	77,770
222,624	199,416	195,869	179,610	173,301	173,858	170,426
47.1%	43.1%	44.4%	41.2%	44.5%	48.3%	50.8%
1.6%	1.8%	1.8%	3.2%	3.4%	3.5%	3.6%
51.3%	55.1%	53.8%	55.6%	52.1%	48.2%	45.6%
51,329	51,350	48,828	48,097	45,222	43,589	44,602
45,595	45,978	48,254	50,744	50,782	50,328	49,983
96,924	97,328	97,082	98,841	96,004	93,917	94,585
353,300	348,600	344,800	337,800	334,200	330,300	326,100
4,700	3,800	7,000	3,600	3,900	4,200	4,000
$352	$337	$330	$337	$330	$319	$313
$1,251	$1,198	$1,140	$1,098	$1,058	$1,007	$973
581	565	550	534	528	525	522

**MANAGEMENT'S DISCUSSION AND ANALYSIS OF FINANCIAL
CONDITION AND RESULTS OF OPERATIONS**

BUSINESS

California Water Service Company is a public utility supplying water service through 20 separate water systems to 362,900 customers living in 38 communities in California. These systems, or districts, are located throughout the state as shown in the tabulation on page 11.

The Company's rates and operations are regulated by the California Public Utilities Commission (Commission) with the rates for each district determined separately. A detailed discussion of Regulation and Rates begins on page 6 of this report.

The six-year drought in California which required water rationing in a number of the Company's districts was declared officially ended after above average precipitation in the first three months of 1993. A detailed discussion of Water Supply is on page 4 of this report.

RESULTS OF OPERATIONS

Earnings and Dividends

The Company's earnings per share for 1993 were $2.70 compared with $2.18 in 1992 and $2.42 in 1991. Net income was $15,501,000 in 1993 compared with $12,529,000 in 1992 and $13,928,000 in 1991. Earnings and revenue in 1991 and 1992 were impacted by mandatory water rationing in some Company districts and water conservation in all districts.

In January 1993, the Board of Directors increased the dividend rate for the twenty-sixth consecutive year. The annual rate paid in 1993 was $1.92 per share, an increase of 3.2% compared with the 1992 dividend of $1.86 per share, which represented an increase of 3.3% over the 1991 dividend of $1.80 per share. The dividend payout ratio was 71% in 1993 compared with 85% in 1992 and 74% in 1991. These increases were based on projections that the higher dividend could be sustained while still providing the Company with adequate financial flexibility.

Operating Revenue

Operating revenue was a record $151.7 million in 1993, compared with $139.8 million in 1992 and $127.2 million in 1991. The increase was $11.9 million, or 9%, in 1993. Step and general rate increases accounted for $2.7 million of added revenue. Offset rate adjustments, primarily for purchased water and pump tax cost increases, added $7.3 million. Average water consumption per customer increased 3%, adding $2.3 million to revenue. However, rationing loss recoveries declined $1.2 million from 1992 due to the ending of rationing. Sales to 2,200 new customers accounted for $0.8 million in additional revenue.

In 1992, operating revenue increased $12.6 million from 1991. Step and general rate increases accounted for $3.4 million of added revenue. Offset rate adjustments, primarily for purchased water and pump tax cost increases, added $7.0 million. Average water consumption per customer increased 6%, adding $3.9 million to revenue. The discontinuance of mandatory rationing in four districts in April 1992 helped account for higher water consumption. However, this also resulted in lower rationing loss recoveries of $4.0 million compared with $6.9 million in 1991. Sales to 3,100 new customers accounted for $1.2 million in additional revenue.

In 1991, an October decision of the Commission authorized the Company to recover a portion of revenue lost through water rationing and conservation. In December, after the Commission approved district water management plans, $6,951,000 of revenue lost since August 8, 1990, was recorded as revenue. This included the transfer of $3,195,000 in penalty charges collected from customers who had exceeded their monthly allotments, while the remaining $3,756,000 was accrued as unbilled revenue. Surcharges on customers' water bills were authorized by the Commission beginning in 1992, to allow recovery of this accrued unbilled revenue in addition to future revenue losses. Water rationing and conservation in the fifth drought year lowered average water consumption per customer by 14% causing an $11.9 million reduction in revenue. Additional revenue from drought rate relief in 1991 was $5.6 million. General and step rate increases added $4.1 million to 1991 revenue. Sales to 4,300 new customers accounted for $1.3 million in additional revenue.

OPERATING REVENUE
(MILLIONS OF DOLLARS)

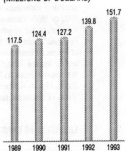

Operating and Interest Expenses

Operating expenses in 1993 increased $7.8 million compared with increases of $13.2 million in 1992 and $1.8 million in 1991.

Purchased water expense continued to be the largest component of operating expense at $38.5 million, an increase of $5.4 million. This was attributable to a 19% increase in water purchases to 48 billion gallons and to wholesale water suppliers' rate increases. Total water production, including well production and surface supplies was up 3% from 1992 to 95 billion gallons. Total cost of water production, including purchased water, purchased power and pump taxes, was $52.9 million in 1993, $50.2 million in 1992, and $38.8 million in 1991. Commission regulatory procedures allow offset rate adjustments for changes in these costs through use of balancing accounts. However, there was a delay in recovery of some cost increases as discussed under the caption Regulation and Rates on page 6.

Employee payroll and benefits charged to operations and maintenance expense was $26.2 million in 1993 compared with $24.8 million in 1992 and $23.5 million in 1991.

Bond interest expense in 1993 increased $1.5 million due to the sale of $20 million new bonds in November 1992 and the sale of additional new bonds in 1993 as discussed under the caption Liquidity and Capital Resources. However, this was partially offset by a $336,000 reduction in interest on short-term debt due to reduced borrowings. Bond interest coverage before income taxes was 3.2 in 1993, 2.9 in 1992 and 3.2 in 1991.

New Accounting Standards

The Financial Accounting Standards Board has issued three new statements which affect the financial statements in 1992 or 1993. These are Statements No. 106 "Employers' Accounting for Postretirement Benefits Other Than Pensions", Statement No. 107 "Disclosures About Fair Value of Financial Instruments", and Statement No. 109 "Accounting for Income Taxes". The effect of these Statements is discussed in Notes to Financial Statements: Note 5— Income Taxes; Note 6— Employee Benefit Plans and Note 7— Fair Value of Financial Instruments.

LIQUIDITY AND CAPITAL RESOURCES

The Company's liquidity is primarily provided by cash generated from operations and the utilization of a short-term line of credit of $30 million as described in Note 3 to the financial statements. The credit line was temporarily increased to $40 million during the bond refinancing periods in May and November to cover short-term requirements between the calling of bonds and the issuance of new bonds.

A major refinancing program was completed in 1993. Eight series of bonds in the principal amount of $49,593,000 and bearing coupons ranging from 8.6% to 12⅛% were called prior to maturity with a portion of the proceeds from the sale of three $20 million dollar bond issues. The Series EE 7.9% first mortgage bonds were issued in June 1993, the Series FF 6.95% bonds were issued in October 1993 and the Series GG 6.98% bonds were issued in November 1993. Interest savings from the refunding will be approximately $1.9 million annually. Standard & Poor's and Moody's maintained their bond ratings of AA- and Aa3 respectively on the new Series GG bond issue. Capital requirements consist primarily of new construction expenditures for replacing and expanding the Company's utility plant facilities. They also include refunds of advances for construction and retirement of bonds.

During 1993, utility plant expenditures totaled $28.8 million including $21.5 million covered by Company funding and $7.3 million being recovered from developers through refundable advances and contributions in aid of construction. Company funding was through cash generated from operations, the use of the short-term line of credit and a portion of the proceeds from the sale of new bonds.

The 1994 Company construction program has been authorized for $21.6 million. The funds for this program are expected to be provided by cash from operations and a new issue of common stock. Additionally, new subdivision construction will be financed by developers' refundable advances and contributions.

GROSS ADDITIONS TO UTILITY PLANT
(MILLIONS OF DOLLARS)

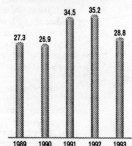

1989	1990	1991	1992	1993
27.3	26.9	34.5	35.2	28.8

Capital Structure

The Company's total capitalization at December 31, 1993, was $257.1 million. Capital ratios were: common equity 48.2% preferred stock, 1.4%; and first mortgage bonds, 50.4%. The rate of return on year-end common equity was 12.4% compared with 10.4% in 1992 and 11.7% in 1991.

CALIFORNIA WATER SERVICE COMPANY
BALANCE SHEET
December 31, 1993 and 1992

(In Thousands)

ASSETS

	1993	1992
Utility plant:		
Land	$ 6,742	$ 6,838
Depreciable plant and equipment	522,614	495,212
Construction work in progress	3,466	4,123
Intangible assets	391	978
Total utility plant	533,213	507,151
Less depreciation	141,510	132,538
Net utility plant	391,703	374,613
Current assets:		
Cash and cash equivalents	1,461	899
Accounts receivable:		
Customers	8,984	8,407
Other	1,851	3,336
Unbilled revenue	7,548	6,744
Materials and supplies at average cost	2,853	2,784
Taxes and other prepaid expenses	3,716	3,763
Total current assets	26,413	25,933
Other assets:		
Regulatory assets	23,404	—
Unamortized debt premium and expense	4,467	1,187
Other	632	1,715
Total other assets	28,503	2,902
	$446,619	$403,448

See accompanying notes to financial statements.

16

CAPITALIZATION AND LIABILITIES

	1993	1992
Capitalization:		
Common stock	$ 25,059	$ 25,059
Retained earnings	98,940	94,515
Total common shareholders' equity	123,999	119,574
Preferred stock without mandatory redemption provision	3,475	3,475
First mortgage bonds	129,608	122,069
Total capitalization	257,082	245,118
Current liabilities:		
Short-term borrowings	15,000	11,500
Accounts payable	11,234	9,110
Accrued taxes	2,810	2,520
Accrued interest	1,788	2,088
Other accrued liabilities	7,124	8,452
Total current liabilities	37,956	33,670
Unamortized investment tax credits	3,341	3,413
Deferred income taxes	11,045	—
Regulatory liabilities	11,467	—
Advances for construction	90,812	89,127
Contributions in aid of construction	34,916	32,120
	$446,619	$403,448

CALIFORNIA WATER SERVICE COMPANY
STATEMENT OF INCOME
For the years ended December 31, 1993, 1992 and 1991

(In Thousands, except per share data)

	1993	1992	1991
Operating revenue	$151,716	$139,805	$127,176
Operating expenses:			
Operations:			
Purchased water	38,454	33,065	23,947
Purchased power	11,852	12,766	11,683
Pump taxes	2,601	4,370	3,206
Administrative and general	16,910	16,349	15,023
Other	19,718	19,051	18,107
Maintenance	7,250	6,965	7,175
Depreciation	10,304	9,412	8,795
Income taxes	10,600	8,250	9,550
Property and other taxes	6,172	5,803	5,369
Total operating expenses	123,861	116,031	102,855
Net operating income	27,855	23,774	24,321
Other income and expenses, net	273	169	384
Income before interest expense	28,128	23,943	24,705
Interest expense:			
Bond interest	11,992	10,443	10,564
Other interest	635	971	213
Total interest expense	12,627	11,414	10,777
Net income	$ 15,501	$ 12,529	$ 13,928
Earnings per share of common stock	$ 2.70	$ 2.18	$ 2.42
Average number of common shares outstanding	5,689	5,689	5,689

See accompanying notes to financial statements.

18

STATEMENT OF COMMON SHAREHOLDERS' EQUITY
For the years ended December 31, 1993, 1992 and 1991

(In Thousands, except shares)

	Common Shares Outstanding	Common Stock	Retained Earnings	Total
Balance at December 31, 1990	5,688,754	$25,059	$89,185	$114,244
Net income			13,928	13,928
Dividends paid: preferred stock			153	153
common stock			10,240	10,240
Total dividends paid			10,393	10,393
Income reinvested in business			3,535	3,535
Balance at December 31, 1991	5,688,754	25,059	92,720	117,779
Net income			12,529	12,529
Dividends paid: preferred stock			153	153
common stock			10,581	10,581
Total dividends paid			10,734	10,734
Income reinvested in business			1,795	1,795
Balance at December 31, 1992	5,688,754	25,059	94,515	119,574
Net income			15,501	15,501
Dividends paid: preferred stock			153	153
common stock			10,923	10,923
Total dividends paid			11,076	11,076
Income reinvested in business			4,425	4,425
Balance at December 31, 1993	5,688,754	$25,059	$98,940	$123,999

See accompanying notes to financial statements.

CALIFORNIA WATER SERVICE COMPANY
STATEMENT OF CASH FLOWS
For the years ended December 31, 1993, 1992 and 1991

(In Thousands)

	1993	1992	1991
Operating activities:			
Net income	$15,501	$12,529	$13,928
Adjustments to reconcile net income to net cash provided by operating activities:			
Depreciation	10,304	9,412	8,795
Deferred income taxes and investment tax credits, net	12,355	(821)	(4,135)
Regulatory assets and liabilities, net.	(11,937)	—	—
Change in operating assets and liabilities:			
Accounts receivable	908	(2,633)	(126)
Unbilled revenue	(804)	842	(3,708)
Accounts payable	2,124	1,218	(444)
Other current liabilities	(1,338)	1,084	(346)
Other changes, net	247	645	143
Net adjustments	11,859	9,747	179
Net cash provided by operating activities	27,360	22,276	14,107
Investing activities:			
Utility plant expenditures	(28,829)	(35,188)	(34,459)
Financing activities:			
Net short-term borrowings	3,500	(2,500)	14,000
Proceeds from sale of first mortgage bonds	60,000	20,000	—
Advances for construction	5,024	8,187	10,425
Refunds of advances for construction	(3,428)	(3,443)	(3,234)
Contributions in aid of construction	3,402	3,446	3,075
Retirement of first mortgage bonds including premiums	(55,391)	(1,458)	(1,421)
Dividends paid	(11,076)	(10,734)	(10,393)
Net cash provided by financing activities	2,031	13,498	12,452
Change in cash and cash equivalents	562	586	(7,900)
Cash and cash equivalents at beginning of year	899	313	8,213
Cash and cash equivalents at end of year	$ 1,461	$ 899	$ 313
Supplemental disclosures of cash flow information:			
Cash paid during the year for:			
Interest (net of amounts capitalized)	$ 12,763	$ 11,042	$ 10,292
Income taxes	9,188	11,384	13,316

See accompanying notes to financial statements.

NOTES TO FINANCIAL STATEMENTS *December 31, 1993, 1992 and 1991*

Note 1. **SUMMARY OF SIGNIFICANT ACCOUNTING POLICIES**

The accounting records of the Company are maintained in accordance with the uniform system of accounts prescribed by the California Public Utilities Commission (Commission). Certain prior years' amounts have been reclassified, where necessary, to conform to the current presentation.

Revenue

Revenue consists of monthly cycle customer billings for water service at rates authorized by the Commission. Revenue from metered accounts includes unbilled amounts based on the estimated usage from the latest meter reading to the end of the accounting period. Flat rate accounts which are billed at the beginning of the service period are included in revenue on a prorata basis for the portion applicable to the current accounting period.

In October 1991 the Commission issued a decision on its investigation into the effects of the drought on water utilities which permitted the Company to recover revenue lost through water conservation as recorded in memorandum accounts. As a result, $6,951,000 of revenue lost since August 8, 1990 was recorded as revenue in December 1991 after the Commission approved district water management plans. Penalty charges totaling $3,195,000 collected from customers who had exceeded their monthly allotments were transferred to revenue while the remaining $3,756,000 was accrued as unbilled revenue in current assets. Of this amount $3,337,000 was recovered in 1992 by surcharges on customer water bills and transfers of penalty charges.

During 1992, $4,087,000 of revenue lost due to water conservation was recorded as revenue and accrued in unbilled revenue. Of that amount, $2,355,000 was recovered through customer surcharges and penalty charge transfers. As of December 31, 1992 a total of $2,151,000 of revenue lost due to water conservation was included in unbilled revenue.

In 1993, $2,904,000 was recorded as lost water conservation revenue and accrued in unbilled revenue, while $2,631,000 was recovered through customer surcharges and penalty charge transfers. As of December 31, 1993, $2,424,000 of lost water conservation revenue remains in unbilled revenue.

Utility Plant

Utility plant is carried at original cost when first constructed or purchased, except for certain minor units of property recorded at estimated fair values at dates of acquisition. Costs of depreciable plant retired are eliminated from utility plant accounts and such costs are charged against accumulated depreciation. Maintenance of utility plant, other than transportation equipment, is charged to operating expenses. Maintenance and depreciation of transportation equipment are charged to a clearing account and subsequently distributed primarily to operations. Interest is capitalized on plant expenditures during the construction period and amounted to $141,000 in 1993, $523,000 in 1992 and $293,000 in 1991.

Intangible assets arising during the period of initial development of the Company and those acquired as parts of water systems purchased are stated at amounts prescribed by the Commission. All other intangibles have been recorded at cost.

Bond Premium, Discount and Expense

The discount and expense on first mortgage bonds is being amortized over the original lives of the related bond issues. Premiums paid on the early redemption of bonds and unamortized original issue discount and expense of those bonds are amortized over the life of new bonds issued in conjunction with the early redemption.

Cash Equivalents

Cash equivalents include highly liquid investments, primarily a money market mutual fund, stated at cost with original maturities of three months or less.

Depreciation

Depreciation of utility plant for financial statement purposes is computed on the straight-line remaining life method at rates based on the estimated useful lives of the assets. The provision for depreciation expressed as a percentage of the aggregate depreciable asset balances was 2.4% in 1993 and 2.3% in 1992 and 1991. For income tax purposes, the Company computes depreciation using the accelerated methods allowed by the respective taxing authorities.

Advances for Construction

Advances for construction of water main extensions are primarily refundable to depositors over a 20-year or 40-year period. Refund amounts under the 20-year contracts are based on annual revenues from the extensions. Unrefunded balances at the end of the contract period are credited to Contributions in Aid of Construction and are no longer refundable. Contracts entered into since 1982 provide for full refunds at a 2½% rate per year for 40 years. Estimated refunds for 1994 for all water main extension contracts are $3,600,000.

Income Taxes

Effective January 1, 1993, the Company adopted the provisions of Statement of Financial Accounting Standards (SFAS) No. 109, "Accounting for Income Taxes". Statement 109 requires a change from the deferred method of accounting for income taxes under APB Opinion 11 to the asset and liability method. Under SFAS 109 deferred tax assets and liabilities are recognized for the future tax consequences attributable to differences between the financial statement carrying amounts of existing assets and liabilities and their respective tax bases. Measurement of the deferred tax assets and liabilities is at enacted tax rates expected to apply to taxable income in the years in which those temporary differences are expected to be recovered or settled. Under Statement 109, the effect on deferred tax assets and liabilities of a change in tax rates is recognized in the period that includes the enactment date.

Due to the implementation of SFAS 109 as of January 1, 1993, the Company recorded an increase in both net regulatory assets and net deferred income taxes of $9,905,000. There was no impact on the results of operations. It is anticipated that future rate action by the Commission will reflect revenue requirements for the tax effects of temporary differences recognized under SFAS 109 which have previously been flowed through to customers.

Prior to 1993, the provision for income taxes was based on income and expenses included in the Statement of Income as prescribed by APB Opinion 11. In accordance with Commission requirements, deferred taxes were not provided for items flowed through for rate-making and accounting purposes. Flow through items included excess state tax depreciation and excess federal depreciation on assets placed in service prior to 1981. Prior year amounts have not been recomputed to apply the provisions of SFAS 109.

The Commission has granted the Company customer rate increases to reflect the normalization of the tax benefits of the federal accelerated methods and available investment tax credits (ITC) for all assets placed in service since 1980. ITC are deferred and amortized over the lives of the related properties.

Advances for Construction and Contributions in Aid of Construction received from developers subsequent to 1986 are taxable for federal income tax purposes and subsequent to 1991 subject to state income tax.

Earnings per Share

Earnings per share is calculated using the weighted average number of common shares outstanding during the year after deducting dividend requirements on preferred stock.

Note 2. **PREFERRED AND COMMON STOCK**

As of December 31, 1993, 399,200 shares of preferred stock were authorized. Dividends on outstanding shares are payable quarterly at a fixed rate before any dividends can be paid on common stock. Preferred shares are entitled to eight votes each with the right to cumulative votes at any elections of directors.

The outstanding 139,000 shares of $25 par value cumulative, 4.4% Series C preferred shares are not convertible to common stock. A premium of $243,250 would be due upon voluntary liquidation of Series C. There is no premium in the event of an involuntary liquidation.

The Company is authorized to issue 8,000,000 shares of no par value common stock. As of December 31, 1993 and 1992, 5,688,754 shares of common stock were issued and outstanding.

Note 3. **SHORT-TERM BORROWINGS**

As of December 31, 1993 the Company maintained a bank line of credit which provided for unsecured borrowings of up to $30,000,000 at the prime lending rate or lower rates as quoted by the bank. The agreement does not require minimum or specific compensating balances.

The maximum short-term borrowings outstanding during 1993, 1992 and 1991 were $33,500,000, $24,500,000, and $14,000,000, respectively.

The average amount outstanding during each of the three years was $11,746,000, $17,431,000 and $1,269,000, respectively, with weighted average interest rates on the daily balances of 4.31%, 4.85% and 5.90%, respectively.

Note 4. **FIRST MORTGAGE BONDS**

As of December 31, 1993 and 1992 first mortgage bonds outstanding were:

		In Thousands 1993	In Thousands 1992
Series I, 4.65%	due 1993	$ —	$ 2,565
Series J, 4.85%	due 1995	2,581	2,596
Series K, 6¼%	due 1996	2,595	2,610
Series L, 6¾%	due 1997	2,177	2,189
Series M, 9½%	due 1999	—	2,213
Series N, 9¼%	due 2000	—	2,670
Series O, 9¼%	due 2000	—	2,670
Series P, 7⅞%	due 2002	2,685	2,700
Series S, 8½%	due 2003	2,700	2,715
Series U, 9¼%	due 2003	—	2,080
Series V, 8.60%	due 2006	—	1,785
Series W, 9⅜%	due 2007	—	2,380
Series X, 10%	due 2005	—	2,755
Series AA, 12⅞%	due 2013	—	33,425
Series BB, 9.48%	due 2008	17,370	17,460
Series CC, 9.86%	due 2020	19,600	19,700
Series DD, 8.63%	due 2022	19,900	20,000
Series EE, 7.90%	due 2023	20,000	—
Series FF, 6.95%	due 2023	20,000	—
Series GG, 6.98%	due 2023	20,000	—
		129,608	122,513
Less: Series AA discount		—	444
Total first mortgage bonds		$129,608	$122,069

Aggregate maturities and sinking fund requirements for each of the succeeding five years 1994 through 1998 are $663,000, $3,215,000, $3,197,000, $2,759,000 and $620,000, respectively. The first mortgage bonds are secured by substantially all of the Company's utility plant.

Note 5. INCOME TAXES

Income tax expense consists of the following:

1993	Federal	State	Total
	In Thousands		
Current	$6,800	$2,408	$9,208
Deferred	1,400	(8)	1,392
Total	$8,200	$2,400	$10,600
1992			
Current	$3,371	$1,650	$5,021
Deferred	3,229	—	3,229
Total	$6,600	$1,650	$8,250
1991			
Current	$4,939	$1,750	$6,689
Deferred	2,861	—	2,861
Total	$7,800	$1,750	$9,550

Income tax expense differs from the amount computed by applying the current federal tax rate to pretax book income. The difference is listed in the table below:

	1993	1992	1991
	In Thousands		
Computed "expected" tax expense	$9,135	$7,065	$7,983
Increase (reduction) in taxes due to:			
State income taxes net of federal tax benefit	1,565	1,089	1,155
Investment tax credits	(100)	(85)	(85)
Other	—	181	497
Total income tax	$10,600	$8,250	$9,550

The components of deferred income tax expense in 1993, 1992 and 1991 were:

	1993	1992	1991
	In Thousands		
Depreciation	$3,858	$3,314	$2,946
Developer advances and contributions	(3,951)	—	—
Bond redemption premiums	1,333	—	—
Other	224	—	—
Investment tax credits	(72)	(85)	(85)
Total deferred income tax expense	$1,392	$3,229	$2,861

The tax effects of temporary differences that give rise to significant portions of the deferred tax assets and deferred tax liabilities at December 31, 1993 are presented in the following table:

	In Thousands
Deferred tax assets:	
Developer deposits for extension agreements and contributions in aid of construction	$25,532
Federal benefit of state tax deductions	3,798
Book plant cost reduction for future deferred ITC amortization	1,811
Insurance loss provisions	668
Miscellaneous	1,686
Total deferred tax assets	33,495
Deferred tax liabilities:	
Utility plant, principally due to depreciation differences	42,796
Premium on early retirement of bonds	1,487
Miscellaneous	257
Total deferred tax liabilities	44,540
Net deferred tax liability	$11,045

A valuation allowance was not required during 1993. Based on historical taxable income and future taxable income projections over the periods in which the deferred assets are deductible, management believes it is more likely than not the Company will realize the benefits of the deductible differences.

Note 6.   **EMPLOYEE BENEFIT PLANS**

Pension Plan

The Company provides a uniform pension plan for substantially all employees. The cost of the plan was charged to expense and utility plant. The Company makes annual contributions to fund the amounts accrued for pension cost. Plan assets are invested in pooled equity, bond and short-term investment accounts. The data below includes the supplemental executive retirement plan.

Net pension cost for the years ending December 31, 1993, 1992 and 1991 included the following components:

	In Thousands		
	1993	1992	1991
Service cost-benefits earned during the period	$1,167	$1,076	$1,044
Interest cost on projected obligation	2,153	1,970	1,855
Actual return on plan assets	(3,672)	(1,410)	(4,629)
Net amortization and deferral	2,132	(262)	3,385
Net pension cost	$1,780	$1,374	$1,655

The following table sets forth the plan's funded status as of December 31, 1993 and 1992:

	In Thousands	
	1993	1992
Accumulated benefit obligation, including vested benefits of $20,719 in 1993 and $15,849 in 1992	$(21,386)	$(16,281)
Projected benefit obligation	$(31,179)	$(26,652)
Plan assets at fair value	29,319	25,349
Projected benefit obligation in excess of plan assets	(1,860)	(1,303)
Unrecognized net gain	(4,556)	(5,665)
Prior service cost not yet recognized in net periodic pension cost	3,925	4,307
Remaining net transition obligation at adoption date January 1, 1987	2,288	2,574
Accrued pension liability recognized in the balance sheet	$ (203)	$ (87)

The projected long term rate of return on plan assets used in determining pension cost was 8.0% for the years 1992 to 1993. Discount rates of 7% in 1993 and 8.0% in 1992, and future compensation increases of 4.75% in 1993 and 6.0% in 1992, were used to calculate the projected benefit obligations for 1993 and 1992.

Savings Plan

The Company maintains employee savings plans which allow participants to contribute from 1% to 14% of pre-tax compensation. The Company matches fifty cents for each dollar contributed by the employee up to 6% of the employee's compensation. Company contributions were $606,000, $561,000 and $522,000 for the years 1993, 1992 and 1991, respectively.

Other Postretirement Plans

The Company provides substantially all active employees medical, dental and vision benefits through a self-insured plan. Employees retiring at or after age 60 with 10 or more years of service are offered, along with their spouses and dependents, continued participation in the plan. Prior to 1993 the Company's share of the costs of this plan were recorded as expense as they were paid. Retired employees are also provided with a $5,000 life insurance benefit.

In 1993 the Company adopted SFAS No. 106, "Employers' Accounting for Postretirement Benefits Other Than Pensions" which requires that the costs of postretirement benefits be accrued during the employees' years of active service. The Commission has issued a decision which authorizes rate recovery of tax deductible funding for postretirment benefits and permits recording of a regulatory asset for the portion of costs that will be recoverable in future rates.

Net postretirement benefit cost for 1993 included the following components:

	In Thousands
Service cost-benefits earned during the year	$ 85
Interest cost on accumulated postretirement benefit obligation	384
Net amortization of transition obligation	248
Net periodic postretirement benefit cost	$717

Postretirement benefit expense recorded in 1993 was $480,000. The remaining $237,000, which is recoverable through future customer rates, was recorded as a regulatory asset. The Company intends to make annual contributions to the plan up to the amount deductible for tax purposes. Plan assets are invested in high grade, short-term money market instruments and commercial paper.

The following table sets forth the plan's funded status and the plan's accrued liability as of yea-end:

	In Thousands
Accumulated postretirement benefit obligation:	
Retirees	$(2,850)
Other fully eligible participants	(657)
Other active participants	(1,542)
Total	(5,049)
Plan assets at fair value	215
Accumulated postretirement benefit obligation in excess of plan assets	(4,834)
Unrecognized net gain	(119)
Remaining unrecognized transition obligation	4,716
Net postretirement benefit liability included in current liabilities	$ (237)

For 1994 measurement purposes, an 8% annual rate of increase in the per capita cost of covered benefits was assumed; the rate was assumed to decrease gradually to 5% in the year 2020 and remain at that level thereafter. The health care cost trend rate assumption has a significant effect on the amounts reported. Increasing the assumed health care cost trend rates by one percentage point in each year would increase the accumulated postretirement benefit obligation as of December 31, 1993 by $423,000 and the aggregate of the service and interest cost components of the net periodic postretirement benefit cost for the year ended December 31, 1993 by $59,000.

The weighted average discount rate used in determining the accumulated postretirement benefit obligation was 7% at December 31, 1993 and the long term rate of return on plan assets was 8%.

Note 7. FAIR VALUE OF FINANCIAL INSTRUMENTS

For those financial instruments for which it is practicable to estimate a fair values the following methods and assumptions were used to estimate the fair value.

Cash and Cash Equivalents. The carrying amount of cash and cash equivalents approximates fair value because of the short-term maturity of the instruments.

First Mortgage Bonds. The fair value of the Company's first mortgage bonds is estimated at $133,415,000 using a discounted cash flow analysis, based on the current rates available to the Company for debt of similar maturities.

Advances for Construction. The fair value of advances for construction contracts is estimated at $22,000,000 based on data provided by brokers.

Note 8. QUARTERLY FINANCIAL AND COMMON STOCK MARKET DATA (Unaudited)

(In thousands, except per share amounts)

The Company's common stock is traded in the over-the-counter market and is quoted in the National NASDAQ list with the symbol CWTR. There were approximately 5,500 holders of common stock at December 31, 1993. Quarterly dividends have been paid on common stock for 196 consecutive quarters and the quarterly rate has been increased during each year since 1968. The 1993 and 1992 quarterly range of common stock market prices was supplied by NASDAQ.

1993	First	Second	Third	Fourth
Operating revenue	$27,833	$40,504	$47,431	$35,948
Net operating income	4,116	7,747	9,377	6,615
Net income	979	4,689	6,221	3,612
Earnings per share	.17	.82	1.09	.62
Common stock market price range:				
High	37¼	36¾	40½	41¼
Low	32½	32¼	33½	37½
Dividends paid	.48	.48	.48	.48

1992	First	Second	Third	Fourth
Operating revenue	$26,867	$36,972	$42,772	$33,194
Net operating income	4,620	6,437	7,076	5,641
Net income	1,811	3,617	4,225	2,876
Earnings per share	.31	.63	.74	.50
Common stock market price range:				
High	31	33¼	34¼	35
Low	26¼	28	29½	29¼
Dividends paid	.46½	.46½	.46½	.46½

APPENDIX C

Sample Government-Owned Utility Annual Report

This appendix contains excerpts from a recent Seattle Water annual report. It is presented as an example financial statement from a government-owned water utility (as discussed in chapter 15, Financial Statement Reports).

FINANCIAL HIGHLIGHTS

Seattle Water's 1992 financial results were strong, especially considering a water supply shortage discussed below. Net income for Seattle Water was $1,078,476, compared with $5,487,220 in 1991. Debt service coverage was 190 percent, well above our financial target of 170 percent, and the 130 percent legal requirement. Capital additions totalled $55,899,677, reflecting a continuing major commitment to our Capital Improvement Program (CIP).

During 1992, Seattle Water faced revenue losses due to demand curtailments as well as additional costs to administer water-use restrictions and to bring emergency pumps to standby status. Due to the financial consequences of the water shortage and the desire to use the pricing system to encourage customers to cut back on water use, Seattle Water levied an emergency rate increase for the summer months. The "drought" surcharge boosted residential and commercial summer rates by 60% and added a third step to the residential rate as a penalty for high use.

Year-end figures for 1992 provide a summary of the financial impacts of the drought. Annual water consumption for 1992 was 16% below normal. The summer rate surcharge prevented revenue from falling as dramatically as consumption. Revenue fell by seven percent relative to our annual projection. As intended, revenue from the surcharge kept net income and debt service coverage close to their financial policy target levels.

In the midst of a very active year, Seattle Water put together a rate proposal which the Mayor and City Council acted on in November 1992. New rates went into effect at the beginning of 1993 and are intended to meet Seattle Water's financial needs for 1993 and 1994. The approved rate increase is expected to increase revenues by $19 million over the two-year period for an average increase of 20%. Included in the rate and revenue calculation is a projected five percent reduction in consumption associated with changed customer behavior learned in the drought. To provide insurance against an even greater reduction in consumption, the City Council approved the rate proposal with a step increase in 1993 followed by a second step in 1994 with the intention of augmenting the 1994 increase if ongoing monitoring indicates the need to do so. In the process of putting together the rate proposal, Seattle Water called upon a panel of retail and wholesale customers for advice on critical issues. In addition, a team lead by the rate consulting firm of Ernst and Young was engaged to review the need for and adequacy of the CIP, to compare Seattle Water's overall performance with other utilities in the country, and to advise the utility on its cash management practices.

Seattle Water prepared, for the first time, a biennial, programmatic budget for 1993-94. The budget was organized and ultimately appropriated in programmatic terms rather than by the line item format traditionally used in the City. In addition, the budget was reviewed for a two-year period to coincide with the rate proposal and anticipated a large debt issuance in 1993 to fund the capital program. The programmatic structure of the budget reflected major service components, and identified key service levels, resource requirements, productivity initiatives and accountability measures.

Capital and Operating Costs *(millions)*

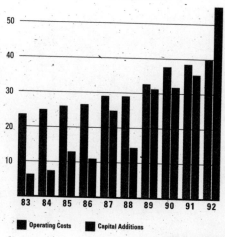

■ Operating Costs   ■ Capital Additions

BALANCE SHEET

ASSETS	DECEMBER 31,	
	1992	1991
Utility Plant (Note 4)	$321,292,310	$276,565,897
Nonoperating Properties (Note 6)	3,462,955	3,130,951
Second Lien Water Revenue Bond Fund (Note 3)		
Cash deposited with City Treasurer		110,472
Long- and short-term U.S. Government and agency securities and other investments, at cost (approximates market) plus accrued interest		1,524,483
		1,634,955
Water Revenue Bond Reserve Fund (Note 3)		
Cash deposited with City Treasurer	419,750	208,373
Long- and short-term U.S. Government and agency securities and other investments, at cost (approximates market) plus accrued interest	9,610,768	9,064,121
	10,030,518	9,272,494
Construction Funds		
Cash deposited with City Treasurer	11,633,717	876,277
Long- and short-term U.S. Government and agency securities and other investments, at cost (approximates market) plus accrued interest	3,268,259	56,198,323
Amount receivable from (payable to) Operating Fund, net	(1,033,709)	350,890
	13,868,267	57,425,490
Current assets		
Cash deposited with City Treasurer - Operating Funds	5,662,020	1,314,182
Customer and vendor deposits	1,588,762	1,040,988
Long- and short-term U.S. Government and agency securities and other investments, at cost (approximates market) plus accrued interest	287,928	556,881
Water sales receivable (Note 2)	5,221,948	7,546,119
Utility Local Improvement District Assessments due within one year (Note 3)	31,000	33,121
Current portion of other receivables (Note 2)	2,402,990	3,239,761
Amount receivable from (payable to) Construction Funds, net	1,033,709	(350,890)
Materials and supplies, at average cost	3,421,694	3,149,175
Prepayments and other	36,543	36,343
	19,686,594	16,565,680
Other assets		
Other receivables, net of current portion (Note 2)	1,108,951	1,206,530
Utility Local Improvement District assessments due after one year (Note 3)	158,449	198,839
Intangible assets (Note 5)	11,245,433	8,696,028
Deferred charges relating to advance refunding of 1975 and 1981 bonds and defeasance of 1961 bonds (Note 3)	510,393	632,060
Other	42,000	42,000
	13,065,226	10,775,457
	$381,405,870	$375,370,924

See accompanying notes to financial statements.

12

BALANCE SHEET

EQUITY AND LIABILITIES	DECEMBER 31, 1992	1991
Equity		
Retained earnings	$83,705,688	$82,627,212
Contributions in aid of construction-		
Locall Improvement Districts	25,217,488	25,217,488
Other	80,878,653	76,652,137
	189,801,829	184,496,837
Long-term debt (Note 3)		
Revenue bonds, due serially	171,680,000	177,100,000
Less - Bond discount and premium, net	(1,434,547)	(1,709,009)
	170,245,453	175,390,991
Less - Bonds due within one year	(4,280,000)	(4,220,000)
	165,965,453	171,170,991
Current liabilities		
Accounts payable, accrued taxes, payroll and other	10,074,666	12,026,683
Interdepartmental borrowings (Note 7)	9,000,000	
Accrued bond interest	2,230,433	3,410,877
Revenue bonds due within one year (Note 3)	4,280,000	4,220,000
	25,585,099	19,657,560
Other liabilities	53,489	45,536
Contingencies (Note 9)		
	$381,405,870	$375,370,924

See accompanying notes to financial statements.

Long-Term Debt/Equity
(in millions)

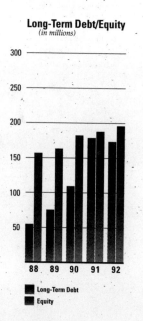

- Long-Term Debt
- Equity

Utility Plant
(Net of Depreciation)
Long-Term Debt
(in millions)

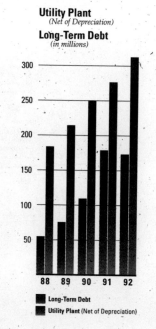

- Long-Term Debt
- Utility Plant (Net of Depreciation)

13

STATEMENT OF INCOME AND RETAINED EARNINGS

	YEAR ENDED DECEMBER 31, 1992	1991
Operating revenues		
Direct service	$34,106,416	$33,129,676
Wholesale	12,340,606	14,631,242
Other	777,315	372,178
	47,224,337	48,133,096
Operating expenses		
Supply	6,998,752	6,533,195
Distribution	6,521,248	6,603,064
Water treatment	1,239,341	1,114,230
Commercial	2,453,452	3,120,914
General and administrative	7,463,039	6,774,986
Engineering	2,108,540	2,651,398
City occupation tax	3,377,888	2,962,724
Other taxes	969,877	1,079,377
Depreciation and amortization	9,124,677	7,396,785
	40,256,814	38,236,673
Operating income	6,967,523	9,896,423
Other income		
Interest income	2,557,804	3,574,426
Timber income and other, net	1,060,756	643,449
	3,618,560	4,217,875
Income before debt expense	10,586,083	14,114,298
Interest expense and amortization of debt issue costs and net discount	9,507,607	8,627,078
Net income	1,078,476	5,487,220
Retained earnings		
Balance at beginning of the year	82,627,212	77,139,992
Balance at end of the year	$83,705,688	$82,627,212

See accompanying notes to financial statements.

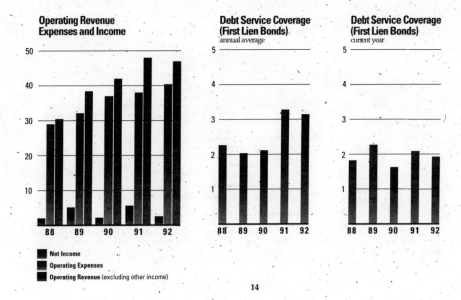

Operating Revenue Expenses and Income

- Net Income
- Operating Expenses
- Operating Revenue (excluding other income)

Debt Service Coverage (First Lien Bonds) annual average

Debt Service Coverage (First Lien Bonds) current year

14

STATEMENT OF CASH FLOWS

	YEAR ENDED DECEMBER 31,	
	1992	1991
Cash flows from operating activities		
Cash received from customers	$49,314,683	$46,212,976
Cash payments to suppliers for goods and services	(11,961,633)	(7,682,273)
Cash payments to employees for services	(21,454,511)	(19,299,528)
Net cash provided by operating activities	15,898,539	19,231,175
Cash flows from capital and related financing activities		
Proceeds from sale of revenue bonds		59,000,000
Proceeds from interdepartmental borrowings	9,000,000	
Acquisition and construction of utility plant	(51,765,791)	(32,478,618)
Additions to intangible assets	(4,133,886)	(3,554,152)
Principal paid on revenue bond maturities	(4,070,000)	(3,815,000)
Defeasance of Second Lien Bonds	(1,350,000)	
Loss on defeasance of Second Lien Bonds	85,000	
Interest paid on revenue bonds, net of amount capitalized	(10,309,698)	(6,855,473)
Contributions in aid of construction	3,725,698	3,769,727
Payments of bond issue and selling costs		(547,921)
Timber sales and other, net	1,723,668	(94,314)
Net cash provided by (used for) capital and related financing activities	(57,095,009)	15,424,249
Cash flows from investing activities		
Purchase of investment securities	(81,824,130)	(155,503,523)
Net proceeds from sale and maturities of investments	135,277,785	114,405,006
Interest and dividends on investments	3,281,002	2,964,170
Net change in nonoperating properties	(332,004)	(140,711)
Net cash provided by (used for) investing activities	56,402,653	(38,275,058)
Net increase (decrease) in cash deposited with the City Treasurer	15,206,183	(3,619,634)
Cash deposited with City Treasurer at the beginning of the year	2,509,304	6,128,938
Cash deposited with City Treasurer at the end of the year	$17,715,487	$2,509,304
Cash deposited with City Treasurer at the end of the year consists of		
Second lien water revenue bond fund		$110,472
Water revenue bond reserve fund	$419,750	208,373
Construction funds	11,633,717	876,277
Operating funds	5,662,020	1,314,182
	$17,715,487	$2,509,304
Reconciliation of operating income to net cash provided by operating activities		
Operating income	$6,967,523	$9,896,423
Adjustments to reconcile operating income to net cash provided by operating activities		
Depreciation	7,540,196	6,565,780
Amortization	1,584,481	1,016,603
Provision for uncollectible accounts	(9,263)	1,235
Change in assets and liabilities		
(Increase) decrease in customer and vendor deposits	(547,774)	205,940
Decrease (increase) in water sales receivable	1,670,522	(687,931)
Decrease in ULID assessments	42,511	50,304
Decrease (increase) in other receivables	934,350	(1,465,185)
Increase in materials and supplies	(272,519)	(264,888)
Increase in prepayments and other	(200)	(250)
(Decrease) increase in accounts payable, accrued taxes, payroll and other	(1,952,017)	3,497,645
(Decrease) increase in other assets and liabilities	(59,271)	415,499
Total adjustments	8,931,016	9,334,752
Net cash provided by operating activities	$15,898,539	$19,231,175

Supplemental schedule of noncash investing and financing activities

The Department received contributions of utility plant in the amount of $500,818 and $247,292 during the years ended December 31, 1992 and 1991, respectively. The Department has recorded these contributions as an increase in utility plant and contributions in aid of construction.

See accompanying notes to financial statements.

NOTES TO FINANCIAL STATEMENTS DECEMBER 31, 1992 AND 1991

1. SUMMARY OF SIGNIFICANT ACCOUNTING POLICIES

The City of Seattle, Water Department (Department) is a public utility of the City of Seattle (City). The Department receives certain services from other departments and agencies of the City, including those normally considered to be general and administrative. The utility is generally charged for services received from other City agencies and additionally must pay an occupation tax to the City General Fund. Water services provided by the Department to other City departments and agencies are billed at rates prescribed by City ordinances. Under direction of the Seattle City Council, no charges are made to the City for water services for public fire protection.

The Department is subject to regulation by city and state agencies. Accounting policies and financial reporting are regulated by the Washington State Auditor's Office, Division of Municipal Corporations, and are in accordance with generally accepted accounting principles for public utilities. Descriptions of the Department's principal accounting policies are as follows:

Utility plant and depreciation

Property and equipment is stated at cost or, if contributed, at donor cost or appraised value at date of acquisition. Interest relating to the financing of projects under construction is capitalized due to the Department's capital financing plans and rate-setting methodology. The cost of current repairs and maintenance is charged to expense, while the cost of replacements and betterments is capitalized. At such time as property is retired and removed from service, the original cost of the property, together with removal cost less salvage value, is charged to the depreciation reserve.

Depreciation of utility plant is computed on the straight-line method, using composite rates based on estimated lives as follows: earthen source of supply developments - 100 years; transmission and distribution reservoirs, tanks and mains - 50 to 100 years; and buildings, fixtures and equipment - 5 to 50 years.

Revenues

Service rates are authorized by ordinances passed by the Seattle City Council. Billings are made to customers on a monthly or bimonthly cyclical basis. Revenues for water sold to customers between the last billing date and the end of the year are estimated and accrued in the accompanying financial statements.

Contributions in aid of construction

The donor cost or appraised value of contributed property and equipment is included in contributions in aid of construction. Depreciation of contributed assets is charged to operating expense.

Construction in progress

Capitalizable costs incurred on projects which are not in use or ready for use are held in construction in progress. When the asset is ready for use, costs relating thereto are transferred to utility plant. Upon determination that a project will be abandoned, the related costs are charged to expense.

Capitalized information systems costs

The Department capitalizes all direct and incremental costs and the related overhead incurred in connection with the development of significant information systems projects that are to be used internally. Such costs are amortized over the projects' estimated useful lives of primarily six years.

Conservation programs

Conservation program costs which result in long-term benefits and reduce or postpone other capital expenditures are capitalized and amortized over their expected useful lives of five years, commencing when each program is in place. Costs of administering the overall program are expensed as incurred.

Investments

The City invests all temporary cash surpluses for City departments. The City may, at various times, enter into repurchase or reverse repurchase agreements. The City may also transfer investments between the Department's funds and/or other City departments in order to make cash available to the Department from maturing investments. All investments of the Department are held by banks or trust companies as the City's agent and in the City's name. It is the City's intent to hold all investments to maturity. The market value of investments is determined based upon the bid price on the last day of the year.

Timber sales

Contracts are entered into, from time to time, with outside timber purchasers for the harvesting of timber owned by the Department within its watershed and from nonoperating properties. Revenue is recognized based on terms of the harvesting contract. The cutting schedules and associated revenues and expenses are for the most part determined by market and other factors. Income arising from timber operations may vary significantly from year to year.

Net revenues from commercial thinning, salvage and timber harvest in the Cedar River Watershed are currently obligated, in compliance with City ordinance, to support land and habitat acquisition within the Watershed.

Reclassification

Certain of the balances in prior year financial statements have been reclassified for comparative purposes.

2. ACCOUNTS RECEIVABLE

Accounts receivable arising from water sales comprise:

	DECEMBER 31,	
	1992	1991
Receivables arising from billings of metered water sales	$3,456,097	$4,799,531
Allowance for doubtful accounts	(94,149)	(103,412)
	3,361,948	4,696,119
Accrual for estimated unbilled water revenue	1,860,000	2,850,000
	$5,221,948	$7,546,119

Other receivables comprise:

	DECEMBER 31,	
	1992	1991
Watermain assessments	$787,361	$768,975
Timber sales receivable	71,690	716,400
Richmond Beach surcharge	514,009	536,600
Due from the Municipality of Metropolitan Seattle	173,645	343,478
Due from other City departments	1,593,815	1,092,491
Other	371,421	988,347
	3,511,941	4,446,291
Less—Current portion	(2,402,990)	(3,239,761)
Total other receivables, net of current portion	$1,108,951	$1,206,530

16

NOTES TO FINANCIAL STATEMENTS DECEMBER 31, 1992 AND 1991

3. LONG-TERM DEBT

Long-term debt consists of the following:

	COUPON RATES	DECEMBER 31, 1992	1991
First Lien Revenue Bonds, varying annual principal payments, due 1992 to 2020	3.25%–10.00%	$112,680,000	$116,750,000
Second Lien Revenue Bonds, defeased in May 1992	7.75%–9.00%		1,350,000
Subordinated Revenue Bond Anticipation Notes, principal due May 1, 1994	5.5%	59,000,000	59,000,000
		$171,680,000	$177,100,000

The combined long-term debt had an effective interest rate of approximately 6.50% as of December 31, 1992. The fair market value of the long-term debt, based upon market prices at the end of the year, was $180,000,000.

Maturities of revenue bonds over the next five years and thereafter are as follows:
Year ending December 31,

1993	$4,280,000
1994	63,515,000
1995	4,815,000
1996	5,120,000
1997	5,455,000
Thereafter	88,495,000
	$171,680,000

In July 1991, the Department issued $59,000,000 of Municipal Water Revenue Bond Anticipation Notes which bear interest at the rate of 5.5% per annum. The proceeds of this issuance are being used to fund capital improvement projects. The notes are subordinate to the First Lien Bonds. Gross revenues, net of charges for operation and maintenance of the Department and payments of principal and interest on First Lien Bonds are pledged to make principal and interest payments on the notes. The notes are due May 1, 1994.

The Department is required to accumulate over a five-year period, starting in April 1990, and then maintain in the Water Revenue Bond Reserve Fund a balance of not less than the total debt service requirement on First Lien Bonds in the next year. The debt service requirement in 1993 for First Lien Bonds is $12,098,245 and the Water Revenue Bond Reserve Fund balance at December 31, 1992 is $10,030,518.

The Department defeased the Second Lien Revenue Bonds in May 1992 and, accordingly, these bonds are no longer included in the accompanying financial statements. Funds in the amount of $823,212 at December 31, 1992 are held in a trust to make future debt service payments. A loss of approximately $85,000 was recorded in 1992 in connection with the defeasance transaction. At December 31, 1992, the remaining Second Lien Revenue bonds totaled $780,000.

The Department is required to produce revenues of not less than the greater of 1) 140% of the average annual debt service required on all First Lien Bonds outstanding or 2) 130% of the amount of principal and interest requirements for the current year on all First Lien Bonds. Net revenues available for debt service, as defined by the respective bond covenants, for the year ended December 31, 1992 represented 307% of the average annual debt service for First Lien Bonds ($7,503,180), 190% of the 1992 principal and interest payments required ($12,108,959) and were calculated as follows:

Net revenue available for First Lien debt service

Net income	$1,078,476
Add:	
City occupation tax	3,377,888
Depreciation and amortization	9,124,677
Interest on revenue bonds, net of interest capitalized	9,035,142
Amortization of bond discount, premium and issue costs	336,278
Amortization of deferred charge on advance refunding of 1975 and 1981 bonds and defeasance of 1961 bonds	133,827
	23,086,288
Less:	
Interest income from ULID assessments and related investments	(47,534)
Net revenue available for First Lien debt service	$23,038,754

4. UTILITY PLANT

Utility plant consists of the following:

	DECEMBER 31, 1992	1991
Equipment	$378,430,351	$337,797,596
Buildings, fixtures and grounds	14,589,047	14,254,665
Land	4,389,135	4,389,135
Right of way	1,139,345	1,139,345
Property held for future use	273,562	272,998
	398,821,440	357,853,739
Less - Accumulated provision for depreciation	(111,529,352)	(104,018,146)
	287,292,088	253,835,593
Construction in progress	34,000,222	22,730,304
	$321,292,310	$276,565,897

In 1992 and 1991, interest of $2,300,695 and $1,700,838, respectively, was capitalized using an effective interest rate of 7.17%.

17

NOTES TO FINANCIAL STATEMENTS DECEMBER 31, 1992 AND 1991

5. INTANGIBLE ASSETS

Intangible assets consist of the following:

	DECEMBER 31,	
	1992	1991
Capitalized information systems costs	$11,187,345	$8,978,161
Capitalized conservation costs	1,761,977	
Other	541,750	548,872
	13,491,072	9,527,033
Less - Accumulated amortization	(2,245,639)	(831,005)
	$11,245,433	$8,696,028

6. NONOPERATING PROPERTIES

The United States Congress passed a bill in late 1992 directing the U.S. Forest Service to exchange at market value certain properties which it owns in the Cedar River Watershed for certain nonoperating properties owned by the Department. The nonoperating properties consist of acreage the Department has acquired throughout the state of Washington for this purpose. Management believes that the market value of the Department's nonoperating properties is sufficient to accomplish the exchange, although the appraisal process has not yet been completed.

7. INTERDEPARTMENTAL TRANSACTIONS

Weather conditions in 1992 resulted in an extreme drought year. As a result, mandatory conservation measures were imposed and a surcharge on water use was levied from June 1992 to August 1992. The surcharge did not entirely mitigate the lower consumption, primarily due to higher than anticipated conservation levels, and therefore revenues were below projection in 1992. Management believes that lower consumption will continue to impact the financial position and results of operations of the Department.

Interdepartmental borrowings at December 31, 1992 represent funds advanced from other City departments to cover operating cash flow requirements. These borrowings were repaid on January 1, 1993.

The Department is borrowing City funds under an arrangement with the City Finance Department to cover expenditures as required. Interest cost is being incurred on these borrowings at a rate which approximates the Treasurer's average rate on invested funds.

In 1992, the Department received approximately $440,000 from the Seattle City Light Department as partial compensation for permission to construct a hydropower facility within the Department's South Fork Tolt Supply System. This has been included in other income.

8. PENSION COSTS

All Department full-time employees participate in the Seattle City Employees Retirement System (the System), a single-employer public employee retirement system. The payroll for Department employees covered by the System for 1992 and 1991 was $21,177,488 and $19,106,610, respectively.

All City full-time employees are eligible to participate in the System except uniformed Police and Fire Department personnel. City employees may retire after 30 years of service regardless of age; after age 52 with 20 years or more of service; after age 57 with 10 or more years of service; and after age 62 with 5 or more years of service. Benefits fully vest on reaching 5 years of service. Vested

employees may retire at or after age 55 and receive reduced retirement benefits. The System also provides death and disability benefits. Benefits are established by City ordinance.

Covered employees are required by City ordinance to contribute 8.03% of their annual basic salary to the plan. The Department is required by the same ordinance to contribute 8.91% of covered payroll. The Department's contribution requirement for 1992 and 1991 was $1,765,714 and $1,561,964, respectively.

The "pension benefit obligation" is a standardized disclosure measure of the present value of pension benefits, adjusted for the effects of projected salary increases and step-rate benefits, estimated to be payable in the future as a result of employee service to date. The measure, which is the actuarial present value of credited projected benefits, is intended to help users assess the System's funding status on a going-concern basis, assess progress made in accumulating sufficient assets to pay benefits when due, and make comparisons among public employees retirement systems and employers. The System does not make separate measurements of assets and pension benefit obligations for individual employers. The pension benefit obligation at January 1, 1992 for the System as a whole, determined through an actuarial valuation performed as of that date was $780.2 million (unaudited). The System's net assets available for benefits on that date were $538.8 million (unaudited), leaving an unfunded pension benefit obligation of $241.4 million (unaudited). The Department's 1992 contribution represented 6.6% of total contributions required of all participating city departments.

Ten-year historical trend information showing the System's progress in accumulating sufficient assets to pay benefits when due is presented in the System's December 31, 1992 component unit annual financial report.

9. CONTINGENCIES

The Department is in the process of negotiating with certain government agencies and Indian tribes concerning the development of measures to mitigate the impact of Department facilities on the Cedar River fishery resource. It is expected that a substantial portion of any costs that might be incurred by the Department will be capitalized.

The Department is currently negotiating with representatives of its wholesale customers over several rate-related issues including the handling of the costs of Tolt Pipeline rehabilitation and future joint facilities. The ultimate effect of these negotiations on future revenues cannot currently be determined.

The Department intends to construct a filtration plant which is expected to become operational in 1998. Expenditures for this project are expected to exceed $80,000,000 and the majority of these expenditures are expected to be paid in 1996 through 1998.

FIVE-YEAR SUMMARY

	1988	1989	1990	1991	1992
FINANCIAL PERFORMANCE (IN THOUSANDS OF DOLLARS)					
Total operating revenues	$30,435	$39,169	$40,685	$48,133	$47,224
Total operating and maintenance expenses	28,995	33,128	37,061	38,237	40,257
Net operating income	1,440	6,041	3,624	9,896	6,967
Other income, net	3,302	2,439	4,152	4,218	3,619
Income, net before debt expense	4,742	8,480	7,776	14,114	10,586
Total funded debt expense	2,870	3,377	5,716	8,627	9,508
Net income for year	1,872	5,103	2,060	5,487	1,078
Net available for first lien debt service	$11,892	$16,471	$16,404	$24,287	$23,039
Ratio of current year first lien debt service to net revenue	1:1.8	1:2.3	1:1.63	1:2.04	1:1.90
Ratio of average annual first lien debt service to net revenue	1:2.3	1:2.04	1:2.12	1:3.18	1:3.07
Utility Plant (net of depreciation)	$184,159	$219,441	$250,406	$276,566	$321,292
Equity in water system at year end	$160,197	$168,928	$174,993	$184,497	$189,802
Utility bonds outstanding at year end	$60,905	$83,495	$121,915	$177,100	$171,680
Operating cost per million gallons	$571	$625	$689	$754	$857

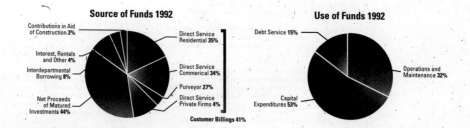

Source of Funds 1992

Contributions in Aid of Construction **3%**
Interest, Rentals and Other **4%**
Interdepartmental Borrowing **8%**
Net Proceeds of Matured Investments **44%**

Direct Service Residential **35%**
Direct Service Commerical **34%**
Purveyor **27%**
Direct Service Private Firms **4%**

Customer Billings **41%**

Use of Funds 1992

Debt Service **15%**
Operations and Maintenance **32%**
Capital Expenditures **53%**

FIVE-YEAR SUMMARY

	1988	1989	1990	1991	1992
SERVICE INFORMATION					
Persons with direct water service	546,000	548,000	569,000	572,000	575,600
Persons served through water districts, cities & towns	585,000	596,000	620,000	645,000	659,400
Total persons served by system	1,131,000	1,144,000	1,189,000	1,217,000	1,235,000
Billed water use (in gallons)					
Total annual use for area	50,819,108,000	53,031,749,000	53,796,617,000	50,683,788,000	46,957,645,000
Average daily use for area	139,230,000	145,292,000	147,388,000	138,860,000	128,651,000
Average daily use per person	123	127	124	114	104
Number of new water services installed	855	835	810	733	660
Number of watermain leaks, breaks, etc. repaired	213	186	165	183	203
FACILITY DATA					
Meters					
Meters in use	171,098	171,806	172,203	172,730	173,230
Percentage of services metered	100%	100%	100%	100%	100%
Mains					
Total miles of supply and distribution	1,808	1,812	1,816	1,823	1,823
Hydrants and Valves					
Hydrants in use	17,855	17,881	17,910	17,932	17,940
Gate valves in use	15,933	16,035	16,189	16,307	16,322
Distribution Transmission Storage					
Reservoirs, standpipes and tanks (gallons)	461,370,000	493,370,000	506,370,000	506,370,000	506,370,000
Total System Source Capacity					
Surface water (IN MGD)	335	335	335	335	335
Ground water (IN MGD)	8	8	8	10	10
WATER QUALITY INDICATORS					
Turbidity complaints	1,086	929	829	1011	1185
Rust complaints	181	134	122	215	119
Taste and odor complaints	325	421	411	355	542
Compliance with Wash. State Board of Health Drinking Water Regulations	Yes	Yes	Yes	Yes	Yes
Number of incidents out of compliance with state drinking water regulation	0	0	0	0	0

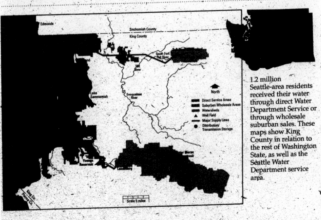

1.2 million Seattle-area residents received their water through direct Water Department Service or through wholesale suburban sales. These maps show King County in relation to the rest of Washington State, as well as the Seattle Water Department service area.

23

ABBREVIATIONS

AICPA	American Institute of Certified Public Accountants
APB	Accounting Principles Board
CAFR	comprehensive annual financial report
CAP	Committee on Accounting Procedure
CEO	chief executive officer
CPR	continuing property record
CUFR	component unit financial report
DDB	double declining balance
EOQ	economic order quantity
ERISA	Employee Retirement Income Security Act of 1974
ERTA	Economic Recovery Tax Act of 1981
FASB	Financial Accounting Standards Board
FICA	Federal Insurance Contribution Act
FIFO	first in/first out
FUTA	Federal Unemployment Tax Act
GAAP	generally accepted accounting principles
GAO	US General Accounting Office
GASB	Governmental Accounting Standards Board
GFOA	Government Finance Officers Association
IT	information technology
ITC	investment tax credit
NARUC	National Association of Regulatory Utility Commissioners
NCGA	National Council on Governmental Accounting
NYSE	New York Stock Exchange
SEC	Securities and Exchange Commission
SFAS	Statement of Financial Accounting Standards
SUTA	State Unemployment Tax Act
SYD	sum of the years' digits
USIRS	United States Internal Revenue Service

INDEX

Note: An *f.* following a page number refers to a figure; an *n.* refers to a footnote; a *t.* refers to a table.

⊠ E

Earnings
  fixed interest charges and, 211
  See also Retained earnings
Economic order quantity (EOQ), 165, 169
Economic Recovery Tax Act (1981) (ERTA), 119
Employees
  benefits for, 78, 79, 213
  receivables from, 158–59
  reporting to, 18, 212–13
  taxes on, 115
  See also Pension entries
Employment Retirement Income Security Act (ERISA) (1974), 213
Engineering costs, 125, 126–27
Enterprise accounting, fund accounting and, 41
EOQ. *See* Economic order quantity
Equity, 39
  owner, 187
  position, 194
  ratios, 194–95
  sales of, 129
Equity accounts, 192
  specifications of, 193
ERISA. *See* Employment Retirement Income Security Act
ERTA. *See* Economic Recovery Tax Act
Expected costs, actual costs and, 69, 81, 138, 163, 230
Expense accounts
  balance-sheet accounts and, 233
  revenues and, 233
Expenses
  authorization for, 139
  classification of, 83
  estimated, 24, 82f
  examples of, 57
  managing/controlling, 27
  multiperiod, 62
  recording, 39
  statement of, 39, 59, 207
Explanatory notes, 203–4, 207
Extension policies, 190–91, 192
External users, reports to, 199, 204–5
Extraordinary items account, 37
Extraordinary property losses account, 104

⊠ F

FASB. *See* Financial Accounting Standards Board
Federal income taxes, 111–12, 115
  estimating, 116–19
  withholding, 159

Federal Insurance Contribution Act (FICA) taxes, 113–14, 115, 120
Federal Power Commission v. *Hope Natural Gas Company* (320 U.S. 591), 219
Federal Unemployment Tax Act (FUTA) taxes, 113–14, 120
FICA taxes. *See* Federal Insurance Contribution Act taxes
FIFO. *See* First in/first out
Finance systems, computerizing, 40
Financial Accounting Standards Board (FASB), ix
  standards by, 2, 50–51, 199, 200, 206
  statements by, 51, 85, 86, 103
Financial condition, 43
  assessing, 49–50, 194, 225
  changes in, 186
  concern about, 231
  management discussion/analysis of, 202
Financial data, 1, 205
  accumulating/recording, 33
  breakdown of, 30
Financial management, ix, 11, 27, 216
  IT function and, 250
  measurement of, 237
  responsibilities of, 1, 20
  utility management and, 3
Financial planning, 24–25, 27, 224, 225, 240
  elements of, 23, 30
  managers and, 228–29
  requirements for, 241
  See also Planning
Financial policy, 3
  accounting-system requirements and, 238
Financial reports, 197, 208–13
  auditing, 199
  for external groups, 221, 222
  format/content of, 43–44
  providing, 43
  required, 209–10
  standards for, 199
  types of, 11, 186
Financial statements, 194, 211, 243
  auditing, 206
  comparative, 202
  debt issues and, 240
  forecasted, 224
  historical, 209
  standards for, 197–99
Financing, 1, 13–15, 18, 237–38
  alternative sources for, 15
  cash for, 146
  differences in, 6t
  external/internal, 179
  rate, 238–39
First in/first out (FIFO), valuation by, 162

mortgaged, 212
personal, 113
Property account, identification by,
131–33
Property additions/retirements,
records for, 142
Property Held for Future Use account,
123
Property insurance expense, 77, 78
Property insurance reserve category, 38
Property records, 139–44
establishing/maintaining, 142–43
Property taxes, 112–13, 115
capitalization of, 127
estimating, 119–20
utility management and, 119–20
Proprietary Capital account, 193
Proprietorships, 192
Protective covenants, 210, 211–12
Public authorities, sales to, 54–55
Public education programs, money
for, 76
Public service commission
ITC and, 118
operating income and, 36
reports to, 198
retirement units and, 130
Public utility approach, 227
revenue requirements under, 60–61
Public Utility Depreciation Practices
(NARUC), 87
Pumping equipment category, 132
Pumping expenses, 68, 72–73
Purchased water, cost of, 72–73
Purchase requisitions, 142, 168
Purchasing
advantages/disadvantages of, 73
policies for, 20, 165
Purchasing agent, work of, 164
Purchasing department, 168
inventory and, 169

⊠ Q

Quantity discounts, considering, 164

⊠ R

Rate base, development of, 215, 218,
227, 238
Rate case, 215
components decided in, 218–19
preparing, 217, 225
Rate-making, 53, 61–62, 116, 131, 176,
200, 201, 217, 220, 226, 240, 241

above-the-line expenses for, 246
compound interest method/sinking
fund method and, 100f
goals of, 215–16
influences on, 227
political process of, 215
Rate of return, 226
determining, 61, 216, 218, 219
overall, 220
Rate regulation, 225
accounting practices and, 200–201
investor-owned utilities and, 215
Rates
changes in, 226, 227
development of, 60, 201, 216, 220, 237
differences in, 6t
revenues from, 237
test period for, 216–17
Rate schedules
applying, 57, 59
determining, 59–63, 225, 226–28
Ratios, 49–50, 194–95
current, 49
income, 195
operating, 50, 195
Reacquired Bonds account, 184
Reacquired Capital Stock account, 193
Receivables, 158–61
nontrade, 160
segregating, 159
types of, 158–59
uncollectible, 159
Receiving report, preparing, 165, 168
Record keeping, 31–42, 164–65
Reduction in Par or Stated Value
of Capital Stock account, 193
Refunds, 191, 201
Regulation, 200
public, 5–6
Regulation S-K (SEC), 202
Regulation S-X, "Form and Content
of Financial Statements" (SEC), 2
disclosure through, 203
on leases, 204
Regulatory accounting, 201
Regulatory agencies
capitalization/depreciation and, 140
information for, 18, 197
Regulatory evaluation process, 215
Remaining-life method, 103
Remittances by mail, 148
Removal, cost of, 88, 93
Rent expense, 73, 77
Repayments, cash for, 146, 147, 155–56
Replacement costs, 62, 68
depreciation and, 103
estimating, 131
Reporting, 1, 18–22
exception, 222–23
external, 222

W

Wages and salaries expense, allocating, 83

Wages/salaries, 72, 74, 77, 185

Wastewater
  accounting process and, 239
  funds for, 42

Wastewater utilities, financial structure of, 7, 9

Water delivered, variations in, 64–65

Water operating revenue accounts, outline of, 262–63

Water property and interdepartmental rents, revenue from, 55

Water pumpage, report on, 233

Water sales, categorizing, 54

Water service billed, 181

Water treatment equipment category, 132

Water treatment expenses, 68, 73–74

Water use
  controlling, 65
  report on, 233

Wells and springs category, 132

Working capital, 37, 49, 189
  determining, 218
  net, 186
  sources and uses of, 186

Working funds, 146
  purchasing through, 165

Work orders, 137, 141, 142

Y

Yellow Book. See *Standards for Audit of Governmental Organizations, Programs, Activities & Functions*